Register Now for O~~nl~~
to Your B~~o~~

Your print purchase of *Social Work and Mental Health* **includes online access to the contents of your book**—increasing accessibility, portability, and searchability!

Access today at:

**http://connect.springerpub.com/content/book/978-0-8261-6443-8
or scan the QR code at the right with your smartphone
and enter the access code below.**

5HM814AJ

If you are experiencing problems accessing the digital component of this product, please contact our customer service department at cs@springerpub.com

The online access with your print purchase is available at the publisher's discretion and may be removed at any time without notice.

Publisher's Note: New and used products purchased from third-party sellers are not guaranteed for quality, authenticity, or access to any included digital components.

*Scan here for
quick access.*

SPC

SPRINGER / PUBLISHING COMPANY
View all our products at springerpub.com

Sylvia I. Mignon, MSW, PhD, is professor of sociology and criminal justice at the University of Massachusetts (UMass) Boston and director of the Forensic Services Graduate Certificate Program. She is the former director of the MS and BA in human services programs at UMass Boston. As a Licensed Independent Clinical Social Worker in Massachusetts, Professor Mignon has worked in mental health, substance abuse, and medical treatment programs. In addition to mental health, her research areas include substance abuse, family violence, child welfare, criminal justice, and the death penalty. She is the author of numerous journal articles and four previous books: *Family Abuse: Consequences, Theories, and Responses*, with Calvin J. Larson and William M. Holmes (Boston, MA: Allyn and Bacon, 2002); *Substance Use and Abuse: Exploring Alcohol and Drug Issues*, with Marjorie Marcoux Faiia, Peter L. Myers, and Earl Rubington (Boulder, CO: Lynne Rienner Publishers, 2009); *Substance Abuse Treatment: Options, Challenges, and Effectiveness* (New York, NY: Springer Publishing Company, 2015); and *Child Welfare in the United States: Challenges, Policy, and Practice* (New York, NY: Springer Publishing Company, 2017).

SOCIAL WORK AND MENTAL HEALTH

Evidence-Based Policy and Practice

Sylvia I. Mignon, MSW, PhD

SPRINGER **PUBLISHING COMPANY**

Springer Publishing Company, LLC
11 West 42nd Street
New York, NY 10036
www.springerpub.com
http://connect.springerpub.com

Acquisitions Editor: Kate Dimock
Compositor: Amnet Systems

ISBN: 978-0-8261-6442-1
ebook ISBN: 978-0-8261-6443-8
DOI: 10.1891/9780826164438

Instructor's Materials: Qualified instructors may request supplements by emailing textbook@springerpub.com.

Instructor's Manual: 978-0-8261-6431-5
Instructor's PowerPoints: 978-0-8261-6440-7
Instructor's Test Bank: 978-0-8261-6432-2

19 20 21 22 / 5 4 3 2 1

The author and the publisher of this Work have made every effort to use sources believed to be reliable to provide information that is accurate and compatible with the standards generally accepted at the time of publication. The author and publisher shall not be liable for any special, consequential, or exemplary damages resulting, in whole or in part, from the readers' use of, or reliance on, the information contained in this book. The publisher has no responsibility for the persistence or accuracy of URLs for external or third-party Internet websites referred to in this publication and does not guarantee that any content on such websites is, or will remain, accurate or appropriate.

Library of Congress Cataloging-in-Publication Data

Names: Mignon, Sylvia I., author.
Title: Social work and mental health : evidence-based policy and practice / Sylvia I. Mignon.
Description: New York, NY : Springer Publishing Company, LLC, [2020] | Includes bibliographical references and index.
Identifiers: LCCN 2019015033 (print) | LCCN 2019015653 (ebook) | ISBN 9780826164438 (eBook) | ISBN 9780826164421 (print : alk. paper) | ISBN 9780826164315 (instructor's manual) | ISBN 9780826164407 (instructor's powerpoints) | ISBN 9780826164322 (instructor's test bank)
Subjects: | MESH: Social Work, Psychiatric | Mental Health | Evidence-Based Practice | Public Policy | United States
Classification: LCC RA790 (ebook) | LCC RA790 (print) | NLM WM 30.5 | DDC 362.2/0425—dc23
LC record available at https://lccn.loc.gov/2019015033

Contact us to receive discount rates on bulk purchases.
We can also customize our books to meet your needs.
For more information please contact: sales@springerpub.com

Sylvia Mignon: https://orcid.org/0000-0003-4845-1735

Publisher's Note: New and used products purchased from third-party sellers are not guaranteed for quality, authenticity, or access to any included digital components.

Printed in the United States of America.

For John, Anna, and Cameron

CONTENTS

PREFACE

Social workers are the number one providers of mental health services in the United States. They work in a variety of environments with clients who have mental illness, including community mental health centers and hospitals, as clinicians in organized therapy groups, and as private practitioners. Often social workers focus solely on their clients and the agencies they work for, such as mental health clinics, and overlook the larger context in which their services are provided. A goal of this textbook is to describe the realities of the contemporary American mental health system and the impacts on clients and social workers. It takes a critical perspective on the lack of quality care for some of society's most vulnerable members, the mentally ill. Unlike other texts that address mental health and illness, this book focuses on the issues and policies that create challenges for social workers in the mental health system and obstacles to providing a continuum of excellent mental healthcare. The text also focuses on ways that social workers can help improve the overall functioning of the mental health system.

One theme of the text is that mental health diagnosis, treatment, and access to care are often lacking due to an insufficient knowledge base. That is, some mental disorders are not yet well understood, so responses to them can be inappropriate or inadequate. Lack of knowledge of the causes of mental illness, challenges in the classification of mental disorders, and the difficult behavioral manifestations of mental illness combine with stigma to result in one of the most intractable health and social problems today. Social workers have always had a role in planning for and arranging services for the mentally ill and over the years have established themselves as mental health professionals.

The development of mental health policy is often overlooked as a part of overall health policy. Social workers can lack input into the development of mental health policy because it is often developed by politicians rather than those with policy expertise. For example, the Mental Health Parity Act of 1996 and the Mental Health Parity Addiction and Equity Act of 2008 have not necessarily translated into better insurance coverage and care for those persons with mental illness. Also included in this text's coverage are an examination of the laws and policies regarding voluntary and involuntary psychiatric hospitalization, professionals' duty to warn potential crime victims, and the rights of the mentally ill to refuse treatment. These are areas in which social work advocacy is essential. As established mental health professionals, social workers can help the field move forward in the improvement of services and the development of policy. This text contributes to that effort.

The critical perspective taken here ensures that an examination of mental health treatments, especially pharmacologic therapy, does not focus exclusively on the benefits to clients taking prescribed medications. Instead, the book digs deeper to ask who benefits when clients take psychotropic drugs. Armed with the knowledge that pharmaceutical companies are the largest profit makers in the world, it clearly is not appropriate to assume they have only altruistic motives.

Another distinguishing characteristic of this text is the attention paid to the "lived experiences" of the mentally ill and their families. This includes descriptions of living with the symptoms and diagnosis of mental illness and the efforts to seek relief through a fragmented system of care. Boxed materials describe the experiences of the mentally ill themselves and their families.

With a focus on social work innovation in mental healthcare, this text provides descriptions of promising policies and practices to improve mental healthcare in the United States. This includes new drug and brain stimulation or neuromodulation techniques and expanded social work prevention efforts.

This textbook is recommended as a primary text for mental health courses in master of social work (MSW) programs. The text can also be used in upper-level undergraduate college courses in social work, typically bachelor of social work (BSW) programs. The text ensures that social work students will not only understand the issues of their clients (micro level), but also understand mental health issues in a broader societal context (macro level). Although the Council on Social Work Education (CSWE) does not issue specific requirements for social work education programs regarding mental health, the nine core competency requirements of CSWE are addressed in the text as described in the 2015 Educational Policy and Accreditation Standards (EPAS).

Chapter 1, Social Work and the Mental Health System, reveals that the mental health system in the United States is not much of a system at all. Any discussion of a system connotes some semblance of planning, interconnection, and collaboration as well as a continuum of care for clients with mental illness. This chapter describes the lack of cohesiveness that characterizes mental health policy and services today—leading to a weak system that is not especially responsive to the needs of clients. Every day social workers confront the challenges of a disorganized system as they provide services to clients. Chapter 1 briefly outlines global ideas about mental health and mental illness, bearing in mind that global mental health issues are far more complex than can be adequately addressed in this text.

Chapter 1 provides an overall picture of mental illness in the United States, including types and prevalence of mental illness. It examines the nature versus nurture controversy, while paying special attention to research on brain chemistry. The chapter highlights that challenges in making a diagnosis can lead to inadequate and even inappropriate treatment. Another significant issue is the role of stigma in the diagnosis and treatment of mental illness. The media also play an important role in how mental illness is portrayed. Class issues in health and mental health are alive and well in the field; those with mental illness receive poorer overall healthcare and suffer from underdiagnosis of physical illness. Mentally ill individuals of color are more likely to lack access to quality mental healthcare and endure discrimination within the system. Improved policies and practices are very much needed within the American mental health system, and social workers are well qualified to provide the needed services and leadership.

Chapter 2, A Short History of Mental Health Policy and Treatment in the United States, reveals a significant transformation in how mental illness has been viewed and understood over time and how the field of social work in mental health has developed. Responses to mental illness were very much rooted in culture and customs during historical periods. The kinds of medical and social help available to the mentally ill have changed over the course of many years. This chapter offers a chronological examination of the highlights in the history of mental health treatment. It details the history up through 1773, when the first person was admitted to the Public Hospital for Persons of Insane and Disordered Minds. In the 1880s, individuals with mental illness could be placed in mental institutions with no opportunity for release in the future, as part of a strong societal effort to keep mental illness hidden from public view. In 1841, the work of Dorothea Dix began to bring attention to the filth in which patients were forced to live and the physical abuse of some patients.

Chapter 2 also details the huge influence of Sigmund Freud, which emerged in the 1930s. In 1936, the first lobotomy was performed; and in 1938, electroshock therapy was developed by an Italian neurologist. In the 1940s and 1950s, drugs were developed to treat mental illness and brought with them the promise of allowing affected individuals to have more normal lives outside of institutions. The year 1955 saw the highest number of public psychiatric facilities for mentally ill patients, 560,000 in the United States. Chapter 2 also summarizes the National Mental Health Act signed by President Harry Truman in 1946, the Community Mental Health Act signed by President John F. Kennedy in 1963, and the Mental Health Systems Act signed by President Jimmy Carter in 1980. The Mental Health Parity Act of 1996 and the Mental Health Parity Addiction and Equity Act of 2008 are examined. The Excellence in Mental Health Act signed into law in 2014 by President Barack Obama to support community mental health funding is also considered. Overall, this chapter examines the development of the mental health system and the national, state, and local policies that address treatment of the mentally ill.

Chapter 3, Views From the Inside: Mental Health Clients and Their Families, shows that while much is written about clients with mental illness and their families, little research gives voice to the clients and families themselves. This chapter explores the challenges encountered when seeking assistance with mental health disorders, including client experiences within mental health programs and the financial barriers to help. The chapter offers a balanced approach by profiling cases where clients were helped as well as cases where clients' experiences in the system were not helpful or exacerbated their problems. Patient and family perspectives on coping with very serious mental health problems such as schizophrenia are included. The chapter also addresses the legal right to refuse treatment and the ramifications of treatment refusal.

Chapter 3 also describes how family members themselves often suffer from high levels of stress, anxiety, depression, constraints on social activities, and living with uncertainty about the course of mental illness. Family members are in need of support, which often is provided by social workers and/or a caregiver's support group. The chapter also discusses mental health consumer rights and advocacy groups, such as the Alliance for the Mentally Ill, the largest national organization that advocates for those with mental illness.

Chapter 4, Mental Illness Across the Life Cycle: Children, Adolescents, Adults, and Older Adults, addresses the relationship of mental illness to specific time periods of life. Attitudes of parents toward young children and their problem behaviors can have significant bearing on whether mental health treatment is sought for children. In extreme cases, parents of children living in poverty may want to have their children diagnosed with a mental disorder to qualify for disability benefits. Parents may seek the assistance of social workers to aid them in applying for these benefits. There is controversy over the age at which children should be prescribed psychotropic medications. Those who have entered into adolescence or young adulthood may, with no earlier warning, develop mental illness such as schizophrenia or bipolar disorder, which then becomes a lifelong challenge. Today there is concern about the effects of technology on children and adolescents and brain development. Access to social media can subject children and adolescents to cyberbullying and sexual victimization. Overall, since the 1990s, more children have been receiving mental health services and prescribed more psychotropic medications.

Chapter 4 addresses mental illness among emerging adults, including college students. In recent years, this population has been gaining more attention; however, overall college students have a hard time seeking treatment, and colleges do not do an especially good job of providing mental health services. Mental health services in the college setting are often provided by social workers. The chapter also discusses young adults in the military who can suffer posttraumatic stress disorder as a result of their war experiences.

Chapter 4 also examines how adult mental health problems can be a continuation of mental illness that develops in earlier life or how problems can emerge in adulthood. Depression and substance use disorder are good examples of problems that can develop either earlier or later in life. The mental health of older adults has only recently been given research attention. There are difficulties in separating normal cognitive aging from forms of dementia, with the problems of the elderly being less likely to attract the interest of physicians. Greater attention needs to be given to the mental health of elders, especially since they consume the majority of prescription drugs. Social work with elderly clients is a subspecialty within the field, and social workers are the professionals most likely to work within elder home care organizations and assess older clients for eligibility for nursing home care.

Chapter 5, Social Work and Mental Illness: Labels and Diagnoses, explores the similarities and differences between labeling and diagnoses of mental disorders. Labeling someone as having a mental disorder is typically seen as negative and contributes to the stigma that those with mental illness must endure. Diagnosis, as a medical term, is intended to provide a common language so that professionals can discuss, categorize, and successfully treat mental disorders. This chapter shows that while the uniqueness of each individual is important, the ability to classify mental disorders can assist in finding the best treatment more quickly.

Chapter 5 describes the development of the *Diagnostic and Statistical Manual of Mental Disorders* (*DSM*), the bible of mental illness classification, whose fifth (current) edition is titled *DSM-5*. Mental health diagnoses reflect the culture in which they were developed, and at times specific diagnoses fall out of favor. For example, "neuroses" are now known as anxiety disorders. The discussion of the *DSM* will illustrate that diagnoses can come and go, and that politics and profit can at times underlie our conceptions of mental illness. Treatment matching, the effort to match types of treatment to specific mental health disorders, is discussed. This includes treatments such as inpatient voluntary or involuntary hospitalization, partial hospitalization and other day programs, and different types of psychotherapy such as cognitive behavioral therapy and dialectical behavior therapy. Co-occurring disorders or dual diagnosis, which refers to both mental health and substance use disorders in individuals, is also examined in this chapter.

Chapter 6, Social Work and Psychiatry: Psychotropic Medications and Brain Stimulation Techniques, reviews classes of drugs and how they are prescribed, used, and abused by those persons with mental disorders. Psychiatric medications were developed in the 1940s and 1950s, and advances in these drugs are correlated with the reduction of psychiatric hospitalization through the years. The effectiveness of psychiatric drugs is examined, as are their side effects. For example, the antidepressant Paxil has been associated with suicide in some individuals for whom the drug is prescribed. There is also a discussion of the huge profits of pharmaceutical companies. In recent years, addiction to pain medications such as oxycodone and fentanyl has led to the current opioid crisis in the United States, which has been responsible for numerous deaths across the country.

Chapter 6 also explores the current use of electroconvulsive therapy for severely depressed patients, the use of lobotomy, and transcranial magnetic stimulation (TMS). TMS is a newer technique that provides brief magnetic impulses to the part of the brain that regulates mood. This technique is typically reserved for patients with major depressive disorder for whom antidepressants did not work or resulted in unacceptable side effects. Social workers can play an important role in gathering psychosocial information from applicants that is critical to screening and assessment for TMS.

Chapter 7, Gender, Race, Ethnicity, and the Mental Health System, shows race and ethnicity are closely correlated with mental health, especially disparities in access to and use of mental health services. This is a relatively new area of research, and it took the National Institute of Mental Health until 2015 to develop a strategic plan for research on mental health disparities. This chapter discusses the reality that racial and ethnic minorities have less access to mental healthcare, and when they do receive care, it is likely to be of lower quality. The chapter draws on the literature on the causes of disparities in the use of mental health services.

Chapter 7 also examines the combination of behavioral problems and the long history of racial discrimination in the United States, which can result in a juvenile justice response to mental illness in minorities rather than mental health interventions. Similarly, adults of color and those living in poverty who have behavioral health problems may be more likely to find their way into correctional facilities rather than programs that treat mental disorders. In the current political climate, which is highly unwelcoming of refugees and immigrants into the United States, mental health problems and treatment needs are likely to be very significant.

Chapter 8, Social Work, Mental Illness, and the Criminal Justice System, discusses the very close association between the criminal justice system and the mental health system. It explores the relationship between violence and mental illness. At times, a criminal justice intervention may occur when a mental health intervention is actually needed, especially for individuals suffering from major mental disorders. Indeed, incarceration can take the place of psychiatric hospitalization. Appropriate police response is critical in cases of challenging or threatening behavior. There is a long history of police doing a poor job of responding to calls where someone has a serious mental disorder. Importantly, there is a current move afoot to include social workers when police respond to calls where mental illness and/or substance abuse may be a factor.

Chapter 8 also examines how most correctional facilities in the United States do a poor job of providing basic physical and mental health services. Psychiatric services within correctional facilities are typically limited and of poor quality. This is especially true for incarcerated women. Another major issue discussed in this chapter is the inappropriate use of solitary confinement in correctional facilities, which is known to exacerbate mental health problems. Mental health and drug courts that employ social workers can divert offenders from incarceration into treatment and are showing good success.

Chapter 9, No Place to Go: Homelessness and Mental Illness, focuses on the very close association between these two problems. Mental illness is a major cause of homelessness in the United States. Social workers are on the front lines of providing assistance to the homeless mentally ill. Numerous studies show that more than 25% of the homeless have mental illness of some kind. According to the Department of Housing and Urban Development (HUD), in January 2016 approximately 20% of the homeless population had severe mental illness, and an additional 20% had a chronic substance use disorder. Mental illness and substance use disorder, known as co-occurring disorders, are heavily intertwined within the homeless population. Engaging the homeless in mental health treatment is especially challenging. The homeless must rely on hospital emergency room medical care, if any medical assistance is even sought; in this setting, mental illness is likely overlooked.

Chapter 9 also examines policies and models of providing housing for the mentally ill as a step toward addressing the mental health and other needs of homeless individuals. Research on Housing First and other models for serving the mentally ill is showing good success.

Chapter 10, Views From the Field: Challenges in Mental Health Social Work, examines the many systemic challenges that social workers encounter within the mental health field. Mental health treatment is provided within the broader context of a changing healthcare system. This chapter examines the economics of the mental health system, including Medicare, Medicaid, and private insurance coverage. It addresses the benefits as well as the liabilities of a managed care system. Social workers often assist clients in obtaining insurance that will cover mental healthcare, a process that can be very complex.

Chapter 10 also addresses the stressful nature of social work, especially within the mental health field. Diagnostic categories are not as clear as we would like, and well-trained and informed professionals can disagree about diagnoses and appropriate treatments. Also, mental healthcare regularly involves responding to crises, which adds to the stress of being a mental health professional. One source of stress for social workers and other mental health professionals is trying to determine whether a client is in need of psychiatric hospitalization or whether outpatient services are sufficient to meet the client's needs. Social workers at times need to determine whether an individual is a danger to himself or herself, or to others, and must be involuntarily committed to a psychiatric hospital. Other sources of stress include being a mandated reporter, who is legally responsible for making reports to an agency of suspected child abuse and/or neglect. Social workers and other professionals also have the duty to warn and protect potential crime victims if a client makes threats during a therapy session, as determined by the 1970s duty-to-warn case, *Tarasoff v. the Regents of the University of California*.

Chapter 11, Innovations in Mental Healthcare, examines how innovations in mental health treatment can come from a variety of sources. Successful implementation of innovations in mental health policy and care often depends upon social work agency leadership and the support of management as well as the availability of resources within organizations. An important innovation is to work toward greater integration of mental health, substance abuse, and primary care services—and here is one place where mental health policy can play a critical role. Primary care physicians are often the gatekeepers to referrals to mental health professionals; although they are the number one providers of antidepressant medications, they typically have little knowledge and training about mental illness and when it is appropriate to seek specialized social work mental health services for their patients.

Chapter 11 also addresses a much-needed innovation in determining ways to access the best medical care for mental and physical illness. Wider access to user-friendly electronic medical records holds the potential to improve communication among health providers, thereby improving all forms of healthcare, including mental health treatment. Other innovations to be discussed include the role of technology in improving mental healthcare, including e-therapy for clients for whom transportation is not available or who live in remote areas. Innovations in neuroimaging will help to identify mental disorders at an earlier point and, one hopes, lead to earlier and improved treatment. Adjunct activities such as exercise, including yoga, are known to aid recovery from mental disorders.

Chapter 12, Prevention and Future Issues in Mental Health Social Work, reveals that the prevention of mental illness falls solidly and almost exclusively within the purview of social work, rather than within other mental health professions such as psychology and psychiatry. This chapter discusses the need for greater emphasis on primary, secondary, and tertiary prevention in mental healthcare and policy. Primary prevention refers to seeking to prevent mental disorders from developing at all. Programs that ensure that children have adequate housing, food, clothing, and medical care can help to prevent the development of mental disorders. Secondary prevention refers to an early intervention to prevent a mental disorder from becoming worse. For chronic mental disorders such as schizophrenia or bipolar disorder, secondary prevention is the effort to prevent recurrent episodes. Tertiary prevention refers to actual treatment for mental disorders that prevent the spread of the consequences of mental illness to family members and others.

Chapter 12 discusses a key factor in prevention—that is, screening in a variety of contexts for mental health and substance abuse problems. Screenings should regularly take place in physicians' offices, hospital emergency rooms, court systems, and local health and mental health clinics. Policies that require medical providers to screen for mental health and substance abuse problems can have a very strong and positive impact on early intervention. Also, we need a better understanding of what obstacles prevent people from seeking mental health treatment.

Chapter 12 also reviews social determinants and how the conditions in which people are born, live, and work affect their health, especially their mental health. These circumstances are shaped by the distribution of power, money, and resources within the United Sates and every nation. A continuum of mental health policies and services is needed with input at the federal, state, and local levels. At the federal level, the Substance Abuse and Mental Health Services Administration (SAMHSA) provides frameworks for prevention and treatment and grants funding for innovative programs. At the state level, mental health services are designed using both federal and state funds, albeit with a wide disparity in the types and amount of mental care that are available in each state. At the community level, innovative programs seek state and federal funding. Community coalitions support improvements in community mental health and support the common goal of prevention. These coalitions often include mental health and substance abuse professionals from local human services organizations as well as parents and other members of the community. They can implement environmental changes such as restricting the number of alcohol outlets to make it more difficult for children and adolescents to obtain alcohol. State and federal funding are crucial to the development of an improved mental health system.

ACKNOWLEDGMENTS

Many people lent their support and helped to strengthen this work. John Kohler provided important insights into the mental health and substance abuse treatment fields. John's professional life underscores that the needs of clients are always paramount. My children, Anna and Cameron, serve as constant reminders of the importance of a healthy family. Cuf Ferguson lent his psychologist's eye to improve and clarify my work. My appreciation to Debra Riegert for helping to formulate the original ideas for this text. I am grateful to Amanda Smart and Wendy Mota Kasongo, University of Massachusetts (UMass) Boston graduate research assistants, for helping to gather source materials. And my gratitude to Marcia Colagiovanni for her very close reading and comments. As always, Marcia elevates my work.

Sylvia I. Mignon

This book also includes, for qualified instructors, an Instructor's Manual, PowerPoint presentations, and a Test Bank, which can be accessed by emailing textbook@Springerpub.com.

CHAPTER 1

SOCIAL WORK AND THE MENTAL HEALTH SYSTEM

LEARNING OUTCOMES

- Compare and contrast definitions of *mental health* and *mental illness*.
- Describe the prevalence of mental illness in the United States.
- Define *stigma* as it applies to individuals with mental illness.
- Analyze the impact of the media on concepts of mental illness.
- Explain social factors that contribute to mental health problems in American society.

INTRODUCTION

The concept of mental illness suggests many different and disturbing images and stereotypes. For example, as shown in television advertisements for antidepressants, there is the image of a woman with her head hanging appearing to be devoid of energy, looking forlorn and hopeless. There is the image of a man seemingly angry and very upset. Media depictions often attribute crimes of violence to those persons whose behavior is out of control due to a raging mental illness. However, mental illness is often a private kind of suffering for individuals and their families. Overall, we prefer to view those with mental illness as somehow different from ourselves. In fact, many of us will endure some form of mental illness in our lifetimes.

What, then, is mental health? Mental health includes our emotional, psychological, and social well-being. It affects how we think, feel, and act. It also helps determine how we handle stress, relate to others, and make choices. Further, mental health is important at every stage of life, from childhood and adolescence through adulthood. Factors that contribute to mental illness include biological factors such as genetics and brain chemistry and may be related to a family history of mental health problems. Life experiences such as childhood abuse and trauma are also associated with mental health problems.

Mental disorders, like mental health, impact a person's thoughts, feelings, moods, and behaviors. For some persons with mental illness, their disorders are chronic, lasting their entire lifetime. Other individuals may function well most of the time, yet have periodic episodes of mental illness that are a challenge for them and others. In reality, mental health cannot be separated from physical health, and mental disorders are underestimated due to a failure to appreciate the connection between other health conditions and mental illness (Prince et al., 2007).

This chapter reviews global ideas about mental health and addresses the stigma associated with mental illness that is often exacerbated by the media. It provides an overview of mental illness in the United States today. The chapter also begins our examination of the role of mental health social workers in providing services and developing policy. Part of this examination seeks to apply the core competencies of social work to mental health as determined by the Council on Social Work Education (CSWE), the accrediting body of social work undergraduate and graduate programs. See Tips for the Field 1.1 for the nine core competencies of social work that can be adapted to address the policy, research, and treatment needs of those with mental illness.

TIPS FOR THE FIELD 1.1

CORE COMPETENCIES OF THE COUNCIL ON SOCIAL WORK EDUCATION

In 2008, the CSWE changed its academic orientation to support competency-based education. Instead of focusing on curriculum design and organization, the CSWE took the position that social work education should focus on student learning outcomes. To reflect this stance, the Educational Policy and Accreditation Standards were revised in 2015, which resulted in the current nine core competencies. These core competencies of the CSWE are easily adaptable to the treatment of mental disorders:

1. *Demonstrate ethical and professional behavior.* The first core competency is a hallmark of the social work profession. With this profession long recognized as having one of the strongest professional codes of ethics, ethical behavior is at the very heart of the social work profession. In this text we will see the challenges of maintaining these ethical standards in the treatment of those with mental illness.

2. *Engage diversity and difference in practice.* The second core competency focuses on cultural competency and encourages equitable treatment for diverse populations. There are numerous examples that illustrate the potential for differential treatment according to race and ethnicity, especially within the criminal justice system. Mental

health services must be provided to individuals and families of color by a diverse group of professionals.

3. *Advance human rights and social and economic environmental justice.* The third core competency addresses the history of the social work profession and its commitment to ensuring access to mental healthcare and the role of social work in developing a just American society. Today's mental health system is not necessarily just and can be rife with prejudice that has long-term negative consequences for the poor and people of color. An essential factor is that justice must be available to all in both access to and quality of care.

4. *Engage in practice-informed research and research-informed practice.* The fourth core competency underlies the social work profession; there is a clear need to determine what works and what does not in the treatment of mental illness. Social work knowledge and skills must be acquired and applied through a continuous learning process that consistently seeks improvement over time.

5. *Engage in policy practice.* The fifth core competency addresses the need for members of the social work profession to acquire leadership and policy development skills in addition to clinical skills. Social workers have the knowledge and experience to make important contributions to mental health policy and need to increasingly seek these kinds of professional policy and leadership positions.

6. *Engage with individuals, families, groups, organizations, and communities.* The sixth core competency corroborates that social workers possess the critical skills needed to engage clients and their families in mental health treatment. Social workers must bring community attention to the needs of the mentally ill and improve mental health advocacy and advocacy organizations.

7. *Assess individuals, families, groups, organizations, and communities.* The seventh core competency supports social workers in their work, including determining the appropriate types of treatment for individual clients and their families. As much as possible, these assessments and recommendations for treatment should be free of bias.

8. *Intervene with individuals, families, groups, organizations, and communities.* The eighth competency addresses the wide variety of social work interventions necessary to ensure the appropriate provision of mental health services. Additionally, interventions must support the effort to overcome individual and community obstacles to providing mental health treatment.

9. *Evaluate practice with individuals, families, groups, organizations, and communities.* The ninth and final competency relates back to the fourth core competency, which states that research and program evaluation are critical in determining effective treatments for those with mental illness. Social workers in clinical settings are in a very good position to assess and implement effective treatment protocols. Overall, social work interventions with the mentally ill must be developed, tested, and evaluated to determine what works best.

SOURCE: Council on Social Work Education. (2015). *2015 education and policy and accreditation standards for baccalaureate and master's social work programs.* Alexandria, VA: Author.

▓ GLOBAL IDEAS ABOUT MENTAL HEALTH

No one is a stranger to stress; indeed, many people today are living under extreme stress. Stress is associated with experiences of mental as well as physical illness, with a host of illnesses being triggered or exacerbated by stress. Stress is clearly a worldwide phenomenon. In 2017 alone, the United Nations refugee agency reported 68.5 million refugees around the world had to flee persecution, violence, and/or war (Associated Press, 2018). It is hard to imagine anything more stressful than having to leave one's homeland with no guarantee of safe passage to a protected environment for oneself and family. We are naive to think these experiences do not pose mental health risks for those who must endure the challenges of being unwanted immigrants and refugees.

Estimates from the World Health Organization (WHO) show the magnitude of mental health problems around the world. Approximately 300 million people worldwide suffer from depression (WHO, 2018a, 2018b). Bipolar disorder affects approximately 60 million people, and schizophrenia is estimated to affect 23 million people (WHO, 2018a, 2018b).

In American society, we are constantly bombarded with images of violence from around the world. This exposure begins at very early ages, with the many images of war and natural disasters that we see on the daily news. We see refugees fleeing worn-torn countries, only to be turned back. On television we watch Syrian children gagging and trying to breathe after being gassed by their own government. We see losses attributed to nature such as the 2017 devastation of Puerto Rico by Hurricane Maria and surviving residents coping with posttraumatic stress, including anxiety and depression (Daily Briefing, 2017; *New York Times*, 2018). We see the stress of immigrants in the United States facing deportation under President Donald Trump and families ripped apart in the process, including the separate detention of parents and children of all ages at the Mexican border (Linsky, 2018).

It is very difficult to determine the number of people across the globe who live with constant stress as well as the myriad health conditions that negatively impact mental health (Anderson & Jane-Llopis, 2011). The development and expansion of research on the impact of natural and human-made disasters on children are of great importance. The vulnerability of children is evident due to their undeveloped or underdeveloped coping skills (Grolnick et al., 2018). Their reactions to stress may include anxiety, depression, and grief that can result in posttraumatic stress disorder (PTSD). Previous mental health problems can worsen or new mental health issues can develop as children react to trauma. The numerous and devastating school shootings in the United States can leave child and adolescent victims as well as witnesses with long-term consequences.

Interventions immediately after trauma, known as *psychological first aid* or *psychological debriefing*, are considered promising; however, more research is needed. The fact that school shootings are now commonplace led to the development of the Cognitive Behavioral Intervention for Trauma in Schools (CBITS), a model for providing services to children and adolescents who have experienced school shootings (Grolnick et al., 2018).

Mental disorders are closely related to other health conditions, but more must be discovered about those connections. Mental illness in every culture can be linked to chronic illnesses associated with lifestyle factors such as poor diet, smoking, obesity, and high blood pressure. A mental illness can make it harder to adhere to a medication regimen (Prince et al., 2007). Physical injury can both be caused by and result from mental illness. Food insecurity, a huge problem in today's world, is also associated with the development of mental health disorders in children and adolescents. The more inadequate children and adolescents' nutrition, the more likely they are to develop a mental health disorder (Burke, Martini, Cayir, Hartline-Grafton, & Meade, 2016).

Unfortunately, mental health is not typically considered an urgent concern in developing countries, where eradicating infectious disease is the priority (Nii-Trebi, 2017; Prince et al., 2007). Key goals of the WHO in 2015 included the promotion of research on mental health and the reduction of substance abuse around the world (WHO, 2018b). The Centre for Global Mental Health (CGMH), located in the United Kingdom, is a pioneer in supporting research, promoting access to care, and ensuring the prevention and treatment of mental health problems, especially in poor countries that have few health resources (CGMH, n.d.). Its Mental Health Innovation Network (MHIN) promotes the sharing of innovations among researchers, clinicians, and policy makers to improve global mental health.

As we will see in this text, culture has strong bearing on attitudes toward mental health and mental illness. In a study comparing mental health professionals in Brazil with mental health professionals in Switzerland, Brazilian professionals held a more positive attitude toward providing psychiatric services within the community, whereas Swiss professionals held greater stigmatizing attitudes and showed a preference for prescribing medications over other interventions (Des Courtis, Lauber, Costa, & Cattapan-Ludewig, 2008).

Overall, more attention must be paid to global mental health and well-being as well as to individual and community resilience. Much more can and should be done to promote the mental well-being of citizens of all nations. This includes promoting strong social networks and living environments that support physical and mental health (Anderson & Jane-Llopis, 2011). These efforts will become even more critical as the world copes with climate change and the knowledge that ice caps in Antarctica are melting three times faster today than they were 10 years ago (Pierre-Louis, 2018). To further promote change, global mental health initiatives must obtain greater prominence, funding, and support from global political leaders (Tomlinson & Lund, 2012). Global strategies are necessary to reduce the stigma of mental illness, develop evidence-based practices, and support innovative approaches to treatment (Tomlinson & Lund, 2012). Unified social justice and human rights approaches are also necessary to gain the attention of policy makers. Lastly, key interventions on a global level must consider local, national, and international politics (Sawyer, Stanford, & Campbell, 2016).

MENTAL ILLNESS IN THE UNITED STATES

The magnitude of mental disorders is underestimated in the United States. This can be attributed in part to the divorcing of mental health disorders from other kinds of health problems (Prince et al., 2007). However, it is clear that concerns for mental health should be an integral part of social and health policies (Prince et al., 2007). Varying estimates of mental health problems can be attributed to the use of different questionnaires, how the questions are administered, and whether findings of specific studies can be generalized beyond a specific sample (Bagalman & Cornell, 2018). There is also a distinction between having symptoms of a specific mental health problem such as depression and not seeking treatment, and having depression diagnosed by a mental health professional. Some surveys include substance use disorders as a mental health problem, whereas others distinguish between mental health and substance use disorders. The distinctions and intersections between mental health disorders and substance use disorders are examined in Chapter 5, Social Work and Mental Illness: Labels and Diagnoses.

The best-known and most comprehensive national survey on mental health and substance abuse is the National Survey on Drug Use and Health, administered through the Substance Abuse and Mental Health Services Administration (SAMHSA). This survey is completed each year and consists of interviews with approximately 68,000 people age 12 and older. The survey collects data on substance use and mental illness. For substance use, data are collected on tobacco use, alcohol use, illicit drug use, substance use disorders, and substance abuse treatment. For mental illness, data are not collected by specific mental health diagnosis but rather according to the following categories: major depressive episode (within the past year), mental illness among adults, co-occurring mental illness and substance use disorders among adults, suicidal thoughts and behavior among adults, and mental health service use among adults. For adolescents, data are collected on major depressive episodes and substance use (SAMHSA, 2017). Thus, data are collected in major categories without a specific focus on clinical diagnosis of individuals.

In 2016, it was estimated that 18.3% of American adults age 18 and older had some kind of mental illness during the previous year. It was estimated that 4.2% of American adults had *serious* mental illness (SAMHSA, 2017). Among adolescents age 12 to 17, 12.8% had a major depressive episode. Of those adolescents, only 40.9% received treatment for depression. The mental health problems of adolescents are addressed in Chapter 4, Mental Illness Across the Life Cycle: Children, Adolescents, Adults, and Older Adults.

Also in 2016, among adults age 18 and older, 14.4% received some form of mental healthcare over the previous year. This percentage was measured by responses to questions about whether respondents sought help for their "nerves," anxiety, or their emotions. For the purpose of the survey, the category of *any mental illness* was defined as a "mental, behavioral, or emotional disorder" that can range from no impairment to mild, moderate, or severe impairment (National Institute of Mental Health, 2017). For adults with any mental illness, 43.1% received treatment services in the past year. *Serious mental illness* was defined as the same "mental, behavioral, or emotional disorder" but has a major impact on one's life that causes serious functional impairment (National Institute of Mental Health, 2017). Examples of serious mental illness include schizophrenia and bipolar disorder. For those adults with serious mental illness, 64.8% received mental health services in the past year (SAMHSA, 2017).

It is very difficult to generalize about mental healthcare because access to services varies widely by state. For example, the highest rates of access to care are found in Vermont, Massachusetts, Maine, Connecticut, and Minnesota (Nguyen & Davis, 2018). The states with the lowest rates of access to mental healthcare and the highest rates of incarceration are among the poorest: Alabama, Arkansas, and Mississippi (Nguyen & Davis, 2018).

Lack of health insurance can directly limit access to mental healthcare. Those persons with private insurance or those with the ability to pay on their own have significantly greater access to mental health resources. The poor have less access to mental healthcare and may receive lower-quality mental healthcare services. One's health insurance status can be related to one's level of stress. In the Stress in America survey conducted in 2017 for the American Psychological Association, 43% of respondents indicated that healthcare concerns were a source of stress and 66% reported that health insurance costs were also a source of stress (American Psychological Association, 2018). Further, having public insurance such as Medicaid can be associated with higher levels of anxiety (Jacobs, Hill, & Burdette, 2015). Not surprisingly, adults without health insurance reported higher levels of overall stress than those adults with health insurance (American Psychological Association, 2018).

Class disparities have significant effects on mental health. The poor and disadvantaged groups live with more stress and problems associated with mental health issues, including gun violence, obesity, smoking, and other health issues (Schroeder, 2016). Chapter 7, Gender, Race, Ethnicity, and the Mental Health System, and Chapter 8, Social Work, Mental Illness, and the Criminal Justice System, discuss class disparities in terms of access to healthcare and the greater likelihood of the poor and minorities having contact with the criminal justice system.

STIGMA AND MENTAL ILLNESS

Often it is the lack of knowledge and understanding of mental illness that is associated with the assignment of stigma to individuals with mental health problems (Rusch, Angermeyer, & Corrigan, 2005). In fact, in many cultures, mental illness is among the most stigmatized conditions. Stigma is based on *stereotypes*—that is, beliefs about certain groups within a society (Corrigan & Shapiro, 2010). *Prejudice* is the negative attitude toward those groups, and *discrimination* is the behavior that results from prejudice (Corrigan & Shapiro, 2010). Prejudice and stereotyping are not sufficient in and of themselves to stigmatize. Instead, stigma is the actual discrimination based upon power differentials (Rusch et al., 2005). It can take the form of discrimination directed toward individuals with mental illness as well as institutional discrimination that, whether intentional or not, reduces life opportunities for those with mental illness (Rusch et al., 2005). It is the structural discrimination toward the mentally ill in American society that results in both the lack of and the poor quality of mental health services (Schulze & Angermeyer, 2003).

So powerful is the stigma of mental illness that it reduces the chances that those with mental illness will seek help. For affected individuals, this can mean missed opportunities for appropriate treatment. In addition, the stigma of mental illness exacerbates the problems associated with determining its prevalence (Baumann, 2007; Jackowska, 2009; Rusch et al., 2005). In some cases, persons with mental disorders may have their physical health problems overlooked by health professionals, with their physical symptoms being erroneously attributed to their mental illness (Thornicroft, Rose, & Kassam, 2007).

Severe mental illness such as schizophrenia can bring rejection to individuals and their families from others and also from mental health professionals themselves (Jackowska, 2009). One survey of people with schizophrenia in Poland found that 58% expected discrimination in their contacts with other people and 50% expected stigma in employment (Cechnicki, Angermeyer, & Bielanska, 2011). Higher levels of perceived stigma by those with schizophrenia can be linked with low self-esteem (Berge & Ranney, 2005).

In a study comparing individuals with bipolar disorder and those with depression, both groups reported that they felt stigmatized. However, those with bipolar disorder felt an even greater psychosocial impact (Lazowski, Koller, Stuart, & Milev, 2012). Another study found that when respondents in the United Kingdom focused on the biomedical causation of bipolar disorder, there was increased compassion and less desire to maintain social distance (Ellison, Mason, & Scior, 2015).

It is hard enough for persons with mental illness to cope with symptoms and behaviors, but stigma adds another layer of stress (Rusch et al., 2005). These effects of stigma can last for many years and even a lifetime. *Self-stigma* is defined as the mentally ill taking on the stigmatized attitudes toward themselves. Internalizing the stigma associated with mental illness can lead to lower self-esteem (Corrigan, Kerr, & Knudsen, 2005; Corrigan & Rao, 2012). Self-stigma can also extend to negative beliefs about one's own character and competency. It fosters negative emotional reactions to the self and results in behavior that restricts opportunities (Corrigan et al., 2005). Perceptions of stigma by those with mental illness can be associated with an overall lower quality of life, including restricted social connections and fewer work opportunities (Alonso et al., 2009; Corrigan et al., 2005).

An individual's choice to disclose mental illness can be empowering and inspiring or, alternatively, negative and self-deprecating, depending on the circumstances (Rusch et al., 2005). Programs to promote self-empowerment may include feeling a sense of control over one's life and treatment, which are discussed in Chapter 11, Innovations in Mental Healthcare, and Chapter 12, Prevention and Future Issues in Mental Health Social Work (Corrigan et al., 2005; Corrigan & Rao, 2012).

Mental health professionals themselves can hold stigmatizing attitudes, most commonly directed toward individuals with schizophrenia (Nordt, Rossler, & Lauber, 2006; Rusch et al., 2005; Schulze & Angermeyer, 2003). As we will learn, some mental health professionals are not willing to serve the most serious mentally ill and drop participation in the Medicaid program (Corrigan et al., 2005). The fact that some psychiatrists can hold the same negative attitudes toward the mentally ill calls into question whether psychiatrists are appropriate role models in antistigma efforts (Lauber, Anthony, Ajdacic-Gross, & Rossler, 2004).

THE MEDIA AND MENTAL ILLNESS

It is common knowledge that the media play to stereotypes of the mentally ill as unpredictable and dangerous (Angermeyer & Schulze, 2001; Ma, 2017). Indeed, when heinous crimes are committed and reported in news outlets, there is always some question as to whether the perpetrator has a history of mental illness. Invariably, someone makes the point that "normal" people do not commit heinous crimes and, therefore, the perpetrator must be mentally ill. When few people have knowledge of mental illness, it is not a surprise that most rely on images from the news, television, and movies. News outlets engage in selective reporting, which then influences the public to believe mental illness should be stigmatized and is a cause of violent crime (Angermeyer & Schulze, 2001). In truth, those persons with mental illness are not more likely to be dangerous than individuals without mental illness (Rueve & Welton, 2008). This issue is explored further in Chapter 8, Social Work, Mental Illness, and the Criminal Justice System.

The association of violent crime with mental illness by the media is not accurate, and more realistic portrayals in the media can reduce the stigma. One study of college students found that almost one fourth obtained their perceptions of mental illness from television and films and were also more likely to think of these as realistic portrayals (Aguiniga, Madden, & Zellman, 2016). Research shows that nonstigmatizing messages about the mentally ill can influence the public to be more supportive of increased funding and services (McGinty, Goldman, Pescosolido, & Barry, 2018).

Evidence-based methods to reduce stigma include working to counteract the negative effects of advertising and media reports about mental illness (Rusch et al., 2005). Education aimed at providing factual knowledge about mental health is known to be more effective among those who start with a strong knowledge base. Research shows that personal contact with the mentally ill has positive effects on attitudes (Rubio-Valera et al., 2016; Rusch et al., 2005). Other suggestions include providing information to address causal beliefs about mental illness (Ellison et al., 2015). See Tips for the Field 1.2 for a list of suggestions for how social workers can help to reduce the stigma of mental illness.

TIPS FOR THE FIELD 1.2

DIGGING DEEPER INTO MENTAL HEALTH STIGMA: WHAT SOCIAL WORKERS CAN DO

1. Social workers can evaluate their own attitudes toward those with mental illness and work to reduce their own stigmatizing attitudes.

2. BA and MSW degree programs can offer more courses on and opportunities to learn about mental illness and infuse mental health issues into the curricula. Academic programs can also increase the availability of field instruction and internships in mental hospitals and outpatient clinics.

3. Social workers can help reduce stigma by working with and supporting family members. This will enable family members to receive the support they need and reduce the stigma felt by family members themselves.

4. Social workers can develop and lead antistigma programs and workshops that challenge misconceptions about mental illness. These programs and workshops can be offered to the general public, to family members, to police and other law enforcement agencies, and to other mental health professionals.

5. Social workers can advocate for change within their own agencies, ensuring that the needs of the mentally ill are a priority within the scope of service.

6. Social workers can advocate for policy change by providing education to legislators and other policy makers and by positioning themselves to contribute to policy development.

7. Social workers can design and carry out research studies that assess stigma and help to enhance the knowledge base regarding stigma.

SOURCES: Ahmedani, B. K. (2011). Mental health stigma: Society, individuals, and the profession. *Journal of Social Work Values and Ethics, 8*(2), 4–16; Rubio-Valera, M., Aznar-Lou, I., Vives-Collet, M., Fernandez, A., Gil-Girbau, M., & Serrano-Blanco, A. (2016). Reducing the mental health-related stigma of social work students: A cluster RCT. *Research on Social Work Practice, 28*(2), 164–172. doi:10.1177/1049731516641492

◼ WHO IS AFFECTED BY MENTAL ILLNESS? PRESIDENT TRUMP AND THE GOLDWATER RULE

Exactly who gets mental illness? There is much debate about how mental illness develops. Is it biological? Is the home life, the community environment, or even a traumatic brain injury that results in mental illness to blame? Is it a combination of these factors? Psychiatrist Thomas Szasz characterized mental illness as simply "problems in living," rather than a disease process (Szasz, 1961). Explanations for mental illness have continued to evolve through the years and are discussed in Chapter 2, A Short History of Mental Health Policy and Treatment in the United States. More recently, WHO (2018b, 2018c) has found that mental health problems can result from human rights violations, crime victimization, financial pressures, gender discrimination, difficult or inadequate employment, social isolation, physical health problems, and genetic predisposition. We will learn in this text that psychiatrists, social workers, psychologists, and mental health counselors do not necessarily agree on how mental illness develops or how to diagnosis and treat the different forms of mental illness.

Even the president of the United States has been the subject of media coverage regarding whether he has a mental disorder. Much controversy exists among the public as well as some mental health professionals regarding the mental health of President Donald Trump (Lee et al., 2017). He has been called "narcissistic," a term that has been extensively discussed by the media (Scharfenberg, 2017). This issue has garnered so much attention that *The Boston Globe* printed a front-page article in February 2017 as Trump began his presidency. *The Boston Globe* staff conducted interviews with 10 psychiatrists and psychologists, some of whom supported Trump and some of whom did not (Begley, 2017). All 10 respondents agreed that Trump has a need to feel superior to other people. However, to warrant a diagnosis of mental illness—in this specific case, narcissistic personality disorder—as described in the *Diagnostic and Statistical Manual of Mental Disorders, Fifth Edition*, the individual must suffer some distress and some level of impairment. In the case of President Trump, he does not appear to display distress, and his behavior has brought financial success and media attention in the business world that served as his stepping-stone to the presidency. In contrast, some political pundits have focused on Trump's business failures that have been downplayed over time and that have resulted in him declaring bankruptcy several times.

As a result of the election of Donald Trump to the presidency, there has been a resurgence of discussion about what is known as the Goldwater Rule. This ethical rule stems from a 1964 survey by *Fact* magazine of 12,356 psychiatrists about whether presidential candidate Barry Goldwater was psychologically fit to serve as president of the United States (Levin, 2016). Responses included that he was a "paranoid schizophrenic," suffering from a "chronic psychosis," and "a megalomaniacal, grandiose omnipotence" (Levin, 2016, pp. 1–2). It appeared that some psychiatrist respondents were taking issue with Goldwater's very conservative politics rather than rendering a true picture of the mental health of the candidate himself. This controversy over the mental health status of a political candidate in 1973 led to what is now known as the Goldwater Rule: Section 7.3 of the American Psychiatric Association's (APA) *Principles of Medical Ethics With Annotations Especially Applicable to Psychiatry* explicitly states that while psychiatrists can share their general expertise, it is unethical to offer a professional opinion unless a psychiatrist has examined an individual and has received that specific individual's permission to make that assessment public (Mayer, 2010).

In March 2017, there was further interpretation of the Goldwater Rule by the APA that psychiatrists cannot and should not diagnose from afar and, further, cannot make any comment on a public figure's "expressed emotion, speech or behavior, even in an emergency" (Lee, Glass, & Fisher, 2018, p. 10). The authors of the controversial 2017 book *The Dangerous Case of Donald Trump* clarify that they were not seeking a diagnosis for President Trump but rather were sounding an alarm about "the dangers of Trump's proximity to weapons of mass destruction" (Lee et al., 2018, p. A10). The authors describe their efforts as a "duty to warn," rather than an effort to formulate a mental health diagnosis.

Regardless of where one stands on the Trump presidency, there are indicators that stress has increased among Americans since his election. The Stress in America survey conducted in 2017 by the American Psychological Association (2018) found that 63% of respondents felt stress over "the future of our nation." Mental health professionals have also reported increases in stress and anxiety attributable to concerns about the future of the United States, leading more people to seek psychotherapy (Arnett, 2017).

CURRENT STATUS OF THE MENTAL HEALTH SYSTEM

Overall, no cohesive national mental health system exists in the United States. Those in need of mental healthcare can face barriers due to lack of insurance or private funds to pay. A 2009 assessment of the mental health system in the United States by the Congressional Research Service, the public policy research division of Congress, found "evidence suggests a comprehensive transformation of the mental health system could be necessary" (Sundararaman, 2009). Recommendations from the report included (a) providing evidence-based practices, (b) increasing the mental health workforce, (c) ensuring access to mental healthcare, (d) increasing professional coordination and collaboration, and (e) improving research evaluation of treatment services. These recommendations have largely gone unnoticed and disregarded, with the result being that no comprehensive systemic delivery of service has been developed. More recently, in 2015 the SAMHSA offered a plan to improve mental health in the United States. See Tips for the Field 1.3 for the SAMHSA recommendations.

TIPS FOR THE FIELD 1.3

THE PLAN OF THE SUBSTANCE ABUSE AND MENTAL HEALTH SERVICES ADMINISTRATION TO IMPROVE MENTAL HEALTH IN THE UNITED STATES

1. *Increase prevention, treatment, and recovery services.* This includes early intervention and integrated treatment to prevent more expensive mental healthcare and to move toward providing services comparable to those that would be provided to individuals with other health conditions. This recommendation aligns with the core competencies of the CSWE) to assess (number 7 in Tips for the Field 1.1) and intervene with individuals, families, and groups (number 8 in Tips for the Field 1.1).

2. *Expand the mental health workforce.* The shortage of mental health professionals must be addressed, and new professionals must be culturally competent and trauma informed. Much more financial and other kinds of investments must be made to ensure the availability of innovative treatment approaches that include crisis prevention, medication management, intervention strategies, community resources, and family and peer supports.

3. *Widen the use of information technology.* Technology can be effectively utilized to fill in the gaps with hard-to-reach groups such as those living in rural areas. For example, these technologies can include telepsychiatry and online psychotherapy. Electronic medical records can help ensure that all medical professionals have access to a client's medical history and problem list. Technology can also bolster the clinical skills of mental health professionals by giving them access to a wide variety of educational and training opportunities such as webinars.

4. *Educate the public.* The stigma of mental illness has long been acknowledged as holding back the development of innovations in treatment. Negative attitudes toward the mentally ill contribute to the lack of medical and social attention to this group, and stigma often prevents those with mental illness from seeking help. Awareness strategies and campaigns need to be mounted in academic environments, workplaces, and faith communities to reduce prejudice.

5. *Invest in research.* Much more needs to be known about genetic predisposition and brain development and their impact on an individual's mental health. We need to further distinguish the types of mental illness and their corresponding best treatments.

SOURCE: Hyde, P. S., & Del Vecchio, P. (2015, February 18). *Five point plan to improve the nation's mental health.* Retrieved from https://blog.samhsa.gov/2015/02/18/five-point-plan-to-improve-the-nations-mental-health

SOCIAL WORKERS IN MENTAL HEALTH

Social workers are the largest group of professional providers of mental health services in the United States. Social workers are uniquely qualified to develop and improve policy and practice. The beginnings of the social work profession included the development of societal responses to mental illness, especially individual treatment for mental disorders (Social Work Policy Institute, 2004).

Mental health social workers must contend with the context in which services are provided, which encompasses legal, policy, political, and social issues (Sawyer et al., 2016). Typically, social workers are not perceived to be those who implement mental health policy. To change this perception, they must strive to develop and expand their expertise and power in the arena of mental health policy. Social workers must influence and work directly with legislators and other policy developers (Powell, Garrow, Woodford, & Perron, 2013), which may mean improving existing policy as well as developing new policy. Social workers can also support their clients by participating in formal policy development. They may develop informal policy by creating specific treatment and referral collaborations with other agencies to ensure continuity of care (Powell et al., 2013).

Since a variety of mental health specialists provide mental healthcare services, there can be controversy over who is best trained and who is in the best position to provide these services (Sawyer et al., 2016). In reality, much remains to be done to develop a continuum of mental health services, and there is room for all kinds of mental health practitioners. Today psychiatrists are often called psychopharmacologists because their practices focus on prescribing medications to treat mental illness rather than providing psychotherapy. Psychologists have the expertise to provide psychological testing that can assist in determining proper diagnoses and also provide psychotherapy. Mental health counselors provide individual and group counseling to clients who have mental illness. Psychiatric nurses are able to prescribe psychotropic medications in some states and also provide psychotherapy.

Social workers have a wide range of expertise, including clinical evaluation, treatment skills, and supervisory skills within agencies. In addition, they can take up the mantle of leadership in the field of mental health, as discussed in Chapter 12, Prevention and Future Issues in Mental Health Social Work. Social workers keep current on the availability of community resources and understand how to circumvent the bureaucratic rules that control access to services. They promote self-advocacy for their clients. They know the importance of strong and supportive families and communities. Social workers understand the relationship between climate change and mental health as they advocate for environmental justice (Anderson & Jane-Llopis, 2011; Jackson, 2018). A core competency as established by CSWE (number 3 in Tips for the Field 1.1) is to advance human rights, as well as social, economic, and environmental justice. See Tips for the Field 1.4 for the principles that guide the provision of mental health services by social workers.

TIPS FOR THE FIELD 1.4

PRINCIPLES OF THE COUNCIL ON SOCIAL WORK EDUCATION TO DIRECT THE PROVISION OF MENTAL HEALTH SERVICES BY SOCIAL WORKERS

The CSWE devised the following principles to guide the role of social work in mental health and behavioral healthcare:

1. *Meet the needs of the individual.* This includes an individual's access to mental healthcare, diagnosis, treatment including medication management, and additional

supportive resources. The CSWE supports the provision of these services by licensed MSWs and states that mental health service provision should not be restricted to those professionals with MDs (psychiatrists or other physicians) and those with PhDs (psychologists). Additionally, the CSWE seeks to ensure that peer-based services are provided by those who have experience, adequate training, and appropriate supervision.

2. *Recognize social determinants of health.* Social determinants of health are circum-stances under which individuals are born, develop physically and mentally, live and work, and become older adults. These experiences are shaped by the distribution of power and money at all societal levels. The CSWE supports services that will address the social determinants as they impact the mentally ill.

3. *Support a team-based approach.* Collaboration with other social workers and other mental health professionals is the best way to ensure the highest quality of care. This includes psychiatrists, primary care physicians, nurses, psychologists, and mental health counselors. All can benefit from educational programs designed for the mental health professions. There is also the need to increase the number of mental health professionals in the United States. For example, the CSWE supports initiatives to develop and expand health training programs such as the Minority Fel-lowship Program of the Substance Abuse and Mental Health Services Administration (SAMHSA), the Mental and Behavioral Health Education Program at Health Resources and Services Administration (HRSA), and the Behavioral Health Workforce Education and Training Program, a collaboration between SAMHSA and HRSA.

4. *Recognize the value of social workers.* Social workers should not only provide clini-cal and supervisory services, but also be involved in policy. This includes serving in advisory and consultative roles to organizational leadership and committee partici-pation.

SOURCE: Council on Social Work Education. (2014, October). *The role of social work in mental and behavioral health care: Principles for public policy.* Alexandria, VA: Author. Retrieved from https://www.cswe.org/getattachment/Advocacy-Policy/RoleofSWinMentalandBehavorialHealth Care-January2015-FINAL.pdf.aspx

Now is the ideal time for more social workers to consider a specialty in mental health treatment and policy. In the coming years, the federal government, through SAMHSA, is making serious mental illness a pri-ority on the national level (Pace, 2017a, 2017b). However, because an inadequate number of all mental health professionals exist, expanding the assessment and treatment skills of social workers will make signifi-cant contributions to the field. Additionally, regarding policy, the NASW recommends offering more policy-type field placements in social work programs to cultivate greater knowledge of policy among social work-ers and to cultivate a link between policy and social work interventions (Pace, 2017b).

SUMMARY AND CONCLUSION

A great deal must be done to improve the quality and access to mental health services on international and national levels. Research on global mental health interventions must be expanded to determine the most appropriate types of treatment. As the largest providers of mental healthcare in the United States, social workers are well qualified to provide these services. The stigma of mental illness has long interfered with help seeking by individuals and their families. Efforts to reduce stigma by social workers can have a positive effect on improving the societal response to mental illness. Together, the CSWE principles and the SAMHSA plan have important contributions to make to improving quality and access to mental healthcare in the United States.

DISCUSSION QUESTIONS/TOPICS

1. Why is it difficult to define mental illness?
2. Discuss your ideas for how global mental health can be improved.
3. What social factors contribute to mental health problems?
4. How can the core competencies defined by the CSWE strengthen the American response to mental health problems?
5. What can be done so that the media offer more realistic portrayals of mental illness?
6. How should the media explore the potential mental health problems of a sitting president of the United States?
7. How can technology improve services for those with mental illness?
8. Discuss some of your own ideas for how social workers can help reduce the stigma of mental illness.
9. Discuss why there has not been much progress in the development of mental health policy in the United States.
10. How can federal agencies such as SAMHSA help to expand and improve mental health services?

REFERENCES

Aguiniga, D. M., Madden, E. E., & Zellman, K. T. (2016). An exploratory analysis of students' perceptions of mental health in the media. *Social Work in Mental Health, 14*(4), 428–444. doi:10.1080/15332985.2015 .1118002

Alonso, J. M., Buron, A., Rojas-Farreras, S., de Graaf, R., Haro, J. M., de Girolamo, G., … Vilagut, G. (2009). Perceived stigma among individuals with common mental disorders. *Journal of Affective Disorders, 118*(1–3), 180–186. doi:10.1016/j.jad.2009.02.006

American Psychological Association. (2018, January 24). *Stress in America: Uncertainty about health care.* www.apa.org/news/press/releases/stress/index

Anderson, P., & Jane-Llopis, E. (2011). Mental health and global well-being. *Health Promotional International, 26*(S1), i147–i155. doi:10.1093/heapro/dart060

Angermeyer, M. C., & Schulze, B. (2001). Reinforcing stereotypes: How the focus on forensic cases in news reporting may influence public attitudes towards the mentally ill. *International Journal of Law and Psychiatry, 24,* 469–486. doi:10.1016/S0160-2527(01)00079-6

Arnett, D. (2017, February 21). Political fears grip therapists' offices. *The Boston Globe,* A1.

Associated Press. (2018, June 20). A record 68.5 million refugees displaced in 2017. *The Boston Globe,* A4.

Bagalman, E., & Cornell, A. S. (2018, January 19). Prevalence of mental illness in the United States: Data sources and estimates. *Congressional Research Service, 7-5700,* R43047. Retrieved from https://fas.org/sgp/crs/misc/R43047.pdf

Baumann, A. E. (2007). Stigmatization, social distance and exclusion because of mental illness: The individual with mental illness as a "stranger." *International Review of Psychiatry, 19*(2), 131–135. doi:10.1080/09540260701278739

Begley, S. (2017, February 13). Executive analysis, from afar: Mental health experts find room for conjecture in Trump's blustering, boasts, and tweets. *The Boston Globe,* A1.

Berge, M., & Ranney, M. (2005). Self-esteem and stigma among person with schizophrenia: Implications for mental health. *Care Management Journal, 6*(3), 139–144.

Burke, M. P., Martini, L. H., Cayir, E., Hartline-Grafton, H. L., & Meade, R. L. (2016). Severity of household food insecurity is positively associated with mental disorders among children and adolescents in the United States. *Journal of Nutrition, 146*(10), 2019–2026. doi:10.3945/jn.116.232298

Cechnicki, A., Angermeyer, M. C., & Bielanska, A. (2011). Anticipated and experienced stigma among people with schizophrenia: Its nature and correlates. *Social Psychiatry and Psychiatric Epidemiology, 46*(7), 643–650. doi:10.1007/s00127-010-02390-2

Centre for Global Mental Health. (n.d.). Centre for Global Mental Health. Retrieved from https://www.centreforglobalmentalhealth.org/about-us

Corrigan, P. W., Kerr, A., & Knudsen, L. (2005). The stigma of mental illness: Explanatory models and methods for change. *Applied and Preventive Psychology, 11,* 179–190. doi:10.1016/j.appsy.2005.07.001

Corrigan, P. W., & Rao, D. (2012). On the self-stigma of mental illness: Stages, disclosure, and strategies for change. *Canadian Journal of Psychiatry, 57*(8), 464–469. doi:10.1177/070674371205700804

Corrigan, P. W., & Shapiro, J. R. (2010). Measuring the impact of programs that challenge the public stigma of mental illness. *Clinical Psychology Review, 30,* 907–922. doi:10.1016/j.cpr.2010.06.004

Council on Social Work Education. (2015). *2015 education and policy and accreditation standards for baccalaureate and master's social work*

programs. Alexandria, VA: Author. Retrieved from https://www.cswe
.org/getattachment/Accreditation/Accreditation-Process/2015-EPAS/
2015EPAS_Web_FINAL.pdf.aspx

Daily Briefing. (2017, November 14). In Puerto Rico, storm left a mental
health crisis in its wake. *The Boston Globe*, A2.

Des Courtis, N., Lauber, C., Costa, C. T., & Cattapan-Ludewig,
K. (2008). *International Review of Psychiatry, 20*(6), 503–509.
doi:10.1080/09540260802565125

Ellison, N., Mason, O., & Scior, K. (2015). Public beliefs about and attitudes
towards bipolar disorder: Testing theory based models of stigma. *Journal of
Affective Disorders, 175*, 116–123. doi:10.1016/j.jad.2014.12.047

Grolnick, W. S., Schonfeld, D. J., Schreiber, M., Cohen, J., Cole, V., Jaycox,
L., … Zatzick, D. (2018). Improving adjustment and resilience in children
following a disaster: Addressing research challenges. *American Psychologist,
73*(3), 215–229. doi:10.1037/amp0000181

Jackowska, E. (2009). Stigma and discrimination towards people with
schizophrenia: A survey of studies and psychological mechanisms.
Psychiatria Polska, 43(6), 655–670.

Jackson, K. (2018). Climate change and public health: How social workers
can advocate for environmental justice. *Social Work Today, 17*(6), 10.

Jacobs, A. W., Hill, T. D., & Burdette, A. M. (2015). Health insurance
status and symptoms of psychological distress among low-income
urban women. *Society and Mental Health, 5*(1), 1–15. doi:10.1177/
2156869314549674

Lauber, C., Anthony, M., Ajdacic-Gross, V., & Rossler, W. (2004). What about
psychiatrists' attitude to mentally ill people? *European Psychiatry, 19*(7),
423–427. doi:10.1016/j.eurpsy.2004.06.019

Lazowski, L., Koller, M., Stuart, H., & Milev, R. (2012). Stigma and discrimination
in people suffering with a mood disorder: A cross-sectional study. *Depression
Research and Treatment, 2012*, 724848. doi:10.1155/2012/724848

Lee, B. X., Glass, L. L., & Fisher, E. B. (2018, February 26). The Goldwater
Rule was never intended as a gag order. Opinion. *The Boston Globe*, A10.

Lee, B. X., Lifton, R. J., Sheehy, G., Doherty, W. J., Chomsky, N., Herman,
J. L., …, Soldz, S. (2017). *The dangerous case of Donald Trump: 27
psychiatrists and mental health experts assess a president*. New York, NY:
Thomas Dunne Books.

Levin, A. (2016, August 25). Goldwater Rule's origins based on long-ago
controversy. *Psychiatric News*. Retrieved from https://doi.org/10.1176/appi
.pn.2016.9a19

Linsky, A. (2018, June 19). Wails of children at border sharpen outcry over
policy. *The Boston Globe*, A1, A6.

Ma, Z. (2017). How the media cover mental illness: A review. *Health
Education, 117*(1), 90–109. doi:10.1108/HE-01-2016-0004

Mayer, J. D. (2010, May 23). The Goldwater Rule: The rationale of the
Goldwater Rule. *Psychology Today*. Retrieved from https://www.psychology
today.com/us/blog/the-personality-analyst/201005/the-goldwater-rule

McGinty, E. E., Goldman, H. H., Pescosolido, B. A., & Barry, C. L. (2018).
Communicating about mental illness and violence: Balancing stigma and
increased support for services. *Journal of Health Politics, Policy and Law,
43*(2), 185–228. doi:10.1215/03616878-4303507

National Institute of Mental Health. (2017, November). *Mental illness definitions*. Retrieved from https://www.nimh.nih.gov/health/statistics/ mental-illness.shtml

New York Times. (2018, November 14). In Puerto Rico, storm left a mental health crisis in its wake. *The Boston Globe*, A2.

Nguyen, T., & Davis, K. (2018). *The state of mental health in America 2017*. Alexandria, VA: Mental Health America.

Nii-Trebi, N. (2017). Emerging and neglected infectious diseases: Insights, advances, and challenges. *BioMed Research International, 2017*, 5245021. doi:10.1155/2017/5245021

Nordt, C., Rossler, W., & Lauber, C. (2006). Attitudes of mental health professionals toward people with schizophrenia and major depression. *Schizophrenia Bulletin, 32*(4), 709–714. doi:10.1093/schbul/sbj065

Pace, P. R. (2017a, June). Summit explores ways to maximize policy impact. *NASW News*, 4.

Pace, P. R. (2017b, November). SAMHSA: More mental health professionals needed. *NASW News*, 4.

Pierre-Louis, K. (2018, June 13). Antarctica is melting three times as fast as a decade ago. *The New York Times*. Retrieved from https://www.nytimes .com/2018/06/13/climate/antarctica-ice-melting-faster.html

Powell, T. J., Garrow, E., Woodford, M. R., & Perron, B. (2013). Policymaking opportunities for direct practice social workers in mental health and addiction services. *Advances in Social Work, 14*(2), 367–378.

Prince, M., Patel, V., Saxena, S., Maj, M., Maselko, J., Phillips, M. R., & Rahman, A. (2007). No health without mental health. *Lancet, 370*, 859–877. doi:10.1016/S0140- 6736(07)61238-0

Rubio-Valera, M., Aznar-Lou, I., Vives-Collet, M., Fernandez, A., Gil-Girbau, M., & Serrano-Blanco, A. (2016). Reducing the mental health–related stigma of social work students: A cluster RCT. *Research on Social Work Practice, 28*(2), 164–172. doi:10.1177/1049731516641492

Rueve, M. E., & Welton, R. S. (2008). Violence and mental illness. *Psychiatry, 5*(5), 34–48.

Rusch, N., Angermeyer, M. C., & Corrigan, P. W. (2005). Mental illness stigma: Concepts consequences, and initiatives to reduce stigma. *European Psychiatry, 20*, 529–539. doi:10.1016/j.eurpsy.2005.04.004

Sawyer, A-M., Stanford, S., & Campbell, J. (2016). Mental health social work: Perspectives on risk, regulation, and therapeutic interventions. *Australian Social Work, 69*(2), 129–132. doi:10.1080/0312407X.2015.1129428

Scharfenberg, D. (2017, March 12). Make narcissism great again. *The Boston Globe*, K1, K4.

Schroeder, S. A. (2016). American health improvement depends upon addressing class disparities. *Preventive Medicine, 92*, 6–15. doi:10.1016.j/ ypmed.2016.02.024

Schulze, B., & Angermeyer, M. C. (2003). Subjective experiences of stigma: A focus group study of schizophrenic patients, their relatives and mental health professionals. *Social Science & Medicine, 56*, 299–312. Retrieved from https://www.ncbi.nlm.nih.gov/pubmed/12473315

Social Work Policy Institute. (2004). *History of social work research in mental health*. Retrieved from http://www.socialworkpolicy.org/research/history -of-social-work-research-in-mental-health.html

Substance Abuse and Mental Health Services Administration. (2017). *Key substance use and mental health indicators in the United States: Results from the 2016 National Survey on Drug Use and Health* (HHS Publication No. SMA 17-5044, NSDUH series H-52). Rockville, MD: Center for Behavior Health Statistics and Quality, Substance Abuse and Mental Health Services Administration. Retrieved from https://www.samhsa.gov/data

Sundararaman, R. (2009, April 21). *The U.S. mental health delivery system infrastructure: A primer.* Washington, DC: Congressional Research Service. Retrieved from https://fas.org/sgp/crs/misc/R40536.pdf

Szasz, T. (1961). *The myth of mental illness: Foundations of a theory of personal conduct.* New York, NY: Hoeber-Harper.

Thornicroft, G., Rose, D., & Kassam, A. (2007). Discrimination in health care against people with mental illness. *International Review of Psychiatry, 19*(2), 113–122. doi:10.1080/09540260701278937

Tomlinson, M., & Lund, C. (2012). Why does mental health not get the attention it deserves? An application of the Shiffman and Smith framework. *PLoS Medicine, 9*(2), e1001178. doi:10.1371/journal.pmed.1001178

World Health Organization. (2018a). *Mental health included in the UN sustainable development goals.* Retrieved from http://www.who.int/mental_health/SDGs/en

World Health Organization. (2018b, March 30). *Mental health: Strengthening our response.* Retrieved from http://www.who.int/news-room/fact-sheets/detail/mental-health-strengthening-our-response

World Health Organization. (2018c, April 9). *Mental disorders.* Retrieved from http://www.who.int/news-room/fact-sheets/detail/mental-disorders

CHAPTER 2

A SHORT HISTORY OF MENTAL HEALTH POLICY AND TREATMENT IN THE UNITED STATES

LEARNING OUTCOMES

- Trace the development of mental health services and the role of social work through American history.

- Analyze the historical role of asylums for the mentally ill within society.

- Discuss the reasons for deinstitutionalization of the mentally ill that began in the 1950s.

- Demonstrate an understanding of the challenges to definitions of mental illness in the 1960s.

- Examine the roles of the films *One Flew Over the Cuckoo's Nest* and *Titicut Follies* in bringing attention to the dreadful treatment of those with mental illness within institutions.

INTRODUCTION

Interpretations of historical events are perceived in various ways, and this is certainly the case when analyzing the evolution of mental health policy and treatment in the United States. Mental health policy and treatment were formulated in ways that reflect historical events, the development of fields such as psychiatry and social work, and political and financial realities and incentives (Mechanic, 1994). As Helmus and Glenn (2005) stated, "events of our past not only remind us of our weaknesses and fallibility but also serve to identify future directions" (p. 9). With no simple and agreed-upon definitions of mental health and mental illness, there are also different views of the purpose and effectiveness of related policies and treatments (Ramon, 2009).

This chapter addresses the history of the U.S. mental health system and the national, state, and local policies that regulate treatment of the mentally ill. It is important to review the history of mental health treatment to assess the system advances as well as the areas in which progress has been lacking. Neither the system of delivering mental health services nor the related financial systems have evolved very quickly (Sundararaman, 2009). Historically, the purpose of these systems has been debated, and that controversy continues today. For example, whose needs are being served by institutionalization? Is it the patients, the families, the community, or the insurance companies? An important concern today is whether treatment programs primarily exist to help clients recover from mental illness or, instead, to make a profit.

Mental health treatment has primarily been within the purview of state and local governments with little national attention or support (Sundararaman, 2009). Not surprisingly, the mental health services available match what local, state, and federal agencies are willing to pay for (Segal & Baumohl, 1981). This means that the mentally ill do not necessarily get the services they need, as treatment decisions are not necessarily made by clinicians but rather by politicians and bureaucrats. While social workers have been very responsive in providing services to the mentally ill, they have had little impact on policy formulation.

▨ THE BEGINNING OF MENTAL HEALTH STATE CARE: ASYLUMS

In 1773, the first person was admitted to the Public Hospital for Persons of Insane and Disordered Minds in Williamsburg, Virginia (Coy, 2006). This marked the beginning of state care for individuals with mental illness (Roberts & Kurtz, 1987). As with the asylums and hospitals that would come later, the intent was to remove the mentally ill from the community to minimize community disruption. In fact, asylums were not initially designed to treat those with mental illness, but rather were designed to separate the mentally ill from their families, communities, and society at large (Lieberman, 2015). Asylums grew and experienced overcrowded conditions in the 1800s. Physical neglect was commonplace, and some patients were subjected to horrific physical abuse (Tuntiya, 2003).

Like the mental health system of today, much of what was available to mentally ill patients depended on their ability to pay for services. In the mid-1800s, state intervention was required to assist in the development of services due to inadequate responses from other organizations (Atwell, 1965). Prior to this time, the mentally ill had been hidden away either at home, in poor houses, or in prisons (Miller & Blanc, 1967).

Families with financial means could care for their mentally ill relatives at home. However, those without financial means had to rely on the growing state asylum system (Lieberman, 2015). By the mid-1800s, asylums cared primarily for patients with chronic mental illness; they were usually both overcrowded and underfunded (Sundararaman, 2009).

In the 1800s, the idea developed that mentally ill patients were in need of "moral" treatment. It was thought that given time away from the daily responsibilities and struggles of life, patients would benefit from the structure, discipline, work, and recreation provided by a supervised environment (Roberts & Kurtz, 1987; Schrift, Cavender, & Hoover, 2013). Dr. Benjamin Rush, a signer of the Declaration of Independence, was the first to advocate for moral treatment of the mentally ill and brought these ideas to the Pennsylvania Hospital in Philadelphia (Roberts & Kurtz, 1987; Trent, n.d.). Moral treatment included the idea that physicians should offer patients good parenting and "genuine philanthropy" (Miller & Blanc, 1967, p. 66).

Dorothea Dix (1802–1887), a strong opponent of the cruel treatment of patients in asylums, such as caging patients and painful use of restraints, helped develop the concept of the state-funded mental hospital to care for the mentally ill. Like Dr. Rush, she subscribed to the importance of moral treatment. Dix became a passionate and successful advocate (Parry, 2006). After seeing that the government took far too long to respond to the mentally ill, beginning in the 1940s, Dix helped to open or expand 32 mental hospitals through her activism and pressure on state legislators (Roberts & Kurtz, 1987). She then turned her efforts toward getting the federal government to provide support for the mentally ill. Unfortunately, these efforts were unsuccessful. Dix's plan was to sell more than 10 million acres of federal land to financially support the needs of the indigent with mental illness. While the legislation received support in the U.S. House of Representatives and Senatet, in 1854 President Franklin Pierce vetoed the land-grant mental health bill because he did not want to expand federal responsibility for the mentally ill and wanted responsibility for care to stay with the states (Miller & Blanc, 1967; Warder, 2014).

In 1860, there were 42 major asylums for the mentally ill in the United States (Bainbridge, 1984). Mental asylums and hospitals were complex organizations that cared for a variety of patients who were "inadvertently thrust upon them by a society seeking solutions to novel problems which grew in part out of rapid social and economic change" (Grob, 1977, p. 35). Patients not deemed mentally ill but still institutionalized included the elderly and those with physical disabilities. Involuntary commitments to mental facilities were most often initiated by families in the 1800s and 1900s for what families considered problem behavior (Grob, 1977).

The 1850s to 1860s brought the decline of moral treatment and the additional growth of large custodial institutions (Miller & Blanc, 1967). This trend has been attributed to increased industrialization and immigration, especially of very poor immigrants, which put more pressure on asylums to admit patients (Roberts & Kurtz, 1987; Trent, n.d.). In the mid-1800s, ideas about mental illness included scientific and religious causes. Stress, it was thought, could overtake a weak nervous and mental system and create problematic behavior. The mid-1880s saw the development of biological psychiatry—the view that abnormalities in the brain are responsible for the development of mental illness, ideas first developed by Wilhelm Griesinger in Germany. Defining psychiatry as the study of brain disease helped to present the field as a medical science (Tuntiya, 2003). It was believed that some patients had inherited their mental illness, whereas others had been subjected to difficult life situations (Bainbridge, 1984).

Some believed that a main cause of mental illness was "religious excitement," stemming from an individual's experience of overpowering religious emotions (Bainbridge, 1984, p. 223). In a review of approximately 15,000 hospital records from 17 asylums between 1833 and 1863, a low of 1% of cases and a high of more than 14% were attributed to religious causes (Bainbridge, 1984). The average proportion of insanity cases presumably caused by religion was 6% across the asylums in the study. Other presumed causes of insanity were financial problems, marital problems, grief over the death of loved ones, and overexertion (Bainbridge, 1984). The identification of presumed religious causes served to lessen the stigma attached to the individual with mental health problems and offered a plausible explanation for that person's troubles.

The last half of the 19th century placed more emphasis on public health and the need for early intervention and prevention. In the 1870s, the Conference of Charities and Corrections was concerned with services provided for the poor insane (Rockmore, 1960). The New York State Care Act of 1890 sought to remove the mentally ill from the almshouses and to provide financial support from New York State rather than rely on county efforts (Brown, 1901). Local governments, it was clear, did not have sufficient funds to pay for asylum care. By the early 20th century, states had passed laws that required them to fund mental asylum care, although care was still inadequate (Sundararaman, 2009).

Toward the end of the 19th century, asylums became increasingly known as "state hospitals." The name change served to emphasize the role of treatment over simply warehousing individuals (Vourlekis, Edinberg, & Knee, 1998). The slow process of patient release to community services involved several issues: (a) lack of interest on the part of hospital administrators, known as superintendents; (b) superintendents' disregard for social work advocates and activists, whom they perceived as infringing on their territory; and (c) the stigma of mental illness among the general public, who preferred to keep the mentally ill out of the community (Vourlekis et al., 1998). See Case Example 2.1 for a description of what Native Americans had to endure in an asylum.

CASE EXAMPLE 2.1

DIGGING DEEPER INTO ASYLUMS: THE CANTON ASYLUM FOR INSANE INDIANS

In 1898, Congress legislated the opening of the Canton Indian Insane Asylum, also known as the Hiawatha Asylum. It opened in 1902 under the auspices of the Bureau of Indian Affairs and was the first and only facility for Native Americans with mental illness in the United States. The legislation was supported by Richard F. Pettigrew, a new senator in the new state of South Dakota. Pettigrew actually had no interest in helping the mentally ill or Native Americans—his concerns were largely economic, specifically to develop employment opportunities to support the new state he represented (Putney, 1984).

Native Americans who were "accepted" into the facility included those without family to care for them, those with physical and intellectual disabilities, rape victims, those with alcohol problems, and the elderly. These patients can also be considered "forced inhabitants," as typically they were not voluntary admissions (Burch, 2014, p. 142). The realities of the experience were poor living conditions, inadequate staff supervision, physical neglect, and abuse of patients via restraints (Burch, 2014; Dunphy, 1984). Over a period of years, Superintendent Hummer himself was the subject of complaints of verbal abuse, inappropriate touching, and affairs outside of his marriage (Burch, 2014).

For example, Elizabeth Fe Alexis Fairbault was locked up due to an apparent drinking problem. Despite considerable efforts on the part of her husband and mother to have her released home to her children, Elizabeth remained in the asylum for 13 years. At the time, Superintendent Hummer insisted she should not be released from the asylum due to her mental condition, yet she was caring for his children (Burch, 2014). Elizabeth became pregnant, reportedly by another inmate, although it has been suggested that Superintendent Hummer was the father of her baby. After her death at age 46 of undetermined causes in 1928, Elizabeth's daughter remained at the asylum until the age of 4, when considerable political pressure was exerted to place the child in an orphanage (Burch, 2014).

Between 1902 and 1934, approximately 374 Native Americans resided at the Canton Asylum for Insane Indians. The asylum was eventually abolished by Commissioner of Indian Affairs John Collier for being outdated and not being able to provide modern therapeutic interventions (Putney, 1984).

SOURCES: Burch, S. (2014). "Dislocated histories": The Canton Asylum for Insane Indians. *Women, Gender, and Families of Color, 2*(2), 141–162; Putney, D. T. (1984). *The Canton Asylum for Insane Indians 1902–1934*. Canton, SD: South Dakota Historical Society.

Gerald Grob (1977), a well-known history professor at Rutgers University, held the view that the history of mental asylums and hospitals may be a "tragedy," which occurred despite the good intentions of those who developed and ran them. Grob (1977) concluded that "mental hospitals were not fundamentally dissimilar from most human institutions, the achievements of which usually fall far short of the hopes and aspirations of the individuals who founded and led them" (p. 40).

▉ THE EARLY 1900s: DEVELOPMENT OF PSYCHIATRY AND MENTAL HEALTH SOCIAL WORK

At the beginning of the 1900s, both psychiatry and social work were seeking professional identities and respect for their expertise and were slowly coming to work together (Black, 1991). It is within this context that social workers took on the responsibility of working with clients and families and of assisting patients with their release from state-run hospitals. This helped to establish a social work specialty in mental health in the early 1900s (Vourlekis et al., 1998).

At this time, another important effort began to reform treatment of the mentally ill, known as the *mental hygiene movement*. Important leadership was provided by Clifford Whittingham Beers. In 1908, Beers published a book titled *The Mind That Found Itself: An Autobiography*. This poignant firsthand account of psychiatric hospitalization revealed the physical abuse and appalling conditions to which he and other patients were subjected (Roberts & Kurtz, 1987). His work led to important advocacy and reform efforts in the mental health system, including improved conditions for hospital staff, such as attendants. Beers established the first mental health association in Connecticut in 1908 and helped other states establish associations to advocate for the mentally ill (Roberts & Kurtz, 1987).

During World War I (1914–1918), mental illness became an acknowledged problem for soldiers, but the allied armies found they were not properly prepared to cope with wartime mental health problems (Black, 1991). Soldiers with no visible signs of physical injury were thought to be suffering from "shell shock," and over time this diagnosis was changed to "war neurosis" (Helmus & Glenn, 2005). Initially, soldiers were removed from battle and taken to hospitals away from battlefronts. However, subsequently this action was thought to weaken a soldier's commitment to fellow soldiers. That thinking began a period in which soldiers with war neuroses were treated closer to the battlefront and then returned to their stations (Helmus & Glenn, 2005).

Through working alongside surgeons and other physicians in war-time, psychiatrists began to garner more attention in World War I (Black, 1991). Since there were not sufficient numbers of psychiatrists to treat the mental health problems of troops, social workers became an important part of the response to mental illness (Black, 1991). In the early part of 1918, it was clear that there were not sufficient facilities to care for American soldiers sent home with war neuroses (Black, 1991, p. 391). In 1919, the U.S. Public Health Service brought about the establishment of the Bureau of Medical Social Work to respond to the needs of returning soldiers and their families (Black, 1991). With more than one third of patients receiving treatment from the Public Health Service having mental or nervous disorders, there was a great need for social workers with expertise in mental health (Black, 1991). Overall, social work responses to the needs of returning soldiers helped to establish the importance of social work services within mental health.

The American Association of Psychiatric Social Workers was established in 1922 as a part of the American Association of Hospital Social Workers and became an independent association in 1926 (Virginia Commonwealth University, n.d.). The National Association of Social Workers, as we know it today, began in 1955 with the merging of seven social work organizations, including the American Association of Psychiatric Social Workers.

THE 1930s: ECONOMIC TURMOIL, LOBOTOMY, AND ELECTROCONVULSIVE THERAPY

The 1930s brought very significant contributions from Sigmund Freud regarding the understanding and treatment of mental illness. Freud saw mental illness as unconscious mechanisms that are in conflict. Through psychoanalysis, the conflicts of individual patients could be classified, analyzed, and even purged (Gay, 1988; Lieberman, 2015). Freud's work focused on individuals who coped with anxiety and/or depression, yet could function in society, rather than on those individuals with chronic, severe mental illness.

In the 1930s, the economic turmoil of the Great Depression led to new social laws (Rockmore, 1960). This decade saw the further development of psychiatric social work modeled after the English system. In community child guidance clinics, psychiatric social workers worked alongside psychologists and psychiatrists (Howarth, 1944). In the names of some organizations, the word *charity* was replaced by *community service* (Rockmore, 1960, p. 71). These partnerships often developed through years of experience with child guidance clinics, where social workers provided the core clinical services and psychiatrists served as clinic directors (Roberts & Kurtz, 1987; Rockmore, 1960).

The 1930s also brought about what some considered major advances in mental healthcare: Both lobotomy and electroconvulsive treatment were introduced at about the same time (Lieberman, 2015). Dr. Egas Moniz, a Portuguese neurologist, began to offer lobotomy in 1935, known then as *leucotomy*. The primary purpose of lobotomy was to make patients more docile and more easily managed in large, overcrowded institutions. The surgery consisted of drilling two holes in the patient's skull, inserting the sharp leucotome instrument, and cutting the frontal lobes away from the other parts of the brain (Levinson, 2011). Dr. Moniz went on to win the Nobel Prize for inventing lobotomy in 1949.

In 1936, the first lobotomy was performed in the United States at George Washington University on a 63-year-old woman (Mahan, 2016). Approximately 50,000 lobotomies were performed in the United States, mostly between 1949 and 1952, which was the highest number of lobotomies of any country in the world (Lenz, 2017; National Public Radio, 2005). Lobotomy then fell out of favor because of negative outcomes, such as severe disability and some deaths, and the introduction of medications that could control patients' behavior (Levinson, 2011).

Perhaps the best-known fictitious example of lobotomy appeared in the 1975 classic film *One Flew Over the Cuckoo's Nest*, based on Ken Kesey's 1962 novel of the same name. Actor Jack Nicholson gives a very powerful performance as Randle McMurphy, a prison inmate who hopes to have an easier time serving his sentence in a mental hospital. Obviously, he has no idea of the consequences. McMurphy's unwillingness to follow the hospital rules and his knack for stirring up other inmates cause serious disruption to his hospital ward as well as great consternation from the controlling and oppressive Nurse Ratched. Ultimately, McMurphy is subjected to a lobotomy; his fellow patient and friend smothers him with a pillow to save him from the indignity of living a lobotomized existence.

In the history of mental health treatment, real-life experiences with lobotomy are important to acknowledge. One attendant at the Southwestern Virginia Mental Health Institute provided a disturbing account of how patients after lobotomy were assigned their own special attendant for several days. The attendant stated that "that was the most gruesome thing I have ever seen" (Schrift et al., 2013, p. 98). The attendant went on to describe the severe pain for the lobotomized patients, the great sensitivity to light that kept their eyes shut for days and then required them to wear sunglasses, and the need to feed and help patients walk. See Case Example 2.2 for a description of Rose Marie Kennedy and the lobotomy she was subjected to at the age of 23.

CASE EXAMPLE 2.2

THE LOBOTOMY OF ROSE MARIE KENNEDY

Rose Marie Kennedy, also known as Rosemary, was born September 13, 1918, at the Kennedy home in Brookline, Massachusetts. She was deprived of oxygen at birth, apparently because the nurse did not want her mother, Rose Fitzgerald Kennedy, to deliver her third child without the presence of a doctor. The nurse delayed the birth by 2 hours, telling Rose she had to keep her legs closed until the doctor arrived (Larson, 2015). It was recognized within a short period of time that Rosemary was not achieving normal developmental milestones. She had learning issues as well as behavioral problems. Since she did not have the academic and sports potential of her siblings, she was mostly kept out of public view so as not to damage the image of the Kennedy pedigree. Through the years, she also experienced an extraordinary number of tutors, services, and supervision funded by her parents. They perceived Rosemary as "delayed" in learning, not as a child with developmental disabilities or what was then called "mental retardation" (Larson, 2015). At age 11, she began a succession of boarding school and convent placements (Lenz, 2017). As she grew into her teenage years, she began sneaking out of the convent at night and going to bars (Lenz, 2017). Rosemary grew into a very attractive young woman, and her father, Joseph Kennedy Sr., was concerned about the possibility of her becoming pregnant. Certainly, this outcome would have a damaging impact on the political careers he planned for his sons (Larson, 2015).

Joseph Kennedy Sr. was informed by physicians that a lobotomy would reduce Rosemary's moodiness, outbursts, and other behavioral issues. The surgery was performed in November 1941 at George Washington University Hospital when Rosemary was 23. An account from one of the doctors detailed the actual surgery, which consisted of two small incisions on both sides of her skull. An instrument "that looked like a butter knife" cut into Rosemary's brain tissue while she was awake, responding to questions and reciting prayers. When Rosemary became "incoherent," the surgery was concluded. Reports indicate that her intellectual capacity was diminished to that of a 2-year-old child. While Rosemary's parents had discussed a possible lobotomy for her, it was only after the procedure was completed that Joe Kennedy Sr. informed his wife (Lenz, 2017). The lobotomy left Rosemary unable to talk or walk. After therapy, she regained only the partial use of one arm, and she walked with a limp that required the assistance of others. Rosemary was institutionalized in New York and then was moved to the St. Coletta School in Wisconsin, where her father had a house built for her and her caretakers on the grounds (Larson, 2015). She died at the age of 86 on January 7, 2005.

SOURCES: Larson, K. C. (2015). *Rosemary: The hidden Kennedy daughter*. Boston, MA: Houghton Mifflin Harcourt; Lenz, L. (2017, March 31). The secret lobotomy of Rosemary Kennedy. *Marie Claire*. Retrieved from https://www.marieclaire.com/celebrity/a26261/secret-lobotomy-rosemary-kennedy

Electroconvulsive therapy (ECT) was first developed in 1938. It was intended to induce seizures that would provide relief from mental illness, especially severe depression. Initially, no sedatives were given to patients. However, in recent years, ECT technology has advanced considerably. While lobotomy is disavowed today, ECT has been refined and touted as a successful treatment for intractable depression that does not respond to other treatments, including medication. ECT also spawned the newer technique of transcranial magnetic stimulation (TMS), which is receiving much attention as a successful treatment. Both ECT and TMS are discussed in Chapter 5, Social Work and Mental Illness. From a historical perspective, ECT and lobotomy were considered significant efforts to help the mentally ill when nothing else seemed to work (Lieberman, 2015).

▨ THE 1940s: FROM CHILD GUIDANCE TO MENTAL HYGIENE

Child guidance clinics served as the underpinning for community mental health programs in the 1940s (Roberts & Kurtz, 1987). When the United States entered World War II, child guidance clinics became "mental hygiene units" (Rockmore, 1960, p. 71). The American Association of Psychiatric Social Workers developed the War Service Office to meet the needs of men in the military and their families (Rockmore, 1960). With national and state resources redirected toward the war effort, the quality of mental healthcare declined during the Great Depression and World War II. Exposés in the late 1940s shone light on the horrible conditions in state mental facilities (Isaac & Brakel, 1992). Across the Atlantic Ocean, Hitler was already hard at work to end the lives of the mentally ill and disabled in Germany. See Case Example 2.3 for a description of Hitler's views on and treatment of the mentally ill.

CASE EXAMPLE 2.3

HITLER'S TREATMENT OF THE MENTALLY ILL

The disabled and mentally ill were a special target of Hitler. In the late 1930s, in secrecy, Hitler had disabled children murdered (Rees, 2017). He then turned his attention to murdering disabled adults, including those with mental illness (History Channel, 2018). Hitler thought it was appropriate to use medical interventions to commit murder for the purpose of doing away with "life unworthy of life" (Rees, 2017, p. 166). Hitler noted the financial savings to hospitals and the better use of time by doctors and nurses if they did not have to care for mentally ill patients. Known as "T4," after the headquarters where the plan was devised, the strategy focused on "euthanizing" mental patients by discharging carbon monoxide gas into the wards and killing patients as they slept (Rees, 2017). When that murderous tactic was determined to not be a very practical solution, the idea evolved into gassing the mentally ill through a room built to look like a shower. From there, five "euthanasia" centers were established in Germany and one in Austria. In the Sonnenstein, Germany center, between June 1940 and August 1941, approximately 14,751 disabled and mentally ill patients were gassed (Rees, 2017).

After protests from the German people, the murders of the mentally ill and physically handicapped orchestrated by T4 ceased (History Channel, 2018). Staff from these centers were then transferred to begin mass killings in concentration camps (Torrey & Yolkin, 2010). As history bears out, this became a primary mode of killing for Hitler and his Nazi Party.

For those individuals with schizophrenia, the murders continued. It is estimated that between 220,000 and 269,500 such persons were sterilized or murdered (Torrey & Yolkin, 2010). That is, 73% to 100% of known schizophrenics in Germany between 1939 and 1945 were murdered by the Nazis. Torrey and Yolkin (2010) conclude in their important article that "the Nazi genocide of psychiatric patients was the greatest criminal act in the history of psychiatry" (p. 26).

SOURCES: History Channel. (2018). *Hitler suspends euthanasia program*. Retrieved from https://www.history.com/this-day-in-history/hitler-suspends-euthanasia-program; Rees, L. (2017). *The Holocaust: A new history*. New York, NY: Public Affairs; Torrey, E. F., & Yolkin, R. H. (2010). Psychiatric genocide: Nazi attempts to eradicate schizophrenia. *Schizophrenia Bulletin, 36*(1), 26–32. doi:10.1093/schbul/sbp097.

By the mid-1940s, professionalism was already developing in the social work field (Ruth & Marshall, 2017). According to Howarth (1944), "we have by now pretty well grown out of the stage when the psychiatric social worker was considered as the useful handmaiden of a Clinic who willingly and self-sacrificingly trailed out in all weathers to collect social histories from homes clean and dirty" (p. 17). Increasingly, social workers were acknowledged for developing their own expertise in mental health.

There were also calls in the early 1940s for psychiatric social workers to participate in mental health research (Howarth, 1944). In 1946, the National Mental Health Act, signed into law by President Harry Truman, provided federal funding for mental health research and education, which then led to the formal establishment of the National Institute of Mental Health in 1949 (National Institutes of Health, 2017; Sundararaman, 2009). Albert Deutsch's book *The Mentally Ill in America*, published in 1949, made significant contributions by pointing out that mental health was not a high priority in American society and that much more funding was required to respond appropriately to the needs of the mentally ill.

THE 1950s: HOSPITAL AND COMMUNITY CARE

The 1950s brought the height of psychiatric institutionalization as well as the beginning of deinstitutionalization and its consequences. The year 1955 marked the peak in the number of public psychiatric facilities, which treated more than 550,000 patients in that year (Isaac & Brakel, 1992). The mid-1950s brought many changes, and with the decrease in the number of patients, hospitals became smaller and more regulated (Schrift et al., 2013). The development of psychotropic drugs and the move to community mental health services were pivotal developments (Atwell, 1965). Yet the system continued to struggle to provide services in the transition from hospital to community care (Rockmore, 1960).

Despite the mid-1950s shift of mental healthcare toward the community and the development of psychiatric medications and shorter-term hospitalizations, not all patients could benefit from these changes. For the most severely ill patients, hospital care could not be entirely replaced by community care (Killaspy, 2006). The 1955 Mental Health Study Act established the Joint Commission on Mental Illness and Health to examine mental illness and to propose solutions (Atwell, 1965). This effort led to a number of reports on schools and mental health, the economics of mental health, and churches and mental health (Atwell, 1965).

The attitude that both hospital care and care within the community were essential to the mental health system also took hold in the 1950s (Mechanic, 1994). Greater attention to community mental health meant a greater focus on less severely mentally ill individuals, who were offered psychotherapy as an alternative to institutionalization. Unfortunately, it also meant the greater neglect of patients with chronic serious illness in hospitals (Mechanic, 1994). Since mental health services were paid for by the states, there was little incentive for private insurers to offer mental health coverage (Barry, Huskamp, & Goldman, 2010).

Finally, the 1950s also saw a call for social work education to include and expand mental health topics. The expansion of social work mental health education focused on the need to engage in collaborations with psychiatrists, psychologists, and psychiatric nurses (Wittman, 1957). In 1956, the American Medical Association defined alcoholism as a disease, which opened another door for collaboration and improved treatment.

THE 1960s: IS MENTAL ILLNESS REALLY AN ILLNESS?

The 1960s were a time of revisiting definitions of mental illness and the controversy over whether mental illness was like any other illness or whether it was a role assigned to individuals by other members of society through a process of labeling. The majority of patients in state psychiatric hospitals in 1960 were committed on an involuntary basis (Isaac & Brakel, 1992). There was an ideological division between support for hospital care and support for care in the community (Mechanic, 1994). Some thought that mental hospitals were instruments for social control of individuals, most specifically poor individuals, who were considered threatening to the existing social order (Grob, 1977).

The 1960s brought considerable social change and strong protests against the Vietnam War. These years included challenges from the field of sociology to the very concept of mental illness. The year 1961 saw the publication of *The Myth of Mental Illness* by Thomas Szasz, who defined mental illness as "problems in living." In his storied career, Szasz continued to reaffirm that "all human actions" are made by choice and to assert that mental illness is a "nonexistent disease" (Szasz, 2001, p. 298). Accordingly, when we do not hold people responsible for their behavior, we can consider them as "victims" of mental illness.

Also published in 1961 was Erving Goffman's book *Asylums*, a collection of four sociological essays on life within "total institutions." Importantly, Goffman described the lived experiences of the institutionalized mentally ill in which they were subjected to abusive and neglectful treatment. For Goffman, this topic was very close to home: His wife had a history of mental illness and hospitalization that ended with her suicide by jumping off a bridge in 1964 (Shalin, 2014). Like Szasz, Goffman did not accept biological definitions of mental illness and instead focused on stigma and the "spoiled identity" of those deemed to have mental disorders. Goffman's work sought to expose the abuses endured by those who bore the label of mental illness (Shalin, 2014).

Thomas Scheff's book *Being Mentally Ill: A Sociological Theory* (1966) examined what he saw as symptoms of mental illness that were "labeled violations of social norms" (p. 25). What Scheff called "chronic" or "stable" mental illness became "a social role" (p. 25). Thus, sociologists brought attention to the societal factors that labeled individuals as mentally ill, rather than focusing on relieving symptoms or larger treatment issues.

In 1961, *Action for Mental Health* was the final report issued by the Joint Commission on Mental Illness and Health (Atwell, 1965). A scathing attack on the existing mental health system, it recommended significant federal and state funding to improve state hospitals by reducing patient numbers and also advocated for increasing the quality of services (Atwell, 1965).

In 1963, by signing the Community Mental Health Act, President John F. Kennedy authorized federal funds for the first time for mental health treatment as well as for the building of community mental health centers in "catchment areas" (Segal & Baumohl, 1981; Sundararaman, 2009). The centers were to provide (a) inpatient care, (b) outpatient services,

(c) partial hospitalization (day programs), (d) emergency services, (e) professional case consultation, and (f) education (Segal & Baumohl, 1981). While moving patients out into the community was seen as a positive trend, in reality, communities were poorly equipped with this responsibility, and the services were inadequate. Facilities might discharge patients from hospitals with prescriptions for their medications, but patients may not have had any way to pay for them or been able to take the medications on their own without supervision. An amendment to the Community Mental Health Centers Act in 1975 emphasized screening for mental health problems as well as training and research (Segal & Baumohl, 1981).

Social workers assumed responsibility for assisting patients to return to the community after hospitalization through efforts to coordinate their care. The field of mental health was moving into the social welfare field (Segal & Baumohl, 1981). While the 1960s brought increasing deinstitutionalization, mental hospitals were still providing inappropriate and abysmal care. Case Example 2.4 describes *Titicut Follies*, a 1967 film that showcased the severe abuse and neglect to which mental patients were subjected.

CASE EXAMPLE 2.4

TITICUT FOLLIES: TELLING THE STORY OF BRIDGEWATER STATE PRISON FOR THE CRIMINALLY INSANE

In 1967, a documentary titled *Titicut Follies* was released. At 84 minutes long, it documented the squalor, the abuse, and the neglect of mental patients in Bridgewater State Prison for the Criminally Insane in Massachusetts. The movie title derived its name from a talent show put on by hospital patients. The film showed the effects of long-term incarceration when patients should have been released long before. For example, a patient named Charles was sentenced to Bridgewater in 1910 for 2 years over a breaking and entering charge—he was still a patient in 1967 (New England Historical Society, 2018).

Early efforts to prevent the showing of the film were successful. The Massachusetts Supreme Judicial Court ruled that the documentary was an invasion of patient privacy despite the fact that the filmmaker, attorney Frederick Wiseman, had obtained consent from patients or their legal guardian and the superintendent of the hospital (New England Historical Society, 2018). While legal efforts focused on stated issues of protecting the privacy of the patients, the film's initial ban clearly was an effort to hide from the public the inhumane treatment of patients. The film won awards in both Germany and Italy and inspired a reduction in the number of hospital patients as well as improved treatment (Bernstein, 2016).

Titicut Follies can be purchased from online retailers or through Zipporah Films at www.zipporah.com/films/22.

SOURCES: Bernstein, P. (2016, April 22). Frederick Wiseman on his banned classic *Titicut Follies*. *Filmmaker*. Retrieved from https://filmmakermagazine. com/98264-frederick-wiseman-screening-his-once-banned-classictiticut-follies/#. W1YfkberIVc; New England Historical Society. (2018). Titicut Follies: *The documentary film about a madhouse so shocking it was banned*. Retrieved from http:// www.newenglandhistoricalsociety.com/titicut-follies-documentary-film-madhouse -shocking-banned

In 1965, legislation creating both Medicaid and Medicare was signed into law by President Lyndon Johnson. Medicaid is health insurance for the poor and disabled offered through federal and state programs. Medicare is health insurance for the elderly. Both programs are associated with Social Security; they have been revised through the years and continue to be essential to the provision of mental health services in the United States.

THE 1970s: COMMUNITY WORK

By 1970, 14.2% of mental health professionals working in community mental health centers were social workers (Levenson & Reff, 1970). In the 1970s, legal strides were made to ensure that hospitalized mental patients in almost all states had civil rights (Isaac & Brakel, 1992).

Further, the 1970s built upon the efforts of the 1960s and the sociological explanations for mental illness, which cut deeply into the world of psychiatry. David Rosenhan's experiments had a dramatic impact on the perceptions of mental illness and the ability of the field of psychiatry to treat mental illness. Case Example 2.5 describes the Rosenhan experiments in the 1970s.

CASE EXAMPLE 2.5

ROSENHAN EXPERIMENTS: ILLUMINATING THE PROBLEMS IN DISTINGUISHING THE SANE FROM THE INSANE

Dr. David Rosenhan, a psychologist at Stanford University, arranged for 12 student "pseudopatients" to be admitted to 12 different mental hospitals in five different states in the early 1970s. The "patients" sought voluntary psychiatric hospitalization by feigning symptoms to get admitted. All were admitted and then reverted to their "normal" behavior. They remained in the hospital between 7 and 52 days. One individual was diagnosed with manic depression and the other 11 with schizophrenia, a very severe form of mental illness (Rosenhan, 1973). Rosenhan's work was criticized, and clearly psychiatrists were upset about the problems in distinguishing between the sane and insane.

Rosenhan then challenged an unidentified hospital by arranging to send his students again over the next year, daring the hospital to be able discern the imposters. That next year the hospital evaluated 193 patients, 41 of whom were considered potential imposters. Rosenhan set off another furor when he acknowledged that he had sent no imposter patients.

Rosenhan's work has had a great influence in the field of psychiatry (Lieberman, 2015; Morris, 2018). This "experiment" highlighted the fact that there were no clear guidelines for distinguishing who is sane and who is insane. At the time, there was no discussion of lack of access to psychiatric hospital beds or problems with insurance coverage and inability to pay (Morris, 2018).

SOURCES: Lieberman, J. A., with Ogas, O. (2015). *Shrinks: The untold story of psychiatry*. New York, NY: Back Bay Books; Morris, N. (2018, January 1). This secret experiment tricked psychiatrists into diagnosing sane people as having schizophrenia. *The Washington Post*. Retrieved from https://www.washingtonpost.com/national/health-science/anexperiment; Rosenhan, D. L. (1973). On being sane in insane places. *Science, 179*(4070), 250–258.

In 1977, President Jimmy Carter created the Presidential Commission on Mental Health to review the mental health system and to recommend policies to overcome systemic problems. Released the following year, its report supported increased funding for research and training of mental health professionals and greater attention to the problems of those with chronic mental illness, specifically the mental health needs of children, adolescents, and the elderly (Mechanic, 1994). Unfortunately, while the report was a strong advocacy document, it did not provide a clear plan for the development of improved mental health services. Professional rivalries; bureaucracies; competing views of the roles of poverty, racism and stigma; as well as politics (Grob, 2005) all underlay the "long and torturous legislative history" of the Mental Health Systems Act (Mechanic, 1994, p. 508). Consequently, a system of care for the treatment of patients with serious mental illness did not result from this effort (Grob, 2005).

THE 1980s: MANAGED MENTAL HEALTHCARE

In 1980, the Carter Presidential Commission was successful in establishing the National Plan for the Chronically Mentally Ill. However, the plan was not especially successful because it was not supported by Carter's successor, President Ronald Reagan (Koyanagi & Goldman, 1991). In fact, in the 1980s, under Reagan, there were major cuts in social services and health programs for the poor (Mechanic, 1994). In the early 1980s, Social Security cut large numbers of the severely mentally ill from its disability benefit rolls. This brought about significant litigation and court decisions that ruled against Social Security and led to improved criteria for the determination of psychiatric disabilities (Mechanic, 1994).

In addition to providing significant portions of mental health services, social workers began to take on other roles at this time. Research in 1982 on staff delivery of services in rural mental health centers in western Pennsylvania found that social workers were providing critical services, including direct care, supportive services, and administrative tasks (Jerrell & Knight, 1985). Those with MSWs were more likely to treat patients with acute illness and have administrative roles, whereas BSWs were more likely to treat chronically ill clients.

In the 1980s, the federal government instituted diagnosis-related groups (DRGs), which set financial limits on the type of care that patients could receive and the length of time that patients could stay in the hospital, based on specific diagnoses. While DRGs focused primarily on physical health problems, mental health hospitalization was included as well. Compensation to hospitals by insurers was based on the average number of days for which patients with a specific diagnosis were expected to need hospital care. Fifteen of 467 DRGs were mental health– or substance abuse–related diagnoses (Taube, Lee, & Forthofer, 1984). Hospitals lost money if a patient stayed beyond the allotted number of days per diagnosis, and hospitals profited when patients were discharged early. By the end of the 1980s, it was established that DRGs for psychiatric diagnoses were a failure for psychiatric wards in general hospitals. This then led to the need for exemptions from the rules (Ashcraft et al., 1989).

While the DRGs are no longer in use, incessant bureaucratic review to keep costs down continues unabated. In the realm of psychiatric care, medical bureaucrats can make treatment decisions for patients they do not know and substitute their own judgment for the professional clinical judgment of those professionals treating mentally ill patients (Schamess, 1996). The 1970s and 1980s private insurance benefits for mental health came about primarily because of the efforts of state legislatures that required a minimum level of benefits for mental health and substance abuse (Barry et al., 2010).

The 1980s also brought the emergence of the advocacy organization known as the National Alliance for the Mentally Ill (NAMI). As a grassroots organization, NAMI advocated for those with mental illness and their families, especially those with severe mental illness who were not receiving the services they needed (Mechanic, 1994). It remains a critical advocacy organization today.

As research developed in the 1980s, we learned from a meta-analysis on the effectiveness of social work practice with the chronically mentally ill that interdisciplinary interventions and halfway houses were often effective in assisting those with chronic mental illness (Videka-Sherman, 1988). However, individual social work treatment with clients was found to be the least effective type of assistance. At that time, the field of mental health was continuing to struggle to find effective treatments.

In 1988, the director of the National Institute of Mental Health, Dr. Lewis Judd, appointed a task force to evaluate the status of social work research. The task force determined that research had not kept pace with the growth of the social work profession (Social Work Policy Institute, 2004). This led to a substantial increase in funding by the National Institute of Mental Health for research and, importantly, for training social workers to become researchers (Social Work Policy Institute, 2004).

THE 1990s: TREATMENT AND PROFIT

In the 1990s, for-profit companies dominated in physical and mental healthcare. Their business model was to try to force competing companies out of business by keeping their insurance premiums as low as possible and by restricting the number of people with serious illness allowed to enroll (Schamess, 1996). Given their primary motive to make a profit, the delivery of services was impacted. Managed care plans continued to limit hospital stays. Nurse case managers were still often are the ones charged with reviewing and restricting hospital stays.

In the words of Gerald Schamess, professor emeritus at the Smith College School of Social Work (1996), "of all the many possible motivations for providing care to people who suffer from serious emotional problems, the pursuit of profit is the most dismal" (p. 215).

THE 2000s: PARITY AND UNIVERSAL HEALTH

The Paul Wellstone and Pete Domenici Mental Health Parity and Addiction Equity Act of 2008 was designed to ensure that those needing substance abuse and mental health treatment, also known as behavioral healthcare, would receive services "on par" with the medical and surgical services received by healthcare patients. This was the culmination of many years of work, building upon the work done for the Mental Health Parity Act of 1996 and continuing legislative efforts up through 2008 (Barry et al., 2010). Health insurers were concerned that this requirement would increase out-of-network spending. In fact, between 2007 and 2012, out-of-network service use dropped from 18% to 12% (Busch et al.,

2017). This likely meant that insurers found other ways to reduce out-of-network service use and/or expanded the number of network providers.

The eventual passage of the Mental Health Parity and Addiction Equity Act can be attributed to finding that the act was not as costly as predicted, the experience of legislators with mental illness in their own families, and the political strategies and persistence displayed by senators and congressional representatives alike (Barry et al., 2010). While this legislation was highly touted, it still has not been able to achieve true parity.

Another effort to increase parity and provide expanded insurance coverage for mental illness and substance abuse treatment was the Excellence in Mental Health Act signed into law in 2014 by President Barack Obama. It was also intended to streamline Medicaid reimbursement and infuse more than $1 billion into the system by creating "certified community behavioral health clinics" to address all levels of intervention from screening to assessment to treatment (CORE Solutions, 2016).

Most recently, a bipartisan bill was introduced, titled the Improving Access to Mental Health Act (S.2613), in March 2018 (National Association of Social Workers, 2018). Approval of this legislation would allow nursing home residents to access mental health services, especially those with Medicare insurance. Additionally, the legislation would increase compensation to social workers, allowing reimbursement to increase 10%—that is, to 85% of what physicians are compensated.

We are frequently reminded that we may not have come as far as we think in terms of providing effective services for the mentally ill. Access to care continues to be a major and controversial issue today for both physical and mental illness. Political controversy continues over the Patient Protection and Affordable Care Act of 2010. It is apparent that some politicians still prefer that some Americans should be left with no health insurance rather than have a national healthcare insurance.

Today, the considerable difficulty of arranging for psychiatric care for patients who have been treated in hospital emergency rooms (ERs) illustrates that we have a long way to go before we can provide care to all those in need. For example, in Massachusetts, the number of patients needing psychiatric inpatient care rose by 13% between 2011 and 2015 (Kowalczyk, 2018). It is a national problem that some patients must wait in hospital ERs for a bed to be available at a psychiatric hospital. Some patients wait for days and some as long as several weeks in an ER. This is especially challenging because ER staff are not equipped to care for these patients. For most patients, this results in watching a lot of television, a poor substitute for what psychiatric hospitalization is intended to be (Kowalczyk, 2018). While the days of severe abuse in asylums may be over, we have yet to establish a comprehensive and coordinated mental health system in which social workers play an important planning and implementation role.

SUMMARY AND CONCLUSION

Social workers consistently work to meet clients' needs, but we have not come as far as we would like. In fact, our society may be turning the clock back when we deny the mentally ill access to safe inpatient care under the guise of helping them by keeping them in the community. The long, painful history of the development of mental health services is a reminder that despite good intentions, there is no substitute for strong and coordinated policy and sufficient funding. Films such as *Titicut Follies* and *One Flew Over the Cuckoo's Nest* brought attention to the inhumane treatment within facilities that were established to treat patients with mental illness in healthy and supportive environments. Deinstitutionalization in the 1950s helped some patients, but not the most severely mentally ill. The increased use of medications to treat mental illness helped some as well, but not others. Some patients were overmedicated to control their behavior and to keep them from annoying and challenging staff.

Overall, mental health policy has developed in haphazard ways rather than through a singular unifying effort by those who subscribe to the critical importance of mental healthcare. Policies were reactive to the times rather than coordinated to meet the needs of those with mental illness.

DISCUSSION QUESTIONS/TOPICS

1. Why is it important to understand the history of providing mental health services in the United States?

2. What was the purpose of the asylums that developed in the 1800s in the United States?

3. How did social workers assist in World War I?

4. Discuss Hitler's views and responses to the mentally ill.

5. Describe the role of lobotomy in the history of American mental health treatment.

6. How have finances impacted the mental health services delivery system in the United States?

7. Discuss the historical impact of sociological theories of mental illness that deny it is real illness.

8. Discuss the successes and failure of the Mental Health Parity Act of 2008.

9. Why do you think electroconvulsive therapy is still available today?

10. What role do health insurers play today in restricting mental health services?

REFERENCES

Ashcraft, M. L. F., Fries, B. E., Nerenz, D. R., Falcon, S. P., Srivastava, S. V., Lee, C. Z., … Errera, P. (1989). A psychiatric patient classification system: An alternative to diagnosis-related groups. *Medical Care, 27*(5), 543–557. doi:10.1097/00005650-198905000-00009

Atwell, R. H. (1965). Recent trends and current problems in mental health services. *Inquiry, 2*(4), 3–12.

Bainbridge, W. S. (1984). Religious insanity in America: The official nineteenth-century theory. *Sociological Analysis, 45*(3), 223–239. doi:10.2307/3711479

Barry, C. L., Huskamp, H. A., & Goldman, H. H. (2010). A political history of federal mental health and addiction insurance parity. *Milbank Quarterly, 88*(3), 404–433. doi:10.1111/j.1468-0009.2010.00605.x

Beers, C. W. (1908). *A mind that found itself: An autobiography*. Retrieved from https://www.gutenberg.org/files/11962/11962-h/11962-h.htm

Black, W. G. Jr. (1991). Social work in World War I: A method lost. *Social Service Review, 65*(3), 379–402. doi:10.1086/603854

Brown, G. (1901). State care of the insane: New York 1901. *The New York Times*. Social Welfare History Project. Retrieved from https://socialwelfare.library.vcu.edu/eras/state-care-insane-1901/

Busch, S. H., McGinty, E. E., Stuart, E. A., Huskamp, H. A., Gibson, T. B., Goldman, H. H., & Barry, C. L. (2017). Was federal parity associated with changes in out-of-network mental health care use and spending? *BMC Health Services Research, 17*, 315. doi:10.1186/s12913-017-2261-9

CORE Solutions. (2016). *Fact sheet: Certified community behavioral health clinics & the Excellence in Mental Health Act*. Retrieved from https://www.coresolutionsinc.com/wp-content/uploads/2016/10/The-Excellence-in-Mental-Health-Act-FactSheet_.pdf

Coy, A. (2006). Mental health in Colonial America. *The Hospitalist*, (5). Retrieved from https://www.the-hospitalist.org/hospitalist/article/123117/mental-health-colonial-america

Deutsch, A. (1949). *The mentally ill in America: A history of their care and treatment from colonial times*. New York, NY: Columbia University Press.

Gay, P. (1988). *Freud: A life for our time*. London, UK: J. M. Dent & Sons.

Goffman, E. (1961). *Asylums: Essays on the social situation of mental patients and other inmates*. New York, NY: Random House.

Grob, G. N. (1977). Rediscovering asylums: The unhistorical history of the mental hospital. *Hastings Center Report, 7*(4), 33–41. doi:10.2307/3560476

Grob, G. N. (2005). Public policy and mental illnesses: Jimmy Carter's Presidential Commission on Mental Health. *Milbank Quarterly, 83*(8), 425–456. doi:10.1111/j.1468-0009.2005.00408.x

Helmus, T. C., & Glenn, R. W. (2005). A look back: A brief history of combat psychiatry. In *Steeling the mind: Combat stress reactions and their omplications for urban warfare* (Chapter 2). Santa Monica, CA: Rand Corporation.

Howarth, H. E. (1944). Present trends in psychiatric social work. *Social Work, 3*(1), 16–20.

Isaac, R. J., & Brakel, S. J. (1992). Subverting good intentions: A brief history of mental health law reform. *Cornell Journal of Law and Public Policy, 2*(1), 89–119.

Jerrell, J. M., & Knight, M. A. (1985). Social work practice in rural mental health systems. *Social Work, 30*(4), 331–337. doi:10.1093/sw/30.4.331

Killaspy, H. (2006). From the asylum to community care: Learning from experience. *British Medical Bulletin, 79–80*, 245–258. doi:10.1093/bmb/ldl017

Kowalczyk, L. (2018, July 18). ER waits for mental health care still long: Patients in crisis can spend days in limbo, despite rules. *The Boston Globe*, A1, B14.

Koyanagi, C., & Goldman, H. H. (1991). The quiet success of the national plan for the chronically mentally ill. *Hospital and Community Psychiatry, 42*(9), 899–905. doi:10.1176/ps.42.9.899

Lenz, L. (2017, March 31). The secret lobotomy of Rosemary Kennedy. *Marie Claire*. Retrieved from https://www.marieclaire.com/celebrity/a26261/secret-lobotomy-rosemary-kennedy

Levenson, A. I., & Reff, S. R. (1970). Community mental health staffing patterns. *Community Mental Health Journal, 6*, 118–125. doi:10.1007/BF01434657

Levinson, H. (2011, November). The strange and curious history of lobotomy. *BBC News*. Retrieved from https://www.bbc.com/news/magazine-15629160

Lieberman, J. A. with Ogas, O. (2015). *Shrinks: The untold story of psychiatry*. New York, NY: Back Bay Books.

Mahan, S. (2016, September 14). The first lobotomy in the US happened at George Washington University. *Washingtonian*. Retrieved from https://www.washingtonian.com/2016/09/14/first-lobotomy-us-george-washington-university

Mechanic, D. (1994). Establishing mental health priorities. *Milbank Quarterly, 72*(3), 501–514. doi:10.2307/3350268

Miller, D., & Blanc, E. (1967). Concepts of "moral treatment" for the mentally ill: Implications for social work with posthospital mental patients. *Social Service Review, 41*(1), 66–74. doi:10.1086/642033

National Association of Social Workers. (2018, May). NASW applauds senators for mental health legislation: Stabenow, Barrasso introduce act to improve access to mental health services. *NASW News*, 4.

National Institutes of Health. (2017, February 17). *The NIH almanac: The National Institute of Mental Health (NIMH)*. Retrieved from https://www.nih.gov/about-nih/what-we-do/nih-almanac/national-institute-mental-health-nimh

National Public Radio. (2005, November 16). *Frequently asked questions about lobotomies*. Retrieved from https://www.npr.org/templates/story/story.php?storyId=5014565

Parry, M. S. (2006). Dorothea Dix (1802–1887). *American Journal of Public Health, 96*(4), 624–625. doi:10.2105/AJPH.2005.079152

Ramon, S. (2009). Adult mental health in a changing international context: The relevance to social work. *British Journal of Social Work, 39*(8), 1615–1622. doi:10.101093/bjsw/bcp066

Roberts, A. R., & Kurtz, L. F. (1987). Historical perspectives on the care and treatment of the mentally ill. *Journal of Sociology & Social Welfare, 14*(4), 75–94.

Rockmore, M. J. (1960). Social work responsibility in mental illness. *Social Work, 5*(3), 70–76.

Ruth, B. J., & Marshall, J. W. (2017). A history of social work in public health. *American Journal of Public Health, 107*(S3), S236–S242. doi:10.2105/AJPH.2017.304005

Schamess, G. (1996). Introduction and editorial: Who profits and who benefits from managed mental health care? *Smith College Studies in Social Work, 66*(3), 209–220.

Scheff, T. J. (1966). *Being mentally ill: A sociological theory.* Chicago, IL: Aldine Publishing.

Schrift, M., Cavender, A., & Hoover, S. (2013). Mental illness, institutionalization and oral history in Appalachia: Voices of psychiatric attendants. *Journal of Appalachian Studies, 19*(1/2), 82–107.

Segal, S. S., & Baumohl, J. (1981). Social work practice in community mental health. *Social Work, 12*(1), 16–24.

Shalin, D. N. (2014). Goffman on mental illness: Asylums and "The Insanity of Place" revisited. *Symbolic Interaction, 37*(1), 122–144. doi:10.1002/symb.84

Social Work Policy Institute. (2004). *History of social work research in mental health.* Retrieved from http://www.socialworkpolicy.org/research/history -of-social-work-research-in-mental-health.html

Sundararaman, R. (2009, April 21). *The U.S. mental health delivery system infrastructure: A primer.* Washington, DC: Congressional Research Service. Retrieved from https://fas.org/sgp/crs/misc/R40536.pdf

Szasz, T. (1961). *The myth of mental illness: Foundations of a theory of personal conduct.* New York, NY: Harper and Row.

Szasz, T. (2001). Mental illness: Psychiatry's phlogiston. *Journal of Medical Ethics, 25*(5), 297–301. doi:10.1136/jme.27.5.297

Taube, C., Lee, E. S., & Forthofer, R. N. (1984). Diagnosis-related groups for mental disorders, alcoholism, and drug abuse: Evaluation and alternatives. *Hospital and Community Psychiatry, 35*(5), 452–455. doi:10.1176/ ps.35.5.452

Trent, J. W. (n.d.). Moral treatment. *Social Welfare History Project.* Retrieved from https://socialwelfare.library.vcu.edu/moral-treatment-insane

Tuntiya, N. (2003). The forgotten history: The deinstitutionalization movement in the mental health care system in the United States. *Graduate theses and dissertations.* Retrieved from http://scholarcommons.usf.edu/ etd/1496

Videka-Sherman, L. (1988). Metaanalysis of research on social work practice in mental health. *Social Work, 33*(4), 325–338.

Virginia Commonwealth University. (n.d.). *National Association of Social Workers history* (1917–1955). Retrieved from https://socialwelfare.library .vcu.edu/social-work/national-association-social-workers-history

Vourlekis, B. S., Edinburg, G., & Knee, R. (1998). The rise of social work in public health through aftercare of people with serious mental illness. *Social Work, 43*(6), 567–575.

Warder, G. (2014). Franklin Pierce's 1854 veto. *Social Welfare History Project.* Virginia Commonwealth University. Retrieved from https://socialwelfare .library.vcu.edu/issues/franklin-pierces-1854-veto

Wittman, M. (1957). Significance of new scientific developments in the mental health field for social work education. *Social Service Review, 31*(2), 135–143.

CHAPTER 3

VIEWS FROM THE INSIDE: MENTAL HEALTH CLIENTS AND THEIR FAMILIES

LEARNING OUTCOMES

- Develop an understanding of the "lived experience" of individuals with mental illness.
- Analyze the impact of mental illness on family members.
- Examine the responses of individuals to the experience of psychiatric hospitalization.
- Describe the reasons why it is very important for individuals with mental illness to participate in developing their treatment plan.
- Identify the special challenges of families coping with schizophrenia.

INTRODUCTION

Like many other people, historical figures and celebrities have had personal experience with mental illness. We know Abraham Lincoln as a president of the United States, but how many of us are aware that President Lincoln suffered from depression and anxiety? How many of us are aware that his wife, Mary Todd Lincoln, had schizophrenia?

Charles Darwin (1809–1882), a biologist and naturalist, had a profound impact on our understanding of how animals evolved from their ancestors. Darwin provided a revolutionary explanation for how humans have developed over time; his theories were revolutionary ideas at the time. Not many of us are aware that he had multiple symptoms of mental illness, including anxiety, obsessive-compulsive disorder (OCD), agoraphobia, and panic attacks (Bergman, 2004). Darwin's contributions to the world were enormous and serve as a reminder that people with mental illness can live rich and accomplished lives and make significant, and even extraordinary, contributions to society.

This chapter highlights the experiences of those with mental illness. It also offers a picture of the families of those with mental illness, and the challenges that family members face. Most often, psychiatrists prefer to focus on the biomedical factors of illness rather than the concerns of the lived experiences of patients (Stanton & Randall, 2016). While social workers and other mental health professionals can seek to understand the symptoms and treatments for individual patients, it is also critical to hear the voices of those with mental illness (Karp & Birk, 2013).

Many celebrities, such as actors, writers, musicians, and sports figures, have come forward to acknowledge and talk about their own mental health challenges. These famous people include, for example, Robin Williams, Dwayne Johnson, Heath Ledger, Ben Stiller, Jim Carrey, Miley Cyrus, and Demi Lovato. Celebrity experience with mental illness serves as a powerful reminder that no one is immune from mental health problems. Celebrities have an important platform from which they can help reduce the social stigma and encourage others to seek help. The individuals who choose to share their most private thoughts and experiences about mental disorders can gain some perspective for themselves as they also try to help others.

Great writers such as Edgar Allan Poe, Sylvia Plath, Virginia Woolf, and Ernest Hemingway were challenged by mental illness. Poe died of a brain tumor that had clearly influenced his erratic behavior. Sylvia Plath, Virginia Woolf, and Ernest Hemingway committed suicide after long struggles with mental illness. These examples of highly creative people with mental illness have led some to question whether indeed there is a relationship between mental illness and creativity, or even genius. See Case Example 3.1 for the mental health issues of Virginia Woolf.

CASE EXAMPLE 3.1

VIRGINIA WOOLF: CHANNELING MENTAL HEALTH ISSUES IN WRITING

As one of the most famous writers in the 1920s and 1930s, Virginia Woolf wrote nine novels, a book of short stories, and other essays. Her most famous novel is perhaps Mrs. Dalloway (1925). Woolf's final novel, Between the Acts (1941), was published after her death in 1941 at the age of 59.

Born in London, Woolf's mother died when she was 13. Other significant losses in her life included her brother, her half sister, and her father. Woolf's gift of writing included her ability and willingness to channel her own mental health issues into the characters in her novels. Woolf had multiple hospitalizations and seemed to be able to anticipate when she was going to experience episodes of depression. For Woolf, writing helped to keep her demons at bay. After previous unsuccessful suicide attempts, Woolf filled her coat pockets with heavy stones and walked into a river to end her life. While there has been debate over her diagnosis, it is widely accepted today that Woolf had untreated bipolar disorder.

SOURCES: A *biological analysis of Virginia Woolf: The impact of mental illness in Woolf's life, marriage, and literature* (2018, January 18). Retrieved from https://owlcation.com/humanities/A-Biographical-Analysis-of-Virginia-Woolf-The-Influence-of-Mental-Illness-on-a-Stable-Marriage; Murphy, B. (2002, April 16). Woolf's mental illness: Obstacle or enabler in her art? *Los Angeles Times*. Retrieved from https://www.latimes.com/archives/la-xpm-2002-apr-16-lv-books16-story.html

Some writers choose to share their experiences of mental illness with their readers. William Styron wrote a poignant book about his own depression, titled *Darkness Visible: A Memoir of Madness* (1992). This highly acclaimed work opened the door to the "depression memoir." Other memoirs of mental illness include Andrew Solomon's *The Noonday Demon: An Anatomy of Depression* (2001), which won the National Book Award. Lewis Wolpert's *Malignant Sadness: The Anatomy of Depression* (1999) chronicles the experience of major depression for someone with a happy family life and successful career as a research biologist.

The personal stories that are shared in mental illness memoirs can be very comforting to those who have mental disorders and also give insights into their experiences to mental health professionals (Donohue-Smith, 2011). In reality, there is no substitute for learning from the ideas and feelings of those with mental disorder: "This narrative voice—the voice of the sufferer—is critical in helping students and clinicians deepen their understanding of both the nature of mental illness and of 'what works' to promote healing" (Donohue-Smith, 2011, p. 138).

Doctors experience mental illness as well, although physicians and medical students with mental health problems are not often acknowledged (Ali, 2017). Some self-prescribe medications, but they may find that medications are not necessarily helpful to them (Stanton & Randall, 2016). The memoir of Kay Redfield Jamison, *An Unquiet Mind: A Memoir of Moods and Madness* (1995), stands out because it is written by a professor of psychiatry who also has bipolar disorder. Nor are social workers immune to mental illness. Social work is an inclusive field, yet it must ensure that both those graduating from schools of social work and active practitioners are capable of providing excellent services

(Reardon, 2012). Social workers can receive assessment and referral for mental health treatment through the National Association of Social Workers (NASW). The Social Workers Assistance Network (SWAN), in Massachusetts, is a free service that provides professional consultations and referrals for social workers with mental health or other personal problems. The issues of social workers are further discussed in Chapter 10, Views From the Field: Challenges in Mental Health Social Work.

PATIENT EXPERIENCES

People with mental illness can experience a wide variety of symptoms. Those with depression talk about loss of interest in life, lethargy, difficulty getting out of bed, and difficulty functioning day to day. As Jamison (1995) put it, "depression is … flat, hollow, and unendurable. It is also tiresome" (p. 218). Those with anxiety can experience excessive and persistent worry, feelings of unease or even dread, heart palpitations, excessive sweating, and panic attacks. Individuals with bipolar disorder can experience periods of manic behavior and depressive periods. Individuals with schizophrenia can experience auditory and visual hallucinations that are confusing and even frightening. Symptoms and diagnoses of specific mental disorders are discussed in Chapter 5, Social Work and Mental Illness: Labels and Diagnoses.

It can be very difficult to acknowledge a mental health problem and ask for help. Those with mental illness may not seek help because they are unaware of their mental illness. This is a form of *anosognosia*, from the Greek word meaning "to not know a disease" (National Alliance on Mental Illness [NAMI], 2018a). When individuals do not understand that they have a mental illness, they lack an accurate understanding of their situation and their need for help. Others with mental illness hope the symptoms will disappear and want to get over it on their own (Sareen et al., 2007). They can be ashamed, embarrassed, and fearful of stigma. Jamison (1995) documents how she refused to take medication for bipolar disorder despite having the clinical expertise to know treatment would help her. The realization of the need for medications can be slow and arduous: "That I owed my life to pills was not, however, obvious to me for a long time; my lack of judgment about the necessity to take lithium proved to be an exceedingly costly one" (Jamison, 1995, p. 89). As one wise mental health social worker put it, "Our hospital is filled with people who won't take their medications."

Some people travel a long and circuitous route before being open to treatment and ultimately finding appropriate treatment. For example, Marya Hornbacher's *Madness: A Bipolar Life* (2008) illustrates the difficulties in obtaining an accurate diagnosis. Hornbacher had her first psychiatric hospitalization at age 16 and endured many years of mental illness with severe behavioral problems before receiving the diagnosis of bipolar disorder. Unfortunately, an accurate diagnosis was not sufficient to convince her to accept treatment. Like many people with bipolar disorder, she did not want to take the medications. It took Hornbacher years to get on an even keel.

It is well known that mental illness can have an impact on a person's job and the perceptions of others in the workplace. Trying to manage this can result in more stress for an employee with mental illness (Malachowski, Boydell, Sawchuk, & Kirsh, 2016). This is compounded when workplace managers are not equipped and not adequately trained to provide the support and assistance that employees may need (Malachowski et al., 2016).

Research that offers the perspectives of those with mental illness can be useful in determining effective ways to combat stigma (Schulze & Angermeyer, 2003). Patients can offer suggestions for more effective treatment. Some individuals with mental disorders can be treated on an outpatient basis or in a day treatment program. The individuals in outpatient treatment can exercise more autonomy because each day, they make the decision to attend. For some people with severe mental disorders, the decision for psychiatric hospitalization is out of their hands.

Inpatient Hospitalization

It can be very frightening to be admitted to a psychiatric hospital. Some patients are admitted on a voluntary basis, but the most severe situations can require mental health professionals to commit a person against his or her own will. For some, this experience creates an overwhelming feeling of powerlessness (Hyde, 2017). Evaluations in hospital emergency rooms (ERs) for psychiatric care can be either cursory or comprehensive. It is not standard practice to ensure that each patient is evaluated by a psychiatrist, social worker, or other qualified mental health professional. That can result in an evaluation completed by someone who is not qualified to make a determination of whether psychiatric hospitalization is necessary. In some cases, emergency psychiatric response teams include social workers and others with strong mental health credentials, but this is not necessarily the case (Geller, 2015). Then begins the search for a psychiatric hospital bed, which can result in waiting for hours, days, and even weeks: "In systems without reasonable functioning mental health services individuals are waiting over 1 month for a psychiatric bed. That means the person is lying on a gurney, or sitting being observed, eating meals, and waiting. No treatment is occurring" (Geller, 2015, p. 916). This experience of waiting in the ER can add to the trauma for patients.

When the process of evaluating a patient in a hospital ER and obtaining a psychiatric bed goes awry, the consequences can be tragic. See Case Example 3.2 for the story of Gus Deeds, the son of Virginia state senator Creigh Deeds.

CASE EXAMPLE 3.2

VIRGINIA STATE SENATOR CREIGH DEEDS AND HIS SON GUS: IMPROVING THE MENTAL HEALTH SYSTEM IN VIRGINIA

Austin "Gus" Deeds, son of Virginia state senator Creigh Deeds, and a student at William and Mary College, had a history of bipolar disorder and suicide attempts. On November 18, 2013, in response to concern about his son's behavior and mental health, a local judge issued an emergency custody order that allowed Gus to be brought to the local Bath Community Hospital (Portnoy, 2016). The emergency mental health evaluator from Rockbridge Area Community Services Board assessed Gus and determined that he was eligible for psychiatric hospitalization, but did not locate a psychiatric bed for him. (Later, it was learned that on that day several hospitals with available beds were not contacted.) Gus was released and went home to his family. The next day Gus stabbed his father 13 times. He then killed himself with a rifle.

Senator Deeds filed a lawsuit against the state of Virginia, the mental health evaluator, and the agency the evaluator worked for. In 2017, Senator Deeds dropped the state of Virginia from his wrongful-death lawsuit. The suit against the mental health evaluator who discharged the senator's son the day before his suicide was settled in October 2018. After originally seeking $6 million, the case was settled for $950,000 (Cloherty, 2017; Vozzella, 2018). Senator Deeds's statement at the conclusion of the lawsuit included the following: "My son is dead. No amount of money can make that right, bring him back, or fill the hole in my heart" (Vozzella, 2018, p. 1).

It is a cautionary tale that not even the child of a powerful politician could obtain appropriate mental health services in a time of crisis. Yet something positive came from this horrific tragedy. As a result of the death of Gus Deeds, much greater financial support was appropriated to the mental health system in Virginia. This included extending time to evaluate psychiatric patients and keeping an up-to-date list of available psychiatric beds (Portnoy, 2016).

SOURCES: Cloherty, M. (2017, July 28). State Senator Deeds drops Virginia from suit over son's death. *WTOP News*. Retrieved from https://wtop.com/virginia/2017/07/deeds-drops-state-death-suit; Portnoy, J. (2016, January 5). Virginia Senator Creigh Deeds sues the state, others for $6 million in son's suicide. *The Washington Post*. Retrieved from https://www.washingtonpost.com/local/virginia-politics/va-sen-creigh-deeds-sues-the-state-others-for-6-million-in-sons-suicide/2016; Vozzella, L.

(2018, October 18). Va. State Senator Creigh Deeds settles lawsuit over his son's death for $950,000. *The Washington Post*. Retrieved from https://www.washingtonpost. com/local/virginia-politics/va-state-sen-creigh-deeds-settles-lawsuit-over-his-sons -death-for-950k/2018/10/17/f75d533e-d243-11e8-8c22-fa2ef74bd

One middle-aged woman evaluated in a hospital ER with a history of suicide attempts and psychiatric hospitalizations had this to say: "I know what these places do for you. You sit there, they throw medication at you and then you leave no better off than when you started" (White, 2013, p. 26). For those who have had negative experiences with psychiatric hospitalization, it is hard to argue with this viewpoint.

Laws have both helped and hindered the mentally ill from receiving the help they need (Grisso & Applebaum, 1991). The mentally ill can be required to accept involuntary mental hospitalization if they are deemed a risk to themselves or to others. Today, patients who are committed are most likely at risk of suicide or homicide. Involuntary hospitalization is fraught with concerns about restricting the personal freedom of the patient, denying the patient's autonomy, and trying to coerce treatment (Wyder, Bland, & Crompton, 2013). It is critical that insofar as it is safe and reasonable, individuals with mental illness must maintain control over their own lives (Davidson, O'Connell, Tondora, Styron, & Kangas, 2006). Different standards can be utilized to determine who should be locked up against their will. For example, patients can be evaluated for involuntary hospitalization by a clinician or be evaluated using a screening instrument. One study utilizing the MacArthur Competence Assessment Tool for Treatment (MacCAT-T) found that patients with dementia, schizophrenia, or depression were much more likely to be judged as having mental impairment when they were evaluated with this tool than when they were evaluated by clinical assessment (Vollmann, Bauer, Danker-Hopfe, & Helmchen, 2003).

Individuals committed involuntarily, based on evidence that they are a danger to themselves or to others, can have more severe symptoms and thus be harder to work with in treatment. It is very difficult to balance patient choice with the fact that someone is hospitalized involuntarily (Bartholomew & Kensler, 2010). Not surprisingly, patients in psychiatric hospitals who were committed can be less satisfied with their experience than voluntary patients (Wykes et al., 2018). In sum, "the use of involuntary treatment has been one of the most contentious legal provisions in psychiatry" (Wyder et al., 2013, p. 580).

Major concerns for inpatients revolve around receiving accurate information, communication with staff, access to activities, level of involvement in formulating treatment plans, quality of the hospital's food, and the physical environment (Walsh & Boyle, 2009). A variety of strategies can help make the hospitalization experience more comfortable. Education on one's diagnosis and medications can be helpful to psychiatric inpatients (Kristiansen, Videbech, Kragh, Thisted, & Bjerrum, 2017). Relationships of patients to hospital clinicians and to each other can be most important for those in hospital treatment (Nordfjaern, Rundmo, & Holes, 2010). Patients, for example, often express their boredom while in the hospital, and having activities available in addition to individual and group therapy can be very helpful (Wykes et al., 2018). For example, music and art therapy can be helpful, as can all forms of physical activity such as yoga, sports, and the use of a gym.

Psychiatric inpatients can also be sensitive to what it takes to run a psychiatric ward and to the issues of staff. Staff clinicians as well as those who provide custodial supervisory care are working in a difficult and demanding closed environment. It is important to balance the needs of the patients and the needs of the staff (Csipke et al., 2016). One inpatient, for example, had this to say: "Everything that happens has to be recorded … they have to cover their back" (Walsh & Boyle, 2009, p. 35). In the best situations, patients and staff avoid adversarial relationships and work collaboratively on the treatment plan (Hyde, 2017).

Involving patients in their own care is much more important than political correctness (Tait & Lester, 2005). Involvement in planning and participating in their own care is important because patients are the experts on their own illness. This type of engagement with patients may in itself be therapeutic. When patients are not included in their treatment planning, a lack of trust may result. For example, a patient being moved to a different unit without being consulted by staff remarked, "I thought I was a member of the treatment team!" (Bartholomew & Kensler, 2010).

Patients have important perspectives about mental illness and its related care that may differ from professional perspectives. Listening to patients can help professionals to expand upon limited ideas about mental illness. In addition, patients often have useful ideas about alternative treatments. Encouraging patients to be involved in their planning and treatment supports social inclusion and can counteract social isolation (Tait & Lester, 2005). The underlying principle is that "recovery requires reframing the treatment enterprise from the professional's perspective to the person's perspective" (Davidson et al., 2006, p. 643). Moreover, patients must be encouraged to maintain hopes and aspirations for the future (Davidson et al., 2006).

In New Jersey, the Recovery Network Project is a program focused on recovered mental health patients providing services to those patients in psychiatric hospitals (Swarbrick & Brice, 2006). The program was developed in response to feedback from patients to whom state hospitals were not offering recovery-related activities. Former patients serve as consultants to hospital staff and work directly with inpatients on recovery strategies. This proactive approach does not focus on patient deficits but instead emphasizes patients' skills, abilities, and motivation within a context of hope for the future (Swarbrick & Brice, 2006).

A variety of supportive programs can go a long way toward ensuring safety, comfort, and the feeling that patients have gained something positive from their psychiatric hospitalization. One patient, Ann Marie, offered very positive comments about her journey to wellness, especially the importance of her poetry writing and artwork: "As I travel the road to recovery I stand tall. Taking this journey seems like it is my life's true calling. When I am down and out these help me see that recovery is possible and that I am not 'less than' because of my illness, I just may have to work a lot harder to get down the road" (South Carolina Department of Mental Health, 2010, p. 7). This provides a good example of how personal the meaning of recovery is to those with mental disorders. Of course, this is not easily measured in scientific studies (Hyde, 2017).

Walsh and Boyle (2009) offer a number of recommendations for the delivery of services within psychiatric hospitals, as seen in Tips for the Field 3.1.

TIPS FOR THE FIELD 3.1

RECOMMENDATIONS FOR THE DELIVERY OF SERVICES IN A PSYCHIATRIC HOSPITAL

These recommendations for nurses to improve the experience of psychiatric hospitalization can extend to social workers as well as all mental health professionals working with clients in psychiatric hospitals.

1. Provide reassurance to the newly arrived inpatient.

2. Ensure that physical problems are evaluated along with the mental health disorder.

3. Family members should be given the opportunity to have their questions answered and be informed of hospital policies and practices, such as visiting hours.

4. Patients should be informed of their rights; rules of the facility should be explained to the patient, including the procedure to make a complaint.

5. Patients should be informed of the roles of the professionals who are a part of their care team.

6. Patients need to be involved in the development of their treatment plan and be aware of all services available.

7. When a recommendation is made to change or modify the medication regimen, the patient must be involved.

8. Discharge planning must include the patient, and a comprehensive written plan should be given to the patient and family regarding follow-up services.

SOURCE: Adapted from Walsh, J., & Boyle, J. (2009). Improving acute psychiatric hospital services according to inpatient experiences. A use-led piece of research as a means to empowerment. *Issues in Mental Health Nursing, 30*(1), 31–38. doi:1080/01612840800250073.

The Health Insurance Portability and Accountability Act (HIPAA) was enacted in 1996 to ensure the privacy and confidentiality of those receiving any kind of health services. While privacy is very important, it does not always work in the best interests of patients with mental illness. For example, the parents and primary caregivers of Chris, a 39-year-old man with schizophrenia, were denied the opportunity to speak with their son's physicians after his hospitalization (Szabo, 2016). Erroneously, the doctors thought Chris did not have health insurance when, in fact, his parents could have verified that he did. This resulted in Chris being prescribed low-cost pills upon release from the psychiatric hospital, even though he had a history of not being willing to take pills. Previously he was given an injectable medication that was used with success and would have been covered either by his insurance or his parents' private funds. Chris committed suicide by carbon monoxide poisoning in the family car in 2012 (Szabo, 2016). In their tragic loss, Chris's parents felt that the HIPAA law took away their opportunity to try to prevent their son's suicide.

In addition to being guided by sometimes confusing HIPAA regulations, psychiatrists may not want to engage with family members for several reasons. Psychiatry has long associated the problems of patients with the behaviors and parenting styles of parents (Romi & Melamed, 2007; Szabo, 2016). Also, taking time to speak with parents may not be a compensated service and can take time and energy away from treating other patients.

Psychiatrists can view those persons with severe mental illness as less able to contribute to their own treatment plan (Gerken, 2017). By contrast, social workers are more likely to accept the long-held notion of client self-determination, a real strength of the profession.

Individuals in need of psychiatric care can go through several stages before taking action. First come the symptoms. Then individuals evaluate the severity of their symptoms. Finally individuals face the consequences. They assess whether treatment is really necessary, evaluate the treatment options, and then determine whether to seek help (Goldberg & Huxley, 1980).

There is a great need for patient preferences and values to be included in the delivery of mental health services, both inpatient and outpatient (Carey, 2016). A change from "patient-centered" care to "patient-per-spective" care is needed. In reality, it is the patient's experience with mental health services that establishes the underpinning for treatment to be effective (Carey, 2016). This patient perspective must be the context within which services are provided and can go a long way toward supporting mentally ill clients in accepting and best utilizing services (Carey, 2016).

FAMILY PERCEPTIONS AND CONCERNS

Family members play critical roles in caring for the mentally ill as well as serving as activists and advocates to obtain services. Family members know the patient best and may provide the care and support that others are unable or unwilling to provide. They are also likely to engage in activities to reduce the stigma of mental disorders.

Generally those with personal experience with a family member or friend with mental illness tend to have a more positive outlook on mental illness (McSween, 2002; Waugh, Lethem, Sherring, & Henderson, 2017). For example, psychiatrist Ken Duckworth wrote about his father's bipolar disorder as part of his application for his medical residency in 1986, something unheard of at the time. Dr. Duckworth is now the medical director of NAMI (Kaltwasser, 2018).

From a political perspective, personal or family experience with mental illness is associated with greater support for mental health treatment as well as support for increased funding (Barry, Huskamp, & Goldman, 2010). As discussed in Chapter 2, A Short History of Mental Health Policy and Treatment in the United States, in the Kennedy family, President John F. Kennedy's sister Rosemary was intellectually disabled and subjected to a lobotomy. President Kennedy and his brother Senator Edward M. Kennedy did much to advance the rights of and services provided to the disabled. Eunice Kennedy Shriver, a sister of Rosemary, established the Special Olympics, an international organization that provides sporting activities to those with intellectual disabilities. Rosemary's nephew and former U.S. congressman (from Rhode Island) Patrick Kennedy has been outspoken about his personal struggle with bipolar disorder and substance use disorder in his efforts to help reduce stigma (Barry et al., 2010).

It is no surprise that family members experience significant levels of stress when a relative has mental illness. Family members use a variety of coping strategies for dealing with a relative in a psychiatric hospital. Some employ avoidance, which limits their exposure to the stress associated with mental illness. This can include reducing or even cutting off contact with the ill family member (Eaton, Davis, Hammond, Condon, & McGee, 2011; Romi & Melamed, 2007). Some families rely upon religious and/or spiritual beliefs, including prayer, to cope. Another strategy is accepting the situation while focusing on changing thinking to manage and respond to the realities of the situation (Eaton et al., 2011).

Therapeutic interventions must take into consideration a family's willingness and readiness to participate (Romi & Melamed, 2007). Engaging in family interventions can help family members feel better by being proactive. One strategy to help determine the readiness for and appropriateness of involvement of family members focuses on four major stages: (a) Complete a detailed family history, including information on the patient and familial relationships; (b) identify the strategies used to communicate and cope within the family; (c) determine the motivation, ability, and willingness of the family members to engage in treatment; and (d) offer recommendations for the type of intervention that may be most useful. This can mean choosing among different types of treatment in different settings (Romi & Melamed, 2007). The Family Crisis Oriented Personal Evaluation Scales (F-COPES), developed in 1981, is an instrument used to measure coping strategies used by family members to respond to difficult situations (McCubbin, Olsen, Larsen, & Fischer, 2000). However, it is not often utilized in clinical practice to assist family members.

Spouses of those with mental illness face challenges on many levels. Spouses can experience the increased burden of household tasks and lack of emotional support (Wittmund, Wilms, Mory, & Angermeyer, 2002). Out of concerns about stigma, spouses can be more hesitant to ask for help from friends and neighbors; this, in turn, leads to increasing social isolation. Also, spouses may have to deal with changing roles due to impairment, perhaps coming to view the mentally ill spouse as another dependent child (Wittmund et al., 2002).

Spouses themselves can be at high risk for developing depressive disorders. One study found that 41.1% of spouses of the mentally ill suffered from depression, 52.2% of women and 32.1% of men (Wittmund et al., 2002). Overall, caring for the mentally ill is more related to how impaired the person is in daily functioning rather than an association with a specific mental health diagnosis (Wittmund et al., 2002).

Parents of children with mental illness also have their own unique challenges. Little is known about parents caring for children who have mental disorders, including their feelings of guilt and inadequacy in their parenting. As one mother put it, "It makes you feel like a failure" (Eaton, Ohan, Stritzke, & Corrigan, 2016, p. 3115). This parental response is not surprising, because for many years psychiatry laid the blame for mental illness at the feet of parents.

It is also difficult to figure out whether it is preferable to disclose or conceal a mental health diagnosis of a child from other family and friends. Despite fears on the part of mothers regarding disclosure, mothers can receive empathy from others (Eaton, Ohan, Stritzke, Courtauld, & Corrigan, 2017). Ensuring that parents have accurate information on the child's behavior, diagnosis, and treatment can reduce parental self-blame. Parent support groups can be especially helpful. Since it is often parents who disclose the diagnosis to their children, it is especially important that they have a good understanding of the illness (Bringewatt, 2017).

When a parent has a mental illness, there can be a great impact on the dependent children. Parents themselves identify their children as important reasons for recovery. Parenting issues and skills should be a part of the recovery plan, but this is often not the case (Mayberry, Reupert, & Goodyear, 2015).

The Special Challenges of Families Coping With Schizophrenia

In families where one member has schizophrenia, the challenges can be even more difficult. Because schizophrenia is among the most severe mental disorders, it is not surprising that family members have to cope with much more stress. In the past, family members, most often parents, were blamed for causing the child to become schizophrenic—for causing the first experience of psychosis as well as subsequent episodes (Brady & McCain, 2004). In a review of the literature on family response to schizophrenia, Brady and McCain (2004) found family responses included living with uncertainty, loss, parental anxiety and depression, family overinvolvement, and a high rate of medical problems. This includes the burden of taking care of the family member, who may be seriously impaired; fear regarding the course of the illness; embarrassment; and lack of social support (Brady & McCain, 2004).

In the 1930s, research began to delve into the causes of schizophrenia. The theories developed at the time suggested that mothers who were overprotective as well as rejecting of their children were "schizophrenogenic mothers" (Johnston, 2013). That is, mental health professionals thought the home environment led to schizophrenia, which represented a way for a child to adapt to a noxious family life. These ideas fell out of favor in the 1970s as biological explanations developed, yet the judgment and fear of judgment still remain strong.

With the onset of schizophrenia, family members can be confused and upset by the strange behaviors and belief systems of the individual, who may stop usual activities, and they may lose motivation (Brady & McCain, 2004). It is often said by a parent, "My child isn't who he used to be." Some schizophrenic patients are alienated from their families, losing an important source of support. For these individuals, life can be especially difficult as they try to get support from others. For example, one mother of a hospital inpatient with a diagnosis of schizophrenia stated that "whenever we came to see our daughter at the hospital, other patients came to her room and congregated around us, craving for personal contact with someone other than their fellow patients" (Schulze & Angermeyer, 2003, p. 304).

An issue that arises is how to distinguish, if possible, the individual's personality from the specific mental illness. This is especially the case for bipolar disorder (Miklowitz, 2011). Sheila Hamilton, author of *All the Things We Never Knew* (2015), illustrates this through a poignant description of her husband's struggles with bipolar disorder, the effects on their family, and his ultimate suicide: "But how much of David's behavior was the illness and how much was the stubborn son of a bitch doing exactly what he pleased? Where did the illness begin and the self disappear?" (Hamilton, 2015, p. 63). Many individuals and families with mental illness continue to ask themselves this question over long periods of time.

Much more attention in treatment and research must be paid to family members of those with mental illness. This is certainly the case where a child, parent, or spouse has a mental disorder. NAMI was established in 1979 by a small group of families, but has since grown into the largest advocacy organization for those with mental disorders. On both a national level and through its active state chapters, NAMI advocates for strengthening national public policy and offers educational programs to individuals, families, and educators. It also offers public awareness activities such as NAMIWalks and Mental Illness Awareness Week. Another critical service is the national free information, support, and referral line available at 1-800-950-6264 or info@nami.org (NAMI, 2018b). See Tips for the Field 3.2 for approaches to assist family members of those with mental disorders.

TIPS FOR THE FIELD 3.2

DIGGING DEEPER INTO SUPPORT SYSTEMS: SOCIAL WORKERS CAN ENCOURAGE FAMILY MEMBERS TO UTILIZE HELPFUL APPROACHES

Social workers and other mental health professionals can encourage family members to utilize the following strategies:

1. Listen to and acknowledge concerns of the individual, and offer understanding.

2. Learn about the causes, treatment, and prognosis for the specific mental illness from trusted sources.

3. Encourage family members to assist the individual to seek professional mental healthcare.

4. Learn the signs and symptoms to recognize when the family member needs help.

5. Encourage the use of supportive services such as peer support.

6. Provide information on the National Alliance for the Mentally Ill, and encourage the family to contact the organization.

7. Maintain hope for a better future.

SOURCES: American Psychological Association. (2018). *Supporting a family member with serious mental illness.* Retrieved from http://www.apa.org/helpcenter/improving-care.aspx; Brady, N., & McCain, G. C. (2004). Living with schizophrenia: A family perspective. *Online Journal of Issues in Nursing.* Retrieved from http://ojin.nursingworld.org/MainMenuCategories/ANAMarketplace/ANAPeriodicals/OJIN/TableofContents/Volume102005/No1Jan05/HirshArticle/LivingwithSchizophrenia.html

Social workers assist families in which a child, parent, or spouse has mental health issues. This assistance can be within the realm of psychiatric hospitalization, a day treatment program, or individual and family therapy. Social workers are more willing to spend time with patients in the hospital and as outpatients, and they tend not be as driven by financial reward. For example, while a psychiatrist seeing a patient in the hospital can be paid per patient visit, social workers are more likely to be in salaried positions and, therefore, are less driven by the number of patients seen.

Several of the core competencies of the Council on Social Work Education (CSWE) relate directly to working with those with mental disorders and their families. Core competency #6 supports utilizing social work skills to engage individuals and families. Core competency #7 supports assessing individuals and families for the types of treatment needed and assessing willingness to accept those services. Core competency #8, intervention with individuals and families, serves as a reminder of the many ways social workers can assist those with mental disorders and their families through screening, assessment, referral, and treatment services.

SUMMARY AND CONCLUSION

When they take the time and make the effort to learn about mental illness, most people are surprised to discover that it is more common than they initially thought. People who know individuals with mental illness are more likely to engage and help to reduce stigma. Celebrities with mental health disorders do much to help reduce stigma in today's world. It can be a very long and challenging process for individuals and families to acknowledge the presence of a mental illness and seek assistance. Psychiatric hospitalization can be very upsetting to both the patient and family members. As much as possible, those with mental illness must be involved in their treatment planning, and their voices and concerns must be heard by mental health professionals. Much more should be done to provide a better-quality environment within psychiatric hospitals, including improving physical comfort.

Treatment of individuals with mental illness must consider the level of involvement of family members. Spouses of those with mental disorders are at high risk of developing depression. Parents of children with mental disorders may have to cope with feelings of guilt and inadequacy. Children who have a parent with mental illness face their own challenges and are in need of support. Finally, social workers are well educated and trained to screen, assess, and provide treatment and support to patients and their families.

DISCUSSION QUESTIONS/TOPICS

1. What do you think is the relationship between creativity and mental illness?

2. Discuss the reasons why some individuals must be admitted to psychiatric hospitals.

3. What can be done to make the experience of psychiatric hospitalization more comfortable and helpful to patients?

4. In what ways do memoirs of authors with mental health problems help the readers of those books?

5. Discuss the unique challenges of parents with mentally ill children.

6. Why are spouses of individuals with mental illness at risk for depression?

7. Discuss the impact on children when a parent has a mental disorder.

8. What services, if any, could have been activated to prevent the suicide of Gus Deeds?

9. What are the special challenges of families coping with schizophrenia?

10. What are your own ideas for what social workers can do to support family members of those with mental illness?

REFERENCES

Ali, U. (2017, April 24). My experience of being a patient on a psychiatric ward. *British Medical Journal, 357,* 1431. doi:10.1136/sbmj.j1431

Barry, C. L., Huskamp, H. A., & Goldman, H. H. (2010). A political history of federal mental health and addiction insurance parity. *Milbank Quarterly, 88*(3), 404–433. doi:10.1111/j.1468-0009.2010.00605.x

Bartholomew, T., & Kensler, D. (2010). Illness management and recovery in state psychiatric hospitals. *American Journal of Psychiatric Rehabilitation, 13*, 105–123. doi:10.1080/15487761003756977

Bergman, J. (2004, January 1). Was Charles Darwin psychotic? A study of his mental health. *Institute for Creation Research*. Retrieved from http://www.icr.org/article/was-charles-darwin-psychotic-study-his -mental-heal

Brady, N., & McCain, G. C. (2004). Living with schizophrenia: A family perspective. *Online Journal of Issues in Nursing*. Retrieved from http:// ojin.nursingworld.org/MainMenuCategories/ANAMarketplace/ ANAPeriodicals/OJIN/TableofContents/Volume102005/No1Jan05/ HirshArticle/LivingwithSchizophrenia.html

Bringewatt, E. H. (2017). Delivering diagnoses: Parents as translators and withholders of children's mental health diagnoses. *Journal of Child and Family Studies, 26*(7), 1958–1969. doi:10.1007/s10826-017-0709-5

Carey, T. A. (2016). Beyond patient-centered care: Enhancing the patient experience in mental health services through patient-perspective care. *Patient Experience Journal, 3*(2), 46–49. Retrieved from http://pxjournal .org/journal/vol3/iss2/8

Csipke, E., Williams, P., Rose, D., Koeser, L., McCrone, P., Wykes, T., & Craig, T. (2016). Following the Francis Report: Investigating patient experience of mental health in-patient care. *British Journal of Psychiatry, 209*(1), 35–39. doi:10.1192/bjp.bp.115.171124

Davidson, L., O'Connell, M., Tondora, J., Styron, T., & Kangas, K. (2006). The top ten concerns about recovery encountered in mental health transformation. *Psychiatric Services, 57*(5), 640–645. doi:10.1176/appi. ps.57.5.640

Donohue-Smith, M. (2011). Telling the whole story: A conceptual model for analyzing the mental illness memoir. *Mental Health Review, 16*(3), 138–146. doi:10.1108/13619321111178096

Eaton, K., Ohan, J. L., Stritzke, W. G. K., & Corrigan, P. W. (2016). Failing to meet the good parent ideal: Self-stigma in parents of children with mental health disorders. *Journal of Child and Family Studies, 25*(10), 3109–3123. doi:10.1007/s10826-016-0459-9

Eaton, K., Ohan, J. L., Stritzke, W. G. K., Courtauld, H. M., & Corrigan, P. W. (2017). Mothers' decisions to disclose or conceal their child's mental health disorder. *Qualitative Health Research, 27*(11), 1628–1639. doi:10.1177/1049732317697096

Eaton, P. M., Davis, B. L., Hammond, P. V., Condon, E. H., & McGee, A. T. (2011). Coping strategies of family members of hospitalized psychiatric patients. *Nursing Research and Practice, 2011*, 392705. doi:10.1155/2011/392705

Geller, J. L. (2015). The first step in health reform for those with serious mental illness: Integrating the dis-integrated mental health system. *Journal of Nervous and Mental Disease, 203*(12), 909–918. doi:10.1097/ NMD.0000000000000

Gerken, A. T. (2017). Open dialogue: A novel approach to treating people with psychotic disorders. *Psych Central Professional*. Retrieved from https:// pro.psychcentral.com/open-dialogue-a-novel-approach-to-treating-people- with-psychotic-disorders

Goldberg, D., & Huxley, P. (1980). *Mental health in the community: Pathways to psychiatric care*. London, UK: Tavistock.

Grisso, T., & Appelbaum, P. S. (1991). Mentally ill and non-mentally-ill patients' abilities to understand informed consent disclosures for medication: Preliminary data. *Law and Human Behavior, 15*(4), 377–388.

Hamilton, S. (2015). *All the things we never knew*. Berkeley, CA: Seal Press.

Hornbacher, M. (2008). *Madness: A bipolar life*. Boston, MA: Mariner Books.

Hyde, B. (2017). *The lived experience of acute mental health care: What's recovery got to do with it*. Doctoral dissertation submitted to Charles Sturt University, Australia.

Jamison, K. R. (1995). *An unquiet mind: A memoir of moods and madness*. New York, NY: Vintage Books.

Johnston, J. (2013). The ghost of the schizophrenogenic mother. *American Medical Association Journal of Ethics, 15*(9), 801–805. doi:10.1001/virtualmentor.2013.15.9.oped1-1309

Kaltwasser, J. (2018, June 28). The challenges, consequences of stigma in mental illness patients. *MD Magazine*. Retrieved from http://www.mdmag.com/medical-news/the-challenges-consequences-of-stigma-in-mental-illness-patients

Karp, D. A., & Birk, L. B. (2013). Listening to voices: Patient experience and the meanings of mental illness. In C. S. Aneshensel, J. C. Phelan, & A. Bierman, A. (Eds.), *Handbook of the sociology of mental health* (pp. 23–40). New York, NY: Springer Publishing Company.

Kristiansen, S. T., Videbech, P., Kragh, M., Thisted, C. N., & Bjerrum, M. B. (2017). Patients' experiences of patient education on psychiatric inpatient wards: A systematic review. *Patient Education and Counseling, 101*(3), 389–398. doi:10.1016/j.pec.2017.09.005.

Malachowski, C. K., Boydell, K., Sawchuk, P., & Kirsh, B. (2016). The "work" of workplace mental health: An institutional ethnography. *Society and Mental Health, 6*(3), 207–222. doi:10.1177/2156869316642265

Mayberry, D., Reupert, A., & Goodyear, M. (2015). Goal setting in recovery: Families where a parent has a mental illness or a dual diagnosis. *Child & Family Social Work, 20*, 354–363. doi:10.1111/cfs.12084

McCubbin, H. I., Olson, D. H., Larsen, D. H., Corcoran, K., & Fischer, J. (2000). Family Crisis Oriented Personal Evaluation Scales (F-COPES) (1987, 1991). In Measures for Clinical Practice: A Sourcebook, 3rd ed., 1, 294–297. NY: Free Press. doi:10.1037/t02213-000

McSween, J. (2002). The role of group interest, identity, and stigma in determining mental health policy preferences. *Journal of Health Politics, Policy and Law, 27*(5), 773–800.

Miklowitz, D. J. (2011). *The bipolar survival guide: What you and your family need to know* (2nd ed.). New York, NY: Guilford Press.

National Alliance on Mental Illness. (2018a). *About NAMI*. Retrieved from https://www.nami.org/About-NAMI

National Alliance on Mental Illness. (2018b). *Anosognosia*. Retrieved from https://www.nami.org/learn-more/mental-health-conditions/related-conditions/anosognosia

Nordfjaern, T., Rundmo, T., & Hole, R. (2010). Treatment and recovery as perceived by patients with substance addiction. *Journal of Psychiatric and Mental Health Nursing, 17*(1), 46–64. doi:10.1111/j.1365-2850.2009.01477.x

Reardon, C. (2012). Supporting social work students with mental health challenges. *Social Work Today, 12*(5), 10. Retrieved from http://www.socialworktoday.com/archive/091712p10.shtml

Romi, T., & Melamed, S. (2007). Involving the family of patients with mental illness in treatment: A model for assessment. *Journal of Family Psychotherapy, 18*(1), 11–26. doi:10.1300Jo85v18n01_02

Sareen, J., Jagdeo, A., Cox, B. J., Clara, I., ten Have, M., Belik, S.-L., ... Stein, M. B. (2007). Perceived barriers to mental health service utilization in the United States, Ontario, and the Netherlands. *Psychiatric Services, 58*(3), 357–364. doi:10.1176/ps.2007.58.3.357

Schulze, B., & Angermeyer, M. C. (2003). Subjective experiences of stigma: A focus group study of schizophrenic patients, their relatives and mental health professionals. *Social Science & Medicine, 56,* 299–312. doi:10.1016/S0277-9536(02)00028-X

Solomon, A. (2001). *The noonday demon: An atlas of depression.* New York, NY: Scribner.

South Carolina Department of Mental Health. (2010). *Connections: Stories of recovery from mental illness.* Columbia, SC: Recovery Steering Committee.

Stanton, J., & Randal, P. (2016). Developing a psychiatrist–patient relationship when both people are doctors: A qualitative study. *British Medical Journal Open, 6*(5), 1–9. doi:10.1136/bmjopen-2015-010216

Styron, W. (1992). *Darkness visible: A memoir of madness.* New York, NY: Random House.

Swarbrick, M., & Brice, Jr., G. H. (2006). Sharing the message of hope, wellness, and recovery with consumers psychiatric hospitals. *American Journal of Psychiatric Rehabilitation, 9,* 101–109. doi:10.1080/15487760600876196

Szabo, L. (2016, February 26). Mental illness: Families cut out of care. Privacy law leaves loved ones on the sidelines—with tragic results. *USA Today.* Retrieved from https://www.usatoday.com/story/news/2016/02/26/privacy-law-leaves-loved-ones-on-the-sidelines

Tait, L., & Lester, H. (2005). Encouraging user involvement in mental health services. *Advances in Psychiatric Treatment, 11*(3), 168–175. doi:10.1192/apt.11.3.168

Vollmann, J., Bauer, A., Danker-Hopfe, H. D., & Helmchen, H. (2003). Competence of mentally ill patients: A comparative empirical study. *Psychological Medicine, 33*(8), 1463–1471. doi:10.1017.S0033291703008389

Walsh, J., & Boyle, J. (2009). Improving acute psychiatric hospital services according to inpatient experiences: A use-led piece of research as a means to empowerment. *Issues in Mental Health Nursing, 30*(1), 31–38. doi:1080/01612840800250073

Waugh, W., Lethem, C., Sherring, S., & Henderson, C. (2017). Exploring experiences of and attitudes toward mental illness and disclosure amongst health care professionals: A qualitative study. *Journal of Mental Health, 26*(5), 457–463. doi:10.1080/09638237.2017.1322184

White, R. (2013). The ethics of involuntary hospitalization. *Journal of Social Work Values and Ethics, 10*(2), 25–35.

Wittmund, B., Wilms, H. U., Mory, C., & Angermeyer, M. C. (2002). Depressive disorders in spouses of mentally ill patients. *Social Psychiatry & Psychiatric Epidemiology, 37*(4), 177–182.

Wolpert, L. (1999). *Malignant sadness: The anatomy of depression.* New York, NY: Free Press.

Wyder, M., Bland, R., & Crompton, D. (2013). Personal recovery and involuntary mental health admissions: The importance of control, relationships and hope. *Health, 5*(3A), 574–581. doi:10.4236/health.2013.53A076

Wykes, T., Csipke, E., Williams, P., Koeser, L., Nash, S., Rose, D., … McCrone, P. (2018). Improving patient experiences of mental health inpatient care: A randomized controlled trial. *Psychological Medicine, 48,* 488–497. doi:10.1017/S003329171700188X

CHAPTER 4

MENTAL ILLNESS ACROSS THE LIFE CYCLE: CHILDREN, ADOLESCENTS, ADULTS, AND OLDER ADULTS

LEARNING OUTCOMES

- Describe the types of mental illness that can develop over the life course.
- Identify the symptoms and responses to attention deficit hyperactivity disorder (ADHD) in children and adolescents.
- Examine trends in mental healthcare for children and adolescents.
- Discuss the mental health problems of those in emerging adulthood, ages 18 to 27.
- Demonstrate an understanding of the difficulties of assessing the mental health problems of older adults, including distinguishing between dementia and depression.

▨ INTRODUCTION

Individuals at specific stages of life can experience different kinds of mental health problems. Almost half of mental health issues arise before a person reaches adulthood. This speaks to the importance of prevention of mental disorders and early intervention with children and adolescents experiencing mental health difficulties.

This chapter reviews the kinds of mental health problems that are most likely to occur throughout the life course. Social workers are the professionals most likely to work with clients and families in all stages of life and can bring considerable expertise to improving and expanding interventions across the life cycle.

▨ MENTAL HEALTH CHALLENGES DURING CHILDHOOD AND ADOLESCENCE

While children are vulnerable members of society in need of protection, they also represent the future of every society (Mechanic, McAlpine, & Rochefort, 2014). If we acknowledge that nothing is more important than the life of a child, mental health of children is of critical importance.

For children and adolescents, mental health concerns correlate with family problems, difficulties in social functioning, and poor academic achievement (Mignon, 2017a). Childhood mental disorders often focus on issues of attention, anxiety, depression, eating disorders, and behavioral problems that cause distress for the child and others. It can be difficult to uncover the causes of mental disorders, which is why we say these factors are "correlated" or "associated with" mental disorders, rather than that they "cause" mental disorders. Today we know that mental illness can have genetic bases, and this linkage is explored in later chapters. We also know that the environment in which a child grows up can promote mental health or mental illness. This is clearly illustrated in the recent documentary film *Three Identical Strangers,* in which three 19-year-olds learn they are actually triplets and were adopted in infancy in 1961 by three different families in New York. The question of why this cruel "experiment" was carried out by the administrators of a New York adoption agency was never adequately answered. Some of the living research staff who appeared in the film said it was to test whether nature or nurture has a greater impact on raising children. Of course, social workers acknowledge the contributions of both nature and nurture in the growth and development of humans.

The World Health Organization (WHO, 2018) estimates that 10% to 20% of children and adolescents around the globe have mental disorders. Approximately 50% of mental disorders begin by age 14, and 75% of all mental disorders begin by the middle 20s (WHO, 2018). The fact that most mental disorders emerge early in life is a compelling reason to ensure that children receive the prevention and intervention services they need.

In the United States, ADHD is the most common mental disorder in children (Stroh, Frankenberger, Cornell-Swanson, Wood, & Pahl, 2008). The Mental Health Surveillance Among Children study (2005–2011) found that 6.8% of children aged 3 to 17 years had ADHD (Perou et al., 2013). Among children aged 3 to 17, 3.5% had behavior/conduct problems, 3% had anxiety, and 2.1% had depression. Autism spectrum disorders were found in 1.1% of the sample (Perou et al., 2013).

Depression is more common in children and adolescents than previously thought. In a recent national survey of adolescents aged 12 to 17, 13.6% of boys had depression, while 36.1% of girls suffered from depression, a large percentage that should get the attention of both parents and mental health professionals (Breslau et al., 2017). Additionally, mental disorders can account for 5.8% to 11.0% of high-school students dropping out and 3.2% to 11.4% of students who leave college without completing their degrees (Mojtabai et al., 2015).

Eating disorders are likely to emerge during the adolescent years and are more prevalent among girls than among boys (Striegel-Moore et al., 2009). The National Comorbidity Survey Adolescent Supplement (NCS-A) found the prevalence of eating disorders to be 2.7% of the American adolescent population, 3.8% for girls and 1.5% for boys (Merikangas et al., 2010). Eating disorders can be related to low self-esteem as well as to hormonal factors during puberty (Klump, 2013). Eating disorders include a wide variety of behaviors, such as overeating; undereating, known as anorexia nervosa; and binging and purging, known as bulimia. These disorders are correlated with a complex web of physical, emotional, and social issues for those who suffer from them. Therefore, it is not surprising that eating disorders negatively affect an individual's quality of life and that professional assistance is needed from social workers or other therapists who specialize in treating eating disorders (Vallance, Latner, & Gleaves, 2011). The National Eating Disorders Association (NEDA) provides a national hotline at 1-800-931-2237.

The decision to seek mental health assistance for children and adolescents can be very complex. It involves an acknowledgment on the part of parents that the child or adolescent is experiencing mental health issues and that some kind of professional assistance is needed (Roberts, Alegria, Roberts, & Chen, 2005). Denial of a mental health problem (or actually any problem) experienced by one's child can be quite strong, and it can take some time to understand that professional help is needed. Many factors come to bear on this, including parental attitudes, social factors such as a concern for stigma, cultural views toward help-seeking, and availability of health insurance or private funds to pay for treatment. The interpretation of a child's behavior is made within a cultural context and is discussed in Chapter 7, Gender, Race, Ethnicity, and the Mental Health System (Roberts et al., 2005). Oftentimes, it takes some kind of crisis, such as a manic episode, car accident, or arrest, to draw the attention of family members to the existence of a substance abuse or mental health problem.

There are also legal concerns. For example, a family may be involved with courts because parents have been accused of child abuse and/or neglect, and there is intervention from a child protection agency (Olfson, Druss, & Marcus, 2015). Specifically, interventions within a family for child abuse and/or neglect can uncover mental illness within individual family members. This scenario serves as a reminder that social workers are often in an excellent position to determine whether a mental disorder is present. This is especially the case since the majority of professionals in child protection agencies are social workers.

The Special Case of ADHD

ADHD has been variously described as a mental illness, a mental condition, a brain disorder, a learning disability, a biologically based neurological disorder, and "a neuro-biological disorder with a possible genetic basis" (Stroh et al., 2008, p. 396). ADHD's symptoms include difficulty focusing in school, restlessness, forgetfulness, and lack of organizational skills. It is distinguished from attention deficit disorder (ADD) by the additional symptoms of physical restlessness and fidgeting. The *Diagnostic and Statistical Manual of Mental Disorders*, Fifth Edition (*DSM-5*), published by the American Psychiatric Association (2013) estimates that 5% of children in the United States have ADHD.

The most common treatment for ADHD is medication, typically methylphenidate, a central nervous system stimulant marketed under the brand names Ritalin and Adderall (Stroh et al., 2008). It is understandable that parents can be hesitant to consent to have their children take medication (Dosreis et al., 2003). Many of the referrals for ADHD assessment and treatment come from the child's teachers, rather than from his or her parents. Parents can prefer a comprehensive approach to treating ADHD, including medication prescribed by a child's psychiatrist rather than another type of provider, parent education and training, and specialized school accommodations (Sarkar, 2016). The Food and Drug Administration (FDA) began to require warnings in 2004 on ADHD medications, calling attention to the increased risk of high blood pressure, heart attack, and stroke associated with their use (Harris, 2006; Stroh et al., 2008). These medications can also put children at increased risk of suicide (Bushe & Savill, 2013; Liang et al., 2018). Parents are often not aware that medication for ADHD can be associated with the slowing of physical growth of a child as well as the development of tics (Stroh et al., 2008). One study found that overall "parents are deciding treatment for their child based on inaccurate information and beliefs" (Stroh et al., 2008, p. 398).

Trends in Mental Healthcare for Children and Adolescents

In an analysis of three time cohorts for trends in mental healthcare use by children and adolescents aged 6 to 17, researchers found evidence that the use of mental health services has increased (Olfson et al., 2015). The three cohorts were from 1996 to 1998, 2003 to 2005, and 2010 to 2012. Comparing the youth from 1996 to 1998, when 9.2% utilized outpatient mental health services, with the 2010 to 2012 group, mental health services utilization increased to 13.3%. Over the same period of time, the portion receiving psychotherapy increased from 4.2% to 6.0%. The use of psychotropic medication, including antidepressants and antipsychotics, increased from 5.5% to 8.9%, especially among youth with severe mental health impairment (Olfson et al., 2015). This could mean increased public acceptance of psychiatric medications and/or could be the result of successful marketing by pharmaceutical companies.

Much attention has been paid to whether antidepressant medication puts youth at increased risk of suicide. In 2004, the FDA mandated its most stringent warning for antidepressants for youth, known as the "black box" warning. In 2006, the FDA extended this warning for individuals up to age 26 (Gibbons & Mann, 2014).

Sometimes medications are misused to serve as chemical restraints on the behavior of children and adolescents. Case Example 4.1 describes the practice of drugging children who have migrated to the United States from Mexico and other Latin American countries.

CASE EXAMPLE 4.1

PSYCHIATRIC MEDICATIONS GIVEN TO MIGRANT CHILDREN AT THE UNITED STATES–MEXICO BORDER

Immigrant children taken from their parents at the U.S. border with Mexico, or arriving alone as unaccompanied minors, have been given psychotropic drugs to control their behavior while in government-funded shelters. This is being done without parental consent and while families are being torn apart by policies of the U.S. government. The Shiloh Treatment Center in Texas is accused of administering psychotropic medications, forcibly and routinely, according to a lawsuit filed by the Center for Human Rights and Constitutional Law in Los Angeles (Reuters, 2018). The facility has a long history of abusing children. In addition, the federal government has provided $3.4 billion to 71 companies since 2014 to institutionalize these immigrant children, despite repeated allegations of serious harm from this practice (Smith & Bogado, 2018).

Some children have been tackled and held down by staff and injected with medication to reduce agitation and aggressive behavior. Some children wanted to sleep constantly, some were made dizzy by the drugs, and some could not walk as a result of their forced medication. One child was prescribed 10 different medications in the form of pills and shots (Smith & Bogado, 2018). Psychiatrist Mark J. Mills, who reviewed records of children for the lawsuit, had this to say: "The facility should not use these drugs to control behavior. That's not what antipsychotics should be used for. That's like the old Soviet Union used to do" (Smith & Bogado, 2018).

SOURCES: Reuters. (2018, June 20). *U.S. centers force migrant children to take drugs: Lawsuit.* Retrieved from https://www.reuters.com/article/us-usa-immigration-medication/u-s-centers-force-migrant-children-to-take-drugs-lawsuit-idUSKBN1JH076; Smith, M., & Bogado, A. (2018, June 20). Immigrant children forcibly injected with drugs, lawsuit claims. *Reveal: The Center for Investigative Reporting.* Retrieved from https://www.revealnews.org/blog/immigrant-children-forcibly-injected-with-drugs-lawsuit-claims; Vaingankar, J. (2018, July 12). Migrant children forcibly given psychotropic drugs. *Children's Rights.* Retrieved from https://www.childrensrights.org/migrant-children-forcibly-given-psychotropic-drugs/

Despite the increase in use of psychotherapy, not everyone in need receives therapy. One study found that only one fourth of youth with the most severe mental health impairment received psychotherapy (Olfson et al., 2015). Minority youth received psychotherapy and medication significantly less often than did white youth. This may be because of blocked access to care due to lack of finances, and also because of parental and child attitudes toward mental healthcare (Olfson et al., 2015). The issues of racial and ethnic minorities with mental disorders and their mental healthcare are discussed in Chapter 7, Gender, Race, Ethnicity, and the Mental Health System.

While the diagnosis of mental disorders tends to focus on a child's deficits, it is very important to also evaluate a child for his or her strengths and assets (Lambert et al., 2015). This idea, which can help improve treatment planning, has attracted more clinical interest within the last 20 years. One tool that can help provide a deeper understanding of a child's issues is known as the Behavioral and Emotional Rating Scale—Second Edition (BERS-2; Lambert et al., 2015). Administering a scale such as this at regular intervals can help keep track of changes the youth undergo over time as well as progress toward treatment goals.

Psychiatric Hospitalization of Children and Adolescents

When it comes to psychiatric hospitalization of children and adolescents, the decision about hospitalization can be very difficult for individuals and their families. Decisions about whether to hospitalize a child or adolescent are also very difficult for professionals assessing an individual's mental health. Involuntary hospitalization today is reserved for those determined to be in danger of hurting themselves or others. This means the most immediate concern is safety of the individual, suicide prevention, and safety of others. Those hospitalized involuntarily may not be able to provide consent because of the severity of their mental illness symptoms (Persi, Bird, & DeRoche, 2016). According to WHO (2005), children should not be hospitalized simply because less restrictive and more appropriate services are not available (Persi et al., 2016). Decisions must stay focused on the needs of the child or adolescent rather than allowing hospitalization because of the desire to remove children from hospital emergency rooms or because of financial incentives (Persi et al., 2016).

Interestingly, Persi et al. (2016) found that children hospitalized involuntarily did not necessarily have more severe problems than voluntary patients, although four out of five referrals for hospitalization were involuntary. In their sample, only 13% of admissions continued to be considered involuntary after psychiatric assessment of the patient (Persi et al., 2016). The fact that involuntary hospitalization is more likely to occur on nights and weekends outside of regular work hours supports the view that issues beyond the child's needs bear on decision-making. The staff of referral agencies may be less available, and there can be greater concern for legal liability issues that results in pressure to opt for hospitalization so as to avoid worry about being sued. Thus, more needs to be learned about how involuntary hospitalization may be related to services that are available at the time (Persi et al., 2016). This is a major concern for social workers, who have an ethical obligation to ensure that the treatment planning needs of the child or adolescent are paramount, rather than the needs of the staff or the facility.

Shepperd et al. (2009), writing of treatment in the United Kingdom, offered a disturbing insight into the psychiatric care of children and adolescents: "The quality of the evidence base currently provides very little guidance for the development of services" (p. 2). These comments pertain to the United States as well, especially since these and other authors note the U.S. health system is fragmented rather than cohesive (Shepperd et al., 2009).

There is great variation in how children, adolescents, and their parents access care for mental disorders; indeed, some without insurance cannot access care at all (Shepperd et al., 2009). To develop and improve services, it is necessary to clarify the myriad and conflicting ways that patients and families access care. This would include developing collaborations among social service agencies and establishing ways to engage children, adolescents, and their families. Standardized definitions of mental disorders in children and adults can improve the quality of mental health research and assist in gaining more accurate estimates of mental disorders (Perou et al., 2013). Further, research on the various types and amounts of mental disorders in children and adolescents will surely support prevention and early intervention efforts. In addition to identifying and monitoring types of services, the quality of research must be improved to include a greater focus on client characteristics and the outcomes that clients experience from using various mental health services (Shepperd et al., 2009).

More recent concerns focus on the use of cell phones and social media. Anecdotal evidence from Texas mental health professionals reflects concern for the negative consequences of using social media (Stone, 2015). One concern is that due to Internet access, children are experiencing bullying at earlier ages than in the past. In August 2018 in Denver, Colorado, a 9-year-old boy committed suicide by hanging after he was bullied for a year at school and after telling his mother he was gay (Turkewitz, 2018).

While social media and Internet addiction have raised concerns, the flip side is that these technologies can also be used to alleviate some of these problems. There are now computer applications to help children and adults cope with mental health problems. For example, My3 is a safety plan for helping children cope with suicidal thoughts. The name is derived from designating the three people closest to you to contact when having thoughts of suicide (National Suicide Prevention Lifeline, n.d.). The site encourages those who use it to develop a support system and to build a safety plan with a mental health clinician. This includes accessing community-based services and 24-hour access to the National Suicide Prevention Lifeline at 1-800-273-8255.

■ MENTAL HEALTH CHALLENGES IN EMERGING ADULTHOOD

The years from ages 18 to 27 are considered the time of emerging adulthood (Luijks et al., 2017). Young people seek their transition to adulthood in multiple ways, whether continuing their education by attending college, entering the workforce, or enlisting in the military. Emerging adults are learning how to be emotionally and financially independent. While most of us prefer to think we can leave behind the problems we had as children and adolescents, sometimes we may bring those problems with us into adulthood. This is also the time when families are likely to see the onset of major mental disorders such as schizophrenia and bipolar disorder, illnesses that are discussed in further detail in Chapter 5, Social Work and Mental Illness: Labels and Diagnoses. Suffice it to say that when their onset occurs in late adolescence and early adulthood, schizophrenia and bipolar disorder can present lifelong challenges.

Emerging adulthood is a time when those with mental illness may "fall through the cracks" and not seek or receive professional assistance. For example, the cutoff for adolescent psychiatric hospitalization is age 18, and mental health systems typically treat 19-year-olds as adults. It is challenging enough to have a first psychiatric hospitalization at any age, but at age 19 to be placed in an environment with significantly older patients can be especially difficult. We are seeing an increase in psychiatric facilities that offer special programs for those age 18 into their early 20s.

Emerging Adults: College Students

College can be a very stressful time for youth. Stress for college students can have a damaging impact on students' mental and physical health. Stress can also affect academic performance (Bruffaerts et al., 2018; Shankar & Park, 2016). For many students, attending college is their first experience living away from home and can bring even heavier academic pressures and expectations than their high school experience (Pedrelli, Nyer, Yeung, Zulaf, & Wilens, 2015). Anxiety disorders are the most common mental health problem among college students, followed by depression (Center for Collegiate Mental Health, 2018; Pedrelli et al., 2015). It is understandable that going away to college in a completely new environment is cause for heightened stress and anxiety. While many may feel anxious about new experiences, for some students, anxiety can be overwhelming, and professional assistance is necessary.

Until recently, little scholarly attention had been paid to the mental health problems of college students. An exception to that rule is a 1930 journal article that pointed out that the college environment is fraught with "mental maladjustments" (Gardner, 1930, p. 102) due to the subjects they study, the newfound freedom of college life, as well as attitudes including "inferiority, cynicism, introversion, and brooding" (p. 120). Gardner recommended (a) a required course on "mental hygiene" (p. 122) for incoming first-year students, (b) weekly meetings between faculty members and the college psychiatrist on recognizing mental health issues of students, and (c) a college mental health clinic to assist students. Today, mental health counseling services are an integral and important component of college services. While today we are not likely to see a mental health course for incoming first-year students or weekly faculty meetings with a psychiatrist, clearly Gardner's ideas, though they date from 1930, still have merit.

For most people, it is hard to seek assistance for a mental health problem, and that is certainly the case for college students. Students want to avoid the stigma of mental illness and especially do not want to be seen entering the office of the college counseling service (Holland, 2016). This reality can be of greater concern for African American college students, who may be more worried about such stigma (Masuda, Anderson, & Edmonds, 2012). Unfortunately, some students can feel paralyzed by their situations and unable to seek help. One student reported that he had anxiety and depression after he arrived at McGill University in Montreal. As an engineering major, he felt lost among the hundreds of students in his classes. He said, "I was totally ashamed of what happened.

I didn't want to let my parents down, so I retreated inward" (Reilly, 2018, p. 5). This student had to withdraw from college in April of his second semester. After receiving treatment, the student improved and went on to attend a community college.

Insomnia can be associated with mental health problems throughout all age groups (Taylor et al., 2011). For college students, there is increasing evidence of an association between mental illness and insomnia (Taylor et al., 2011; Zochil & Thorsteinsson, 2018). Since this young adult age is associated with the onset of mental illness, it is especially important to examine the role of sleep. Taylor et al. (2011) found 9.4% of college students had symptoms of chronic insomnia and had higher levels of depression and anxiety than others not in college. In the fall of 2018, Harvard University instituted a new online course for incoming first-year students, titled Sleep 101. The course discusses the value of sleep and offers recommendations for students to get a sufficient amount of sleep to maximize their grades and their college experience.

Overall, only a small number of college students seek professional help for their mental health issues, although that picture is slowly changing (Hartrey, Denieffe, & Wells, 2017; Pedrelli et al., 2015). The Center for Collegiate Mental Health found in 2015 that while college enrollment grew by less than 6% over the previous 5 years, the use of counseling centers increased by 30% to 40%. The average counseling duration of treatment is two to five appointments (Center for Collegiate Mental Health, 2018). Unfortunately, most colleges and universities do not have sufficient resources to meet the demand for student counseling services (Reilly, 2018; Thielking, 2017).

Mental health situations become even more challenging when students threaten suicide. For example, a graduate student at the Massachusetts Institute of Technology (MIT) had previously attended Stanford University as an undergraduate, where he tried to commit suicide on two occasions (Cramer, 2017). After a difficult conversation with his MIT adviser, the student jumped to his death from the sixth floor of a campus building. In 2017, the student's family filed suit against MIT for wrongful death and failure to protect him from harm. In 2018, the Massachusetts Supreme Judicial Court dismissed the case, stating that the student had not conveyed to anyone that he intended to take his life and that he was receiving treatment from mental health professionals not associated with MIT (Raymond, 2018).

Evidence supports the fact that college counseling can be helpful to students not just for crisis intervention, but also for treatment over a period of months (Winzer, Lindberg, Guldbrandsson, & Sidorchuk, 2018). Importantly, mental health services for college students are often provided by social workers.

Another useful resource for supporting mental health services on college campuses is the Mental Health America's Collegiate Mental Health Innovation Council. The council was established in 2017 to showcase innovative approaches to promoting comprehensive mental health supports on college campuses (Collegiate Mental Health Innovation Council, 2018). Student leaders and recent college graduates can apply for a 6-month appointment and make significant contributions to their campuses by implementing innovative approaches.

Tips for the Field 4.1 provides recommendations for strengthening college mental health services.

TIPS FOR THE FIELD 4.1

POLICY RECOMMENDATIONS FOR STRENGTHENING COLLEGE MENTAL HEALTH: WHAT COLLEGE SOCIAL WORKERS CAN DO

1. Cultivate awareness among administrators that provision of mental health services is complex for both the college and its students. It is not sufficient to simply seek a reduction in a student's symptoms. Colleges must address students' presenting problems, diagnose mental health problems, determine the length of treatment needed, and learn more about how services are utilized by students.

2. College counseling centers must have adequate staff and expertise to address the range of mental health problems among college students. This includes timely availability of appointments to assess a student's issues.

3. The provision of high-quality treatment services can present fiscal challenges to colleges and universities; thus, adequate funding must be made available.

4. All college students should be educated on potential mental health issues and how to contact the counseling center for assistance.

5. Rigid limits on the number of sessions available to students should be avoided so that students can have flexibility in the treatment duration needed for recovery.

6. College policy and funding decisions need to reflect evidence-based practices that are informed by clinical expertise and that are in line with the values of the college and students.

SOURCE: Center for Collegiate Mental Health. (2018, January). *2017 annual report* (Publication No. STA 18-166). University Park, PA: Penn State University.

Emerging Adults: Armed Forces and Veterans

Mental health is a pressing issue for active-duty members of the armed forces as well as for veterans. The National Alliance on Mental Illness (NAMI, 2018) reports that the three major mental health problems for those serving in war zones are posttraumatic stress disorder (PTSD), depression, and traumatic brain injury (TBI). Substance abuse and addiction can be significant problems as well.

Concerns have been raised over whether it is appropriate to accept individuals with a history of mental disorder into the armed services. A review of data by *USA Today* found that 1,064 army recruits had been treated for mood disorders such as bipolar disorder, and 95 recruits had a history of self-mutilation during the period of October 1, 2016, through October 31, 2017. These applicants were issued waivers to be able to join the army. Apparently waivers were given as a response to the failure of the army to meet its recruitment goal (Brook, 2018). The response of Army Secretary Mark Esper did not match the findings of the data review: "We do not allow anybody in who is undergoing therapy, who is a cutter, identified clearly as a cutter or is using drugs. They are not allowed into the service. And I will not accept them. Quality trumps quantity every single day of the week" (Brook, 2018, p. 1A).

PTSD is the most common mental health disorder for which veterans receive disability benefits. Although Social Security disability benefits and worker's compensation benefits can be time limited, that is not the case for veterans' disability benefits (Sayer et al., 2011). Some veterans are reluctant to apply for disability benefits and do not seek assistance for mental health problems due to concern about the stigma of being disabled and having to rely on government assistance. Other veterans can be helpful in assisting veterans to overcome their reticence and apply for the benefits to which they are entitled (Hernandez, Morgan, & Parshall, 2017; Sayer et al., 2011).

Women serving in the military are more likely to experience intimate-partner violence than women who are not in the military. In a review of 8,888 medical records of women receiving care in the Veterans Health Administration (VHA) system (veterans and spouses of veterans), of those who were victims/survivors of intimate-partner violence, 53.5% had a diagnosed mental disorder, compared with 32.6% of those without a history of victimization (Dichter et al., 2017). With these very high rates of mental disorders for women in the military, increased professional attention must be given to these problems.

Suicide is a very important risk factor for those on active duty as well as for veterans. Veterans living in rural areas can have higher rates of suicide than those living in urban areas (McCarthy et al., 2012). In a retrospective study of 9,650 enlisted male and female soldiers who had attempted suicide, 36.3% did not have a history of diagnosed mental illness, a sign that no help had been sought (Ursano et al., 2018). According to Veterans Administration data, there are, on average, 20.6 suicides each day among active members of the military and veterans (Wentling,

2018). Veterans account for 16.8 of the daily suicides, and active military personnel and reservists account for 3.8 daily suicides. The Veterans Crisis Line for veterans, active service members, and their families is 1-800-273-8255.

Social workers offer essential services to those on active duty and to veterans. Currently, the field is developing a specialty in military social work (Jackson, 2013). In this context, social workers assist individuals and their families with making adjustments to living with war wounds, treating PTSD, preventing suicide, providing psychotherapy and support services, and locating additional resources. Social workers who work with the homeless and those with addiction problems are very likely to see veterans in their practices, a reminder that all social workers should have some knowledge of the issues facing individuals and family members in the military (Jackson, 2013). The National Association of Social Workers (NASW, 2018) provides a webpage focused on active military and veterans that offers resources and recommendations for professional development as well as access to the *Handbook of Military Social Work*.

MENTAL HEALTH CHALLENGES IN ADULTHOOD

Adults may have had mental health disorders as children, adolescents, and young adults, but adulthood is also a time when new mental health problems can emerge. Depression is a common mental health disorder in adulthood. Some individuals have experienced depression early in life and continue to endure depression as adults and even as older adults. American lives can be filled with stress, as individuals struggle to balance family obligations such as a spouse and children, work responsibilities, and financial challenges. In what is known as the "sandwich generation," many adults have responsibilities both to their children and to their own aging parents.

In reality, it is not exactly clear when stress and feeling overwhelmed become depression. It is certainly possible for adults to have multiple symptoms, yet not be aware that they have depression. Symptoms of depression include feeling tired all the time, sleeping too much or too little, eating too much or too little to maintain a healthy weight, lack of interest in previously enjoyed activities, and social isolation.

Treating adults with mental illness can bring its own unique challenges. For some adults, the optimism of youth and the enthusiasm for making a better life may have worn off. In clinical practice, the author has seen clients who have come to accept the self-stigma of mental illness, accepting a life without any hope for a better future. See Case Example 4.2 for the story of Ginger.

CASE EXAMPLE 4.2

THE STORY OF GINGER: LIVING WITH CHRONIC MENTAL HEALTH
PROBLEMS

Ginger was a single woman in her 50s who sought counseling at her local community mental health clinic. She had a long history of mental health problems
and alcoholism. Her social worker at the clinic remembered Ginger as a patient
in the detoxification and rehabilitation program, where the social worker was
a substance abuse clinician years before. Time had not been kind to Ginger.
Despite numerous diagnoses, treatment interventions, and medications over
many years, Ginger did not think anything had helped her in the past. Her
health problems were such that she had not had any career or job; she lived
alone, subsisting only on Supplemental Security Income (SSI). Ginger was not
close with her family and had few, if any, friends. Her life, as she described it,
seemed completely devoid of pleasure or hope for the future. Ginger seemed
to accept the role of chronic mental patient and saw no way to improve her life.

Social workers who take a "whole person" approach to mental healthcare recognize that those with mental illness, like everyone, are entitled
to active and full lives. Social workers are very resourceful in locating services and programs that promote better mental health. They can ensure
that those with chronic problems are receiving the physical and mental
healthcare they need. A program in England that focused on providing
home visits to those with mental health disorders concluded that fewer
psychiatric hospitalizations resulted from this intervention (Catty et al.,
2002). Reducing psychiatric hospitalizations is a positive step for clients
and families and an important way to conserve resources. Social workers
are equipped to locate activities for clients to enjoy, and they can encourage forms of exercise to promote good health, such as yoga and tai chi.

An issue for middle-aged adults with serious mental illness is that
they are most likely to be cared for by their own parents. Aging parents typically devote themselves to their adult children with mental illness over a lifetime, and most aging parents act as caregivers for their
children without any support services (Van Pelt, 2011). In fact, a major
worry for older adult parents of severely mentally ill adult children is
who will take care of the adult children when the parents are deceased.

MENTAL HEALTH CHALLENGES IN OLDER ADULTS

Older adults can develop a variety of mental health issues. Some have
had mental health and/or substance abuse issues at a younger age and

carry those problems into their older years. Other older adults develop mental health problems and substance abuse in their later years as a response to increasing medical problems, grief over lost family and friends, and social isolation (Mignon, 2015).

It can be difficult to distinguish between dementia and depression in older adults. Therefore, it is critical to complete a mental health assessment if an older adult is experiencing mental confusion, memory loss, or other symptoms. With dementia, early symptoms may initially be attributed to a natural part of aging rather than perceived to be part of a progressive illness (Canadian Agency for Drugs and Technologies in Health, 2015). Dementia is associated with reduced cognitive functioning, including reduced executive function, learning and memory deficits, and problems with language and social cognition. These signs and symptoms typically get worse over time. Alzheimer's disease is now the most common form of dementia in older adults. Estimates of its prevalence vary, but depression is widely considered to be an issue for 10% to 15% of the older adult population. Older women are at higher risk of depression than are older men (Teixeira, Vasconcelos-Raposo, Fernandes, & Brustad, 2013). Depression and dementia can occur together, and depression is found in approximately 20% of older adults with dementia (Canadian Agency for Drugs and Technologies in Health, 2015).

It is no surprise that rates of depression are higher among older adults living in nursing homes. One study of nursing home residents found that 48% had a diagnosis of depression (Levin et al., 2007). Of those residents, 23% did not receive treatment, 74% were given antidepressant medication, 0.5% were provided psychotherapy, and 2% received both medication and psychotherapy. African American residents, as well as residents who had both cognitive impairments and physical problems, were less likely to be assessed and treated for depression. Overall, depression among nursing home residents can be harder to diagnose because of accompanying mental and physical health problems and a lack of interest on the part of medical providers to determine its causes (Levin et al., 2007; Mignon, 2017b).

Research shows that depression in older adults can be successfully treated and prevented. A good starting point is the Geriatric Depression Scale (GDS), a short screening tool that can determine whether an older adult needs a referral to a mental health professional specializing in the treatment of older adults. The GDS can be used successfully in the offices of primary and specialty physicians as well as in hospital emergency rooms (Greenberg, 2012; Mignon, 2017b).

The field of social work has long had a specialty in working with older adults. Often social workers in nursing homes are responsible for admissions, serve as a liaison to family members, and provide supportive counseling to residents. Social workers can be expected to implement the rules and guidelines established by nursing home owners, many of which are profit-making organizations that give priority to those residents who can pay privately, rather than residents who must rely on Medicaid, which reimburses at lower rates. Social workers should strive to elevate their role in nursing home care to help establish the rules and guidelines that will grant equal access to all those in need of nursing home care, regardless of their ability to pay.

Since social workers provide assistance to clients across the life span, they are well poised to utilize their expertise and experience to transition into policy roles. See Tips for the Field 4.2 for recommendations regarding areas that need greater social work input into public policy.

TIPS FOR THE FIELD 4.2

DIGGING DEEPER INTO POLICY ISSUES: WHAT SOCIAL WORKERS CAN DO

1. Assess the needs of migrant children and their families, uncover maltreatment, and cultivate political clout to ensure a more positive response from federal governmental agencies.

2. Advocate and educate parents and children regarding the appropriate use of medications for ADHD and depression.

3. Participate in the development of college and university policy on interventions with students with mental health issues, and ensure that necessary services are available. Provide psychotherapy and referrals for college students.

4. Work to expand and support the development and use of mental health services for active-duty members of the armed forces and veterans. Provide clinical services to members of the military, veterans, and their families.

5. Develop a specialty in working with chronically mentally ill adults and their families to ensure that clients have the opportunity to create a fulfilling life for themselves, with hope for the future.

6. For social workers with a specialty in the field of gerontology (care of older adults), advocate for appropriate professional assessment of and treatment for depression and dementia.

▨ SUMMARY AND CONCLUSION

The onset of mental disorders often occurs in childhood or adolescence. Therefore, special attention must be paid to the prevention and treatment of mental health problems in this age group. Standardization of definitions of specific mental health disorders can assist in developing a more accurate picture of the type and amount of mental illness in all age categories.

The mental health problems of college students merit more attention than they have received in the past. Anxiety, depression, and eating disorders can successfully respond to treatment. Much more needs to be done to encourage and support students to seek help from their college counseling centers. For active military personnel and veterans, especially women, services need to be developed and expanded to meet the current need.

In addition, far more attention should be paid to accurately diagnosing the mental health problems of older adults, providing services, and ensuring that residents in nursing homes receive appropriate mental healthcare. Depression in older adults can often be successfully treated and prevented with antidepressant medication, psychotherapy, support groups, and exercise.

DISCUSSION QUESTIONS/TOPICS

1. What role do parents play in addressing the mental health problems of their children?

2. Why do you think girls experience much higher rates of depression than boys?

3. Do you consider ADHD to be a mental illness? Why, or why not?

4. Discuss the mental health issues that are likely to arise for college students, and suggest ways to respond to them.

5. What can social workers do to end chemical restraints of children in immigrant detention facilities?

6. In what ways are standardized definitions of mental disorders helpful to social workers and other mental health professionals?

7. What policies would help active-duty military and veterans receive mental health services?

8. What special services may be needed by women in the military?

9. Describe the mental health problems that can arise for older adults.

10. Discuss your own ideas for meeting the mental health needs of nursing home residents.

REFERENCES

Breslau, J., Gilman, S. E., Stein, B. D., Ruder, T., Gmelin, T., & Miller, E. (2017). Sex differences in recent first-onset depression in an epidemiological sample of adolescents. *Translational Psychiatry, 7*, e1139. Retrieved from http://www.nature.com/articles/tp2017105

Brook, T. V. (2018, April 27–29). Army takes recruits with past mental troubles: Service issued waivers for self-mutilators. *USA Today Weekend*, 1A, 2A.

Bruffaerts, R., Mortier, P., Kiekens, G., Auerbach, R. P., Cuijpers, P., Demyttenaere, K., … Kessler, R. C. (2018). Mental health problems in college freshmen: Prevalence and academic functioning. *Journal of Affective Disorders, 225*, 97–103. doi:10.1016/j.jad.2017.07.044

Bushe, C. J., & Savill, N. C. (2013). Suicide related events and attention deficit hyperactivity disorder treatments in children and adolescents: A meta-analysis of atomoxetine and methylphenidate comparator clinical trials. *Child and Adolescent Psychiatry and Mental Health, 7*, 19. doi:10.1186/1753-2000-7-19

Canadian Agency for Drugs and Technologies in Health. (2015, August 24). *Rapid response report: Antidepressants in elderly patients with depression and dementia: A review of clinical effectiveness and guidelines.* Retrieved from https://www.cadth.ca

Catty, J., Burns, T., Knapp, M., Watt, H., Wright, C., Henderson, J., & Healey, A. (2002). Home treatment for mental health problems: A systematic review. *Psychological Medicine, 32*(3), 383–401. doi:10.1017/S0033291702005299

Center for Collegiate Mental Health. (2018, January). *2017 annual report* (Publication No. STA 18-166). University Park, PA: Penn State University.

Collegiate Mental Health Innovation Council. (2018). *Mental Health America.* Retrieved from http://www.mentalhealthamerica.net/collegiate-mental-health-innovation-council

Cramer, M. (2017, November 8). High court issues: Must MIT deter suicides? *The Boston Globe*, B1, B5.

Dichter, M. E., Sorrentino, A., Bellamy, S., Medvedeva, E. Roberts, C. B., & Iverson, K. M. (2017). Disproportionate mental health burden associated with past-year intimate partner violence among women receiving care in the Veterans Health Administration. *Journal of Traumatic Stress, 30*, 555–563. doi:10.1002/jts.22241

Dosreis, S., Zito, J. M., Safer, D. J., Soeken, K. L., Mitchell, J. W. Jr., & Ellwood, L. C. (2003). Parental perceptions and satisfaction with stimulant medication for attention-deficit hyperactivity disorder. *Journal of Developmental and Behavioral Pediatrics, 24*(3), 155–162. doi:10.1097/00004703-200306000-00004

Gardner, G. E. (1930). Causes of mental ill health among college students. *Annals of the American Academy of Political and Social Science, 149*, 102–123.

Gibbons, R. D., & Mann, J. J. (2014, December 31). The relationship between antidepressant initiation and suicide risk. *Psychiatric Times, 31*(12). Retrieved from https://www.psychiatrictimes.com/special-reports/relationship-between-antidepressant-initiation-and-suicide-risk

Greenberg, S. (2012). Best practices in nursing care to older adults. *General Assessment Series, 4*. Retrieved from https://consultgeri.org/try-this/general-assessment/issue-4.pdf

Harris, G. (2006, February. 9). Warning urged on stimulants like Ritalin. *The New York Times*. Retrieved from http://www.nytimes.com

Hartrey, L., Denieffe, S., & Wells, J. S. G. (2017). A systematic review of barriers and supports to the participation of students with mental health difficulties in higher education. *Mental Health & Prevention, 6*, 26–43. doi:10.1016/j.mhp.2017.03.002

Hernandez, S. H. A., Morgan, B. J., & Parshall, M. B. (2017). A concept analysis of stigma perceived by military service members who seek mental health services. *Nursing Forum, 52*(3), 188–195. doi:10.1111/nuf.1287

Holland, D. (2016). College student stress and mental health: Examination of stigmatic views on mental health counseling. *Michigan Sociological Review, 30*, 16–43.

Jackson, K. (2013). Working with veterans and military families. *Social Work Today, 13*(2), 12. Retrieved from http://www.socialworktoday.com/archive/031513p12.shtml

Klump, K. L. (2013). Puberty as a critical risk period for eating disorders: A review of human and animal studies. *Hormones and Behavior, 64*(2), 399–410. doi:10.1016/j.yhbeh.2013.02.019

Lambert, M. C., January, S.-A. A., Epstein, M. H., Spooner, M., Gebreselassie, T., & Stephens, R. L. (2015). Convergent validity of the Behavioral and Emotional Rating Scale for youth in community mental health settings. *Journal of Child and Family Studies, 24*(12), 3827–3832. doi:10.1007/s10826-015-0191-x

Levin, C. A., Wei, W., Akincigil, A., Lucas, J. A., Bilder, S., & Crystal, S. (2007). Prevalence and treatment of diagnosed depression among elderly nursing home residents in Ohio. *Journal of the American Medical Directors Association, 8*(9), 585–594. doi:10.1016/j.jamda.2007.07.0110

Liang, S. H.-Y., Yang, Y.-H., Kuo, T.-Y., Liao, Y.-T., Lin, T.-C., Lee, Y., … Chen, V. C.-H. (2018). Suicide risk reduction in youths with attention-deficit/hyperactivity disorder prescribed methylphenidate: A Taiwan nationwide population-based cohort study. *Research in Developmental Disabilities, 72*, 96–105. doi:10.1016/j.ridd.2017.10.023

Luijks, M.-J. A., Bevaart, F., Zijimans, J., van Duin, L., Marhe, R., Doreleijers, T. A. H., … Popma, A. (2017). A multimodal day treatment program for multi-problem young adults: Study protocol for a randomized controlled trial. *Trials, 18*, 225. doi:10.1186/s13063-017-1950-3

Masuda, A., Anderson, P. L., & Edmonds, J. (2012). Help-seeking attitudes, mental health stigma, and self-concealment among African American college students. *Journal of Black Studies, 43*(7), 773–786. doi:10.1177/0021934712445806

McCarthy, J. F., Blow, F. C., Ignacio, R. V., Ilgen, M. A., Austin, K. L., & Valenstein, M. (2012). Suicide among patients in the Veterans Affairs health system: Rural–urban difference in rates, risks, and methods. *American Journal of Public Health, 102*(S1), S111–S117. doi:10.2105/AJPH.2011.300463

Mechanic, D., McAlpine, D. D., & Rochefort, D. A. (2014). *Mental health and social policy: Beyond managed care* (6**th** ed.). Boston, MA: Pearson.

Merikangas, K. R., He, J. P., Burstein, M., Swanson, S. A., Avenevoli, S., Cui, L., … Swendsen, J. (2010). Lifetime prevalence of mental disorders in U.S. adolescents: Results from the National Comorbidity Survey Replication—Adolescent Supplement (NCS-A). *Journal of the American Academy of Child and Adolescent Psychiatry, 49*(10), 980–989. doi:10.1016/j.jaac.2010.05.017

Mignon, S. I. (2015). *Substance abuse treatment: Options, challenges, and effectiveness.* New York, NY: Springer Publishing Company.

Mignon, S. I. (2017a). *Child welfare in the United States: Challenges, policy and practice.* New York, NY: Springer Publishing Company.

Mignon, S. I. (2017b). Aging and depression. *Annals of Psychiatry and Mental Health, 5*(5), 1113–1116.

Mojtabai, R., Stuart, E. A., Hwang, I., Eaton, W. W., Sampson, N., & Kessler, R. C. (2015). Long-term effects of mental disorders on educational attainment in the National Comorbidity Survey ten-year follow-up. *Social Psychiatry and Psychiatric Epidemiology, 50*(10), 1577–1591. doi:10.1007/s00127-015-1083-5

National Alliance on Mental Illness. (2018). *Veterans & active duty: Mental health concerns.* Retrieved from https://www.nami.org/Find-Support/Veterans-and-Active-Duty

National Association of Social Workers. (2018). *Military and veterans.* Retrieved from https://www.socialworkers.org/Practice/Military-Veterans

National Suicide Prevention Lifeline. (n.d.). *My3.* Retrieved from http://my3app.org/#stay-connected

Olfson, M., Druss, B. G., & Marcus, S. C. (2015). Trends in mental health care among children and adolescents. *New England Journal of Medicine, 21,* 2029–2038. doi:10.1056/NEJMsa1413512

Pedrelli, P., Nyer, M., Yeung, A., Zulauf, C., & Wilens, T. (2015). College students: Mental health problems and treatment considerations. *Academic Psychiatry, 39*(5), 503–511. doi:10.1007/s40596-014-0205-9

Perou, R., Bitsko, R. H., Blumberg, S. J., Pastor, P., Ghandour, R. M., Gfroerer, J. C., ... Huang, L. N. (2013, May 17). Mental health surveillance among children—United States, 2005–2011. *Morbidity and Mortality Weekly Report Supplements, 62*(2), 1–35. Retrieved from https://www.cdc.gov/mmwr/preview/mmwrhtml/su6202a1.htm?s_cid=su6201a1_w

Persi, J., Bird, B. M., & DeRoche, C. (2016). A comparison of voluntary and involuntary child and adolescent inpatient psychiatry admissions. *Residential Treatment for Children and Youth, 33*(1), 69–83. doi:10.1080/0886571X.2016.1167651

Raymond, N. (2018, May 7). Top Massachusetts court clears MIT in student suicide lawsuit. *Reuters.* Retrieved from https://www.reuters.com/article/us-massachusetts-mit-lawsuit/top-massachusetts-court-clears-mit-in-student-suicide-lawsuit-idUSKBN1I81PW

Reilly, K. (2018, March 19). Record numbers of college students are seeking treatment for depression and anxiety—but schools can't keep up. *Time.* Retrieved from http://time.com/5190291/anxiety-depression-college-university-students

Roberts, R. E., Alegria, M., Roberts, C. R., & Chen, I. G. (2005). Mental health problems of adolescents as reported by their caregivers: A comparison of European, African, and Latino Americans. *Journal of Behavioral Health Services & Research, 32*(1), 1–13. doi:10.1007/BF02287324

Sarkar, S. (2016). Psychiatric polypharmacy, etiology, and potential consequences. *Current Psychopharmacology, 6,* 12–26. doi:10.4172/2378-5756.C1.014

Sayer, N. A., Spoont, M., Murdoch, M., Parker, L. E., Hintz, S., & Rosenheck, R. (2011). A qualitative study of U.S. veterans' reasons for seeking Department of Veterans Affairs disability benefits for posttraumatic stress disorder. *Journal of Traumatic Stress, 24*(6), 699–707. doi:10.1002/jts.20693

Shankar, N. L., & Park, C. L. (2016). Effects of stress on students' physical and mental health and academic success. *International Journal of School & Educational Psychology, 4*(1), 5–9. doi:10.1080/21683603.2016.1130532

Shepperd, S., Doll, H., Gowers, S., James, A., Fazel, M., Fitzpatrick, R., & Pollock, J. (2009). Alternatives to inpatient mental health care for children and young people. *Cochrane Database System Review, 2*, CD006410. doi:10.1002/14651858.CD006410.pub.2

Stone, E. (2015, October 13). Experts: Technology affects children's mental health. *Midland Reporter Telegram.* Retrieved from https://www.mrt.com/news/health/article/Experts-Technology-affects-children-s-mental-7414618.php

Striegel-Moore, R. H., Rosselli, F., Perrin, N., DeBar, L., Wilson, G. T., May, A., & Kraemer, H. C. (2009). Gender difference in the prevalence of eating disorder symptoms. *International Journal of Eating Disorders, 42*, 471–474. doi:10.1002/eat.20625

Stroh, J., Frankenberger, W., Cornell-Swanson, L. V., Wood, C., & Pahl, S. (2008). The use of stimulant medication and behavioral interventions for the treatment of attention deficit hyperactivity disorders: A survey of parents' knowledge, attitudes, and experiences. *Journal of Child and Family Studies, 17*, 385–401. doi:10.1007/s10826-007-9149-y

Taylor, D. J., Gardner, C. E., Bramoweth, A. D., Williams, J. M., Roane, B. M., Grieser, E. A. & Tatum, J. I. (2011). Insomnia and mental health in college students. *Behavioral Sleep Medicine, 9*(2), 107–116. doi:10.1080/15402002.2011.557992

Teixeira, C. M., Vasconcelos-Raposo, J., Fernandes, H. M., & Brustad, R. J. (2013). Physical activity, depression and anxiety among the elderly. *Social Indicators Research, 113*(1), 307–318. doi:10.1007/s11205-012-0094-9

Thielking, M. (2017, February 20). Colleges lag on mental health care. *The Boston Globe*, A1, A6.

Turkewitz, J. (2018, August 28). 9-year-old boy kills self after being bullied, his mom says. *The New York Times.* Retrieved from https://www.nytimes.com/2018/08/28/us/jamel-myles-suicide-denver.html

Ursano, R. J., Kessler, R. C., Naifeh, J. A., Mash, H. B. H., Nock, M. K., Aliaga, P. A., … Stein, M. B. (2018). Risk factors associated with attempted suicide among US Army soldiers without a history of mental health diagnosis. *JAMA Psychiatry, 75*(10), 1022–1032. doi:10.1001/jamapsychiatry.2018.2069

Vallance, J. K., Latner, J. D., & Gleaves, D. H. (2011). The relationship between eating disorder psychopathology and health-related quality of life within a community sample. *Quality of Life Research, 20*(5), 675–682. doi:10.1007/s11136-010-9799-x

Van Pelt, J. (2011). Aging parents of adults with serious mental illness. *Social Work Today, 11*(6), 18. Retrieved from http://www.socialworktoday.com/archive/111511p18.shtml

Wentling, N. (2018, June 21). VA reveals its veterans suicide statistic included active-duty troops. *Military.com.* Retrieved from https://www.military.com/daily-news/2018/06/21/va-reveals-its-veteran-suicide-statistic-included-active-duty-troops.html

Winzer, R., Lindberg, L., Guldbrandsson, K., & Sidorchuk, A. (2018). Effects of mental health interventions for students in higher education are sustainable over time: A systematic review and meta-analysis of randomized controlled trials. *PeerJ, 6,* e4598. doi:10.771/peerj.4598

World Health Organization. (2005). *WHO resource book on mental health, human rights and legislation.* Geneva, Switzerland: Author. Retrieved from https://ec.europa.eu/health/sites/health/files/mental_health/docs/who _resource_book_en.pdf

World Health Organization. (2018, October 4). Mental disorders affect one in four people. *World Health Report.* Retrieved from https://www.who.int/whr/2001/media_centre/press_release/en

Zochil, M. L., & Thorsteinsson, E. B. (2018). Exploring poor sleep, mental health, and help-seeking intention in university students. *Australian Journal of Psychology, 70*(1), 41–47. doi:10.1111/ajpy.12160

CHAPTER 5

SOCIAL WORK AND MENTAL ILLNESS: LABELS AND DIAGNOSES

LEARNING OUTCOMES

- Provide an overview of the classification of mental illnesses.

- Discuss the challenges to making accurate diagnoses upon which to develop a treatment plan.

- Demonstrate an understanding of the role of the *Diagnostic and Statistical Manual of Mental Disorders* (*DSM-5*) in the field of mental health.

- Identify the challenges of individuals who have both a mental health disorder and a substance abuse problem.

- Compare and contrast cognitive behavioral therapy (CBT) and dialectical behavior therapy (DBT).

INTRODUCTION

Any discussion of mental health must acknowledge the difficulties in determining an accurate diagnosis. In contrast to labeling that brings with it stigma, a mental health diagnosis is critical to establish a proper treatment plan. Social workers know that an accurate diagnosis, when possible, is essential to figuring out the appropriate treatment. Yet, social workers also must determine whether a diagnosis is in the best interests of their clients (Barsky, 2015).

Ideally, a valid and ethical mental health diagnosis is based upon an understanding of the symptoms, their severity, and how long the individual has been experiencing them. The mental health professional must get to know the individual and his or her history, make clinical observations, and acknowledge the uniqueness of each individual (Aultman,

2016). While this may seem straightforward, there is nothing simple about the process.

This chapter provides an overview of the various types of mental health disorders and their corresponding treatments. We know that there can be a great deal of disagreement regarding a proper diagnosis, as evidenced in the Rosenhan experiments, in which students were hospitalized, diagnosed, and treated, despite having no mental illness. The lack of consensus and clear paths to treatment is a major impediment to advancing the field of mental healthcare. Some mental health problems can have relatively clear pathways to treatment, whereas others do not. This chapter also reviews different types of inpatient and outpatient treatment.

Individuals who share the same mental health diagnosis can lead very different lives. For those individuals who have chronic severe mental illness, the quality of a person's family and friend network, and other social supports, can have very positive impacts (Lauveng, Tveiten, Ekeland, & Ruud, 2015). One of the themes of this text is that social workers are instrumental in helping those with mental illness and their families to locate and utilize supports to improve their lives.

It is beyond the scope of this text to review research findings on genetics, heritable influences, and brain chemistry. On the positive side, research emphasis on the role of biology contributes to a reduction in stigma regarding mental illness (Schmidt, 2007). It is the close association between genetics and mental illness (and the quest for profit) that has led to the development of many psychotropic medications, as discussed in Chapter 6, Social Work and Psychiatry: Psychotropic Medications and Brain Stimulation Techniques.

CLASSIFICATION OF MENTAL DISORDERS

The classification of mental illnesses is important because it provides a common language and the ability to communicate in an organized way. If specific symptoms are associated with specific diagnoses, it is easier to determine incidence (the rate of new cases) and prevalence (the number of existing cases) of those illnesses. If symptoms are grouped together in a meaningful way, far less effort is needed to arrive at a diagnosis, and far less time is needed to determine the appropriate treatment. Accordingly, agreed-upon diagnoses and corresponding treatment options provide the basis for research to compare and contrast findings to determine which treatments are most effective. This approach is not intended to disregard the individual experience of mental illness or the need for professionals to respect the uniqueness of each person. The two most prominent classification systems for mental illness are the *International Classification of Diseases* (*ICD*) and the *Diagnostic and Statistical Manual of Mental Disorders* (*DSM*).

International Classification of Diseases

The *ICD-10* aims to classify all diseases in the world, including mental illness. It is sponsored by the World Health Organization (WHO), which took over responsibility for the *ICD* in 1967. The *ICD-10* was published in 1994, and the United States started to use it in 2015. In June 2018, the *ICD-11* became available; it is scheduled to be implemented in January 2020 (WHO, 2018). The *ICD* has established standards for coding diseases, disorders, and diagnoses. It is used to establish the incidence and prevalence of disease, injuries, and deaths. The most recent revision resulted in changes to coding Alzheimer's disease; substance use, abuse, and dependence disorders; and eating disorders, which are now coded as avoidant/restrictive food intake disorder (Osborne, 2018).

Diagnostic and Statistical Manual of Mental Disorders

The first *DSM* was published in 1952 and has long been known as the "bible" of psychiatry. Published by the American Psychiatric Association (APA), the *DSM* has incredible authority and power associated with it. Now in its fifth edition, the manual holds the key to what is defined as mental illness and who is defined as having mental illness. It can also determine access to mental healthcare and whether insurance will pay for treatment (Reardon, 2014). Revisions to editions of the *DSM* are based on data analysis, literature reviews, and consultations with psychiatrists and others to determine changes in criteria and diagnoses (Lieberman, 2015). The *DSM* also makes an enormous amount of money for the APA. With each new edition of the *DSM*, a wealth of materials and courses are marketed for social workers and therapists to learn how to properly use the *DSM*.

The early *DSM* editions stated specifically that the manual was not for use in billing, but that is exactly what it is used for today. As with previous editions, the 1980 *DSM-III* was designed to coordinate with the *ICD*. The *DSM-III* provided more detailed diagnostic criteria as well as a complex multiaxial diagnostic assessment (APA, 2018). With the acknowledgment that some diagnostic criteria were confusing and inconsistent, the *DSM-III-R* was released in 1987. The *DSM-IV*, which was published in 1994, included 297 mental health disorders (Lieberman, 2015). It reorganized, added, and deleted diagnostic categories (APA, 2018).

The most recent edition, *DSM-5*, was published in May 2013, 19 years after the previous edition, and following much professional angst and controversy (Lieberman, 2015). The APA had actually appointed a task force in 2006 to begin the revision process (Lieberman, 2015), although others trace the development of the *DSM-5* from as early as 1999 (Blashfield, Keeley, Flanagan, & Miles, 2014). Some of the goals of the *DSM-5* were to create more specific criteria, better align criteria with WHO's *ICD*, and update the use of scientific research. The change in title from *DSM-V* to *DSM-5* acknowledged that it would be a "living document" to be revised like computer software in anticipation of a *DSM-5.1*, *DSM-5.2*, and beyond (Lieberman, 2015, p. 272).

In the digital age, in the effort to overcome the secrecy associated with making revisions to the *DSM*, anyone had the opportunity to comment on the *DSM-5* through an online portal. In contrast to past *DSM* editions, for which comments were typically limited to mental health professionals, the *DSM-5* welcomed comments from many stakeholders, including patient advocacy organizations, pharmaceutical companies, the insurance industry, government organizations, and medical organizations (Lieberman, 2015). The APA appeared stunned by the outpouring of public opinion: The public comment period resulted in more than 10,000 comments (Reardon, 2014).

Among the revisions in the *DSM-5* are changes in terminology. Some of the changes between *DSM-IV* and *DSM-5* included removing *Asperger's syndrome* as a separate category and making it part of the new *autism spectrum disorders* category and adding *disruptive mood regulation disorder* for children and adolescents younger than age 18 to avoid the overdiagnosis of bipolar disorder. Additionally, the fifth edition replaced the term *mental retardation* with *intellectual disability disorder*, replaced *gender identity disorder* with *gender dysphoria*, and collapsed the two categories of *substance abuse* and *substance dependence* into one category of *substance use disorder* (Reardon, 2014).

Dr. Jeffrey Lieberman (2015) became president of the APA in 2012, and after his involvement with the *DSM-5*, he concluded, "Despite all the drama, fear, and ambition that played out during the creation of the *DSM-5*, the final product ultimately proved to be a rather modest revision of the *DSM-IV*" (p. 283). This conclusion was reached because the basic definitions of mental illnesses continued to focus on a "consistent and enduring pattern of symptoms that causes subjective distress or impairment of functioning" (Lieberman, 2015, p. 283).

Gary Greenberg (2013) wrote an important exposé of the *DSM-5* with the revealing title *The Book of Woe: The DSM and the Unmaking of Psychiatry*. Greenberg examined the close ties of the publisher of the *DSM*, the APA, to pharmaceutical companies and the nasty politics of elite psychiatry in the United States. A reader is left with the feeling that far more dynamics were at play than accurate assessment and appropriate treatment of those with mental disorders.

With the publication of the *DSM-5*, task force members who were responsible for revisions and additions to the diagnostic categories were, for the first time, required to disclose any financial connections to the pharmaceutical industry (Cosgrove & Krimsky, 2012). An astonishing 69% of task force members acknowledged ties to the drug industry, a 21% increase over the proportion of members who worked on the *DSM-IV* and had such ties! From an ethical point of view, members of *DSM* committees should not receive any financial benefit from their work and recommendations (Cosgrove, 2010). However, disclosure of financial ties is quite different from requiring that *DSM* committee members have no financial ties. This ethical issue remains highly controversial and without a resolution in sight.

In the effort to make the *DSM-5* more accessible, those who are troubled by their own mental health problems can take an initial screening online. The *DSM-5-Based Screening Inventory* is a simple tool that can be used by individuals who are concerned about their mental health. Applying the diagnostic criteria from the *DSM-5* and taking only about 5 minutes to complete, the screening inventory can quickly and easily inform individuals if a professional mental health assessment is needed (Epstein et al., 2017).

Social Workers and the *DSM*

Since social workers provide the majority of services to those with mental health problems, it is important to examine how social workers utilize the *DSM* (Barsky, 2015; Probst, 2013). Many social workers are uncomfortable using the *DSM* because it tends to reduce individuals to their diagnoses while overlooking their uniqueness and the cluster of client feelings that may not make their way into diagnostic categories. Some see the use of the *DSM-5* as acquiescing to psychiatry and medicine, with its focus on disease, while overlooking the strengths-based ecological model often used within social work (Reardon, 2014). It is a hallmark of social work practice, regardless of specialty, that clients be viewed in relationship to their environment.

Social workers do see the value in utilizing the *DSM* for the purposes of billing. Thus, the *DSM* becomes a practical way to receive reimbursement, and at the same time, social workers can focus on a client's symptoms rather than on rigid diagnostic categories (Probst, 2012). In a qualitative study of interviews with 30 clinical social workers, most found the *DSM* useful for helping clients understand their experiences and suffering and to provide hope for recovery (Probst, 2013). Additionally, social workers found the *DSM* helpful in making decisions about the use of medications.

In the future, rather than focusing on simply teaching social workers to use the *DSM-5*, it is preferable to emphasize flexibility in its use in clinical practice (Probst, 2013). Social workers should use the *DSM-5* in the context of "respecting the dignity and worth of clients, empowering clients, putting clients' interests first, and if diagnosis is required, ensuring that the diagnostic process is conducted by a professional with appropriate knowledge and skill" (Barsky, 2015, p. 2). Now is the time for social workers to be more involved in evaluating the usefulness of the *DSM-5* and developing future editions (Probst, 2013). It is also time for social workers to participate in discussions about whether *DSM* task force members should be allowed to have financial interests in the pharmaceutical industry, and they should strive to put an end to this practice.

MAJOR MENTAL DISORDERS

There are literally hundreds of mental disorders, all of which cannot be described in this text. This section presents a very brief overview of some of the major diagnoses and corresponding efforts to treat them. It also serves as a reminder that mental health diagnoses and treatments need to be provided by well-qualified and experienced mental health clinicians, whether they are social workers, psychologists, psychiatrists, psychiatric nurses, or mental health counselors.

Schizophrenia

Schizophrenia has long been considered among the most severe of mental disorders. It has been recognized for many years and was first given the name *schizophrenia* by German psychiatrist Emil Kraepelin in 1887. According to the *DSM-5*, schizophrenia is defined by having one or more of the following five symptoms: (a) hallucinations, (b) delusions, (c) disorganized thinking that can show in speech that does not make sense, (d) abnormal motor behavior such as becoming catatonic and unable to move, and (e) other negative symptoms (APA, 2013). Initial symptoms of schizophrenia, such as a psychotic break, can be so frightening for individuals and others that they often result in psychiatric hospitalization. The *DSM-5* estimates that 0.3% to 0.7% of the total population has schizophrenia in the United States (APA, 2013).

Typically, the onset of schizophrenia is in adolescence or early adulthood, between the ages of 16 and 25; it is seen as a lifelong diagnosis. It can be difficult for individuals and their families to acknowledge this diagnosis, and then to manage the symptoms over the long term. Antipsychotic medications, which are discussed in Chapter 6, Social Work and Psychiatry: Psychotropic Medications and Brain Stimulation Techniques, are seen as the best hope for recovery from and management of schizophrenia. Individuals with schizophrenia are encouraged by medical providers to continue their medications indefinitely. These medications can bring significant side effects such as weight gain, muscle pain, and sexual dysfunction, with the older antipsychotic medications being more likely to cause tardive dyskinesia, the involuntary movements of the mouth, jaw, and tongue (Framingham, 2018; Krebs, Leopold, Hinzpeter, & Schaefer, 2006). Current research is focusing on the development of long-acting medications for schizophrenia that can be administered by injection (Framingham, 2018). However, recent evidence suggests that while initial improvement can occur, long-term treatment with antipsychotics can result in poorer outcomes in schizophrenia treatment (Whitaker, 2015). See Case Example 5.1 for the story of a schizophrenia researcher who experienced the illness himself.

CASE EXAMPLE 5.1

SCHIZOPHRENIA RESEARCHER DIAGNOSED WITH SCHIZOPHRENIA

By age 24, Brandon was already very accomplished. Having graduated from the University of California, Los Angeles, where he majored in molecular biology, Brandon obtained a position at a schizophrenia research lab at the University of California, San Francisco. The research focused on reducing the social isolation of individuals with schizophrenia. Then life changed dramatically. Brandon thought someone was hacking his computer and sending him coded messages, and he experienced symptoms of paranoia. Brandon described feeling that his mind was "covered in mud" (McFarling, 2016, p. 4).

After consulting with a psychiatrist, Brandon was initially incorrectly diagnosed with depression and social anxiety. After receiving the more accurate diagnosis of schizoaffective disorder, which includes symptoms of both mood disorder and schizophrenia, he began a regimen of medications. He experienced some side effects from these medications such as inability to focus, anxiety, and depression, but his paranoia was relieved. Brandon then felt so well he stopped taking his medications, not unlike others with serious mental illness. This decision resulted in a relapse so severe he became uncontrollable at home, and his parents called the police due to his threatening behaviors. Brandon then spent several weeks in a psychiatric hospital, but upon release he very quickly reexperienced out-of-control behavior and was admitted to a different hospital. At this point, Brandon began to respond well to a new medication, olanzapine.

Brandon was able to work himself back to his previous position in the schizophrenia lab. The irony was not lost on him or those who care about him. Reflecting his optimism, Brandon stated, "There is plasticity in the brain. It can change over time if you constantly push. I will not let this illness take my life" (McFarling, 2016, p. 9). Brandon has become a speaker for the National Alliance on Mental Illness (NAMI) and received a standing ovation when he spoke at its national convention. And Brandon went on to attend graduate school.

SOURCE: McFarling, U. L. (2016, June 14). A journey through schizophrenia, from researcher to patient and back. *STAT*. https://www.statnews.com/2016/06/14/schizophrenia-journey

Mood Disorders

Mood disorders are a general category that relate to an individual's emotional state as seen through the lens of distorted or excessive moods such as depression and/or mania (Azam, Qureshi, & Kinnair, 2016). Mood disorders include major depressive disorder and bipolar disorder.

Depression

Major depressive disorder (unipolar depression) is characterized by a depressed mood most of each day, diminished sense of pleasure, and feelings of hopelessness, which can affect an individual's ability to function and which typically last longer than 2 weeks (APA, 2013). The *DSM-5* reports a prevalence of 7% of major depressive disorder in the U.S. population. Some individuals with depression manage to function and receive outpatient care, whereas others require hospitalization for stabilization and then are prescribed antidepressant medication, which they are expected to continue. In addition to medication, psychotherapy can be helpful for depression, as can different forms of physical exercise.

Bipolar Disorder

It is especially difficult to diagnose bipolar disorder because it can easily be confused with unipolar depression. Individuals with bipolar disorder experience alternating periods of depression and periods of mania, with the latter being characterized by symptoms of very high energy and reduced need for sleep. Previously, bipolar disorder was known as manic depression. The prevalence of bipolar disorder in the United States is less than 2% (APA, 2013).

Individuals with bipolar disorder can spend many years seeking an accurate diagnosis and treatment protocol (Thomas, 2016). Misdiagnosis can be common. The average time from onset of symptoms to accurate diagnosis of bipolar disorder can be 5 to 10 years (Phillips & Kupfer, 2013). One reason it is hard to diagnose bipolar disorder is that individuals may present for treatment while in a depressed phase, leading to a diagnosis of unipolar depression. For young people, the onset can be very abrupt, consisting of a manic episode. Today, it can be difficult to differentiate bipolar disorder from reactions that youth have to smoking marijuana laced with other unknown drugs.

Psychiatric hospitalization can be required when an individual experiences an abrupt onset of symptoms. Medication is often utilized during hospitalization and upon discharge, and psychotherapy and physical exercise can be helpful as well.

Anxiety Disorders

Anxiety disorders focus on the experience of excessive fear and anxiety. The *DSM-5* states that excessive fear is a response to a perceived threat of some kind. Anxiety is defined as the anticipation of a threat in the future (APA, 2013). Panic attacks are a specific type of response to fear. There are a number of types of anxiety disorders, including social anxiety disorder and generalized anxiety disorder.

Social anxiety disorder usually takes the form of excessive fear of social situations, in which the individual worries that she or he is being inspected or judged by others. The *DSM-5* estimates the prevalence of social anxiety disorder at 7% of the American population.

In generalized anxiety disorder, the persistent and excessive anxiety and worry are associated with performance at work or school. The prevalence of generalized anxiety disorder is 2.9% for adults and 0.9% for adolescents (APA, 2013).

Individuals with anxiety disorders can be treated on an outpatient basis with therapy and perhaps antianxiety medication and exercise.

Personality Disorders

According to the *DSM-5*, there are 10 types of personality disorders. The characteristics that they share are a pervasive pattern of behaviors and inner thoughts and feelings that are outside of the individual's culture, and that lead to impairment. Personality disorders impact how individuals perceive themselves as well as how they perceive other people. For example, paranoid personality disorder refers to a pattern of distrust of other people. Borderline personality disorder refers to a pattern of unstable relationships with others, instability in one's self-image and emotions, and impulsive behaviors. Antisocial personality disorder is a disregard for the rights of others and the inability to feel guilt. It is a common diagnosis for those who are involved in the criminal justice system. Narcissistic personality disorder is a pattern of grandiose behaviors, a lack of empathy for others, and a strong need for admiration. As discussed in Chapter 1, Social Work and the Mental Health System, some mental health professionals support the view that President Donald Trump has narcissistic personality disorder—an excessive focus on himself as he touts the greatness he sees in himself. Estimates are that approximately 15% of the American population has at least one kind of personality disorder (APA, 2013).

As described by the *DSM*, personality disorders are enduring patterns of behaviors and feelings. Over the years, some experts have questioned whether personality disorders constitute mental illness or instead represent a different personality structure (Kendell, 2002). Effective treatments would support the idea of mental illness, but much more needs to be known. For those who choose to distinguish between mental disorders and personality disorders, experts point out that they can occur at the same time in the same person (Hayward & Moran, 2008).

Suicidal Behavior Disorder

According to the *DSM-5*, a person who has made a suicide attempt within the last 24 months can be diagnosed with suicidal behavior disorder (APA, 2013). However, this diagnosis is described in the section titled *Conditions for Further Study*. If a suicide attempt was made within the last year, the disorder is considered current; if an attempt was made in the previous 12 to 24 months, it is considered to be in early remission. It is challenging for mental health professionals to determine the "degree of intent" of suicidal gestures and attempts (APA, 2013, p. 803).

Suicide attempts can be made at any time during the life course, and suicidal behavior varies across cultures. Suicide attempts are associated with many mental disorders, but they are most closely associated with bipolar disorder, major depressive disorder, schizophrenia, anxiety disorders, and substance use disorders. About 25% to 30% of those who make an initial suicide attempt will make subsequent attempts (APA, 2013).

The Centers for Disease Control and Prevention (CDC) has documented a considerable increase in the rate of suicide among Americans between 1999 and 2016. In all states, except Nevada, suicide rates rose; in some states, such as Vermont, New Hampshire, and Minnesota, rates rose by as much as 38% to 58% (CDC, 2018). Among completed suicides who had known mental health disorders, 69% were male and 31% were female. In those who did not have a history of mental disorders, 84% of suicides were male and 16% were female (CDC, 2018).

INPATIENT TREATMENT

The United States has a long history of psychiatric hospitalization as a response to mental illness—that is, it has a history of institutionalizing individuals without treatment or without hope for the future. The history of custodial treatment based on control of patient behavior within intractable bureaucracies such as state hospitals is a heavy burden to bear (Bartholomew & Kensler, 2010). This is not the kind of environment where typically innovative, evidence-based treatment practices can be found.

We learned in Chapter 4, Mental Illness Across the Life Cycle: Children, Adolescents, Adults, and Older Adults, that persons with mental illness can be admitted to a psychiatric facility voluntarily or involuntarily (against their will). We have previously examined the challenges of psychiatric hospitalization, especially in state hospitals. Many mental health professionals think involuntary hospitalization should be used as a last resort—only when an individual is a danger to himself or herself, or to others. Involuntary hospitalization is the most common type of commitment, but individuals can also be legally required to take medication or accept other forms of treatment such as psychotherapy or electroconvulsive therapy (ECT). Procedural safeguards are critical to prevent abuses (Mental Health America, 2015).

Psychiatric hospitalization, whether involuntary or voluntary, can bring with it feelings of helplessness for the individual. Often there is a lack of personal space, a lack of information, and a lack of activities outside the direct supervision of hospital staff (Salzman-Erikson & Soderqvist, 2017). One woman on an involuntary hospital unit stated, "When you come to the unit, you don't know when you're coming out. Will you ever be well again? It's frightening" (Salzman-Erikson & Soderqvist, 2017, p. 543). There is a delicate balance between involuntary commitment and supporting patients in self-determination regarding their treatment (Bartholomew & Kensler, 2010).

Previously in this text, we made the point that inpatient hospital programs have to balance the needs of patients with the needs of the facility and the staff (Csipke et al., 2016). This is clearly challenging. However, in recent years, private psychiatric facilities have sought to make significant profits, at times at the expense of patient care.

Exploitation of the Mentally Ill and Those With Substance Use Disorders for Profit

As with the correctional system in the United States, some private corporations provide both inpatient and outpatient mental health services. While it can be debated whether it is inherently bad to benefit financially from the difficulties of others, the reality is that today corporations seek to profit from the illnesses of individuals. When the profit motive overtakes caring for patients with mental disorders, social workers must speak up.

Universal Health Services

Universal Health Services (UHS, 2018) is one of the largest healthcare management companies in the United States. Its website boasts about the company having more than 350 health facilities in the United States and the United Kingdom. The website claims this: "Quality healthcare is our passion, improving lives is our reward." If only this were true. The mission and principles of UHS further state the following: "UHS is built on a legacy of integrity and positive outcomes." This statement is highly offensive and absurd when we take a closer look. In reality, severe patient care problems have been documented since 2010 by the Citizens Commission on Human Rights International (CCHR), which serves as a watchdog for mental health issues. Between 2010 and 2017, CCHR has registered more than 4,000 complaints with law enforcement, state and federal legislators and agencies, health officials, and the Federal Bureau of Investigation (FBI). The Department of Justice and the Office of the Inspector General of the Department of Health and Human Services have been investigating UHS mental health facilities since 2013 (CCHR, 2017). Approximately 26 UHS facilities are being investigated for billing fraud.

Currently, Arbour Counseling Services, a mental health clinic in Lawrence, Massachusetts, that is owned by UHS, is suing the Commonwealth of Massachusetts in the U.S. District Court in Boston because Medicaid payments to the clinic were suspended on June 6, 2018 (Kowalczyk, 2018). Nonpayment was the result of Arbor Counseling providing mental health services by staff members who are unqualified, unlicensed, and unsupervised. The decision to stop Medicaid payments was related to a lawsuit against UHS brought by the family of a 19-year-old woman who died in 2009 after receiving care at the Lawrence counseling program. The family claims in their lawsuit that she was given inappropriate medication that resulted in her death (Kowalczyk, 2018). CCHR summed it up this way: "The fact that UHS is allowed to acquire or establish any new psychiatric facility while under investigation is astonishing" (CCHR, 2017, p. 3). It certainly is surprising that lack of proper oversight allows this to occur. See Case Example 5.2 for the closures of UHS psychiatric facilities in Massachusetts for providing poor care.

CASE EXAMPLE 5.2

UNIVERSAL HEALTH SERVICES: CHILD AND ADULT PSYCHIATRIC FACILITIES CLOSED DUE TO INADEQUATE PATIENT CARE

Westwood Lodge, a 12-bed psychiatric facility for children and adolescents, was closed and its license suspended in 2017 by the Commonwealth of Massachusetts after a surprise inspection. The issues were part of a larger set of problems with Arbour Health System, a subsidiary of Universal Health Services (UHS), the largest provider of psychiatric services in the United States. Repeated problems in providing patient care included an insufficient number of staff, poorly trained staff, inadequate supervision of patients, and dirty living conditions (Kowlczyk, 2017). It is challenging enough for children and adolescents to find themselves in a psychiatric hospital, but a neglectful and/or abusive environment surely adds to these challenges.

August 2017 brought the closure of the Westwood Lodge hospital program for adults following a police investigation for sexual assault. The Massachusetts Department of Mental Health had conducted 91 licensing visits to Westwood Lodge between January 1, 2015, and August 24, 2017. Thirteen visits resulted in additional monitoring, the appointment of a clinical monitor, temporary closure of admissions, and suspension of the facility's license (Newman, 2017). Despite the intensive level of oversight, the problems persisted, causing the shutdown. What happened at Westwood Lodge serves as a critical reminder of the exploitation of the most vulnerable, often for financial gain. It is also an illustration that persistent neglect and abuse of psychiatric patients has not yet brought about adequate interventions to improve psychiatric mental healthcare.

SOURCES: Kowalczyk, L. (2017, April 28). State to shut child psychiatric unit at Westwood Lodge. *The Boston Globe*, B2; Newman, A. (2017, August 30). Sexual assault investigation at now-shuttered Westwood Psychiatric Hospital. *Westwood Patch*. https://patch.com/massachusetts/westwood/sexual-assault-investigation-now-shuttered-westwood-psychiatric-hospital

OUTPATIENT THERAPY

There are many types of psychotherapies, far too many to be described in detail here. Some therapies focus on resolving childhood issues and trauma, whereas other therapies focus specifically on resolving current problems that clients are experiencing. For many years, it has been debated and researched which are the most effective in helping clients with mental disorders. Research shows that for all the types of outpatient therapy, the most important factor is the relationship between the client and the therapist, regardless of the type of therapy. It is the quality of the therapeutic relationship that predicts positive outcomes for clients (Ardito & Rabellino, 2011). Cognitive behavioral therapy (CBT) and dialectical behavior therapy (DBT) currently receive the most attention and are briefly reviewed here.

Cognitive Behavioral Therapy

CBT was developed from the behavior modification tradition in the 1970s. It can be used to treat multiple forms of mental illness, including severe forms of mental illness, borderline personality disorder, and substance use disorders (Kredlow et al., 2017; Mignon, 2015). CBT is a short-term treatment that focuses on achieving specific goals, with attention being paid to the present rather than the past. Clients work on changing their negative thoughts, beliefs, and attitudes, which in turn changes their behaviors (Martin, 2018). By learning new and more positive ways of thinking and behaving, clients are able to utilize these tools well into the future. In those with severe mental illness such as schizophrenia, changes are more likely to be behavioral in nature, such as an increase in social activities, rather than to consist of improvement in cognitive abilities (Kingdom & Price, 2009).

Dialectical Behavior Therapy

Some experts consider DBT to be a type of CBT, while others consider it a different therapy that developed from CBT. DBT seeks to bring together two opposites, *acceptance* and *change*. It is the role of the DBT therapist to support clients to achieve a balance between both. Change is supported through behavioral techniques, and acceptance techniques are based on Zen Buddhist practices (Reddy & Vijay, 2017). DBT was developed to treat suicidal individuals with borderline personality disorder; however, today it is utilized with a variety of mental health disorders. It differs from CBT in that it encourages clients to regulate their emotions by accepting uncomfortable thoughts and feelings instead of struggling to overcome them (National Alliance on Mental Illness [NAMI], 2018). DBT has been effective in helping adolescents with oppositional defiant disorder and in helping suicidal adolescents reduce their self-harming behaviors (Marco, Garcia-Palacios, & Botella, 2013; McCauley et al., 2018).

A recent effort to improve mental health services has focused on offering screening and assessment of mental health and other problems within primary care medical offices (Pomerantz, Cole, Watts, & Weeks, 2008). Since it can take weeks or longer to get an appointment for a mental health evaluation on an outpatient basis, there is great value in assessing a patient during a regular medical office visit. One study of a Veterans Administration facility involved moving mental health triage services into a primary care office. This reduced the wait time from an average of 33 days to only 19 minutes, a marked improvement, especially for patients in acute distress. In addition, this approach avoids sending patients to hospital emergency rooms, where adequate mental healthcare may not be available. It also reduces the high costs associated with emergency room treatment.

▨ CO-OCCURRING DISORDERS/DUAL DIAGNOSIS

Until relatively recently, substance abuse problems and mental health problems were seen as two separate issues. With the advent of considerable oversight by health insurance companies, known as managed care, the emphasis is now on positioning mental illness and substance use disorder together and calling the collective entity "behavioral health." While some social workers view substance use disorder as a mental illness, others have been educated and trained to think of substance abuse as a separate problem. The concerns about private corporations financially benefiting from treatment of mental illness extends to substance abuse treatment as well. See Case Example 5.3 for a description of the *Dr. Phil* show.

CASE EXAMPLE 5.3

DR. PHIL MCGRAW: THE QUESTIONABLE METHODS OF DAYTIME TELEVISION

Todd Herzog planned an appearance on the Dr. Phil show in 2013 to receive help for his alcoholism. Having won the television Survivor contest, Todd was no stranger to media attention. However, when the segment was filmed, Todd was so intoxicated that he had to be carried onto the camera set and placed in a chair. He later told the *Boston Globe* staff that he was sober when he arrived but was greeted by a bottle of vodka in his dressing room. He drank it all and also took Xanax that he was given—by whom, it is unclear. While known for his efforts to assist people with addictions, did Dr. Phil McGraw cross the line by ensuring that alcohol was made available to Todd? Was the experience of bringing Todd on the Dr. Phil show really about helping Todd to recover from alcoholism, or was it about ensuring an attention-grabbing show for viewers? This is only one example of the many times that McGraw's guests say they were in drug and alcohol withdrawal and left to their own devices in hotel rooms while waiting to make an appearance on the show.

However, some who made appearances on the show do credit McGraw with helping them get clean and sober. In 2006, the American Psychological Association (APA) gave McGraw an award to recognize that "his work has touched more Americans than any other living psychologist" (Allen & Armstrong, 2017, p. A6). Interestingly, McGraw has a doctorate from the University of North Texas but let his license to practice psychology in Texas expire in 2006. However, this has been no barrier to him becoming the highest-paid personality on daytime television, earning $79 million in 2016 alone.

In 2017, McGraw and his son started what is called "Dr. Phil's Path to Recovery." This program consists of McGraw appearing in a "series of virtual reality scenarios," where patients put on virtual reality goggles and listen to him speak (Allen & Armstrong, 2018, p. A6). Treatment programs can purchase "Dr. Phil's Path to Recovery" at a monthly cost of between $3,500 and $7,000 and then can earn the opportunity to have staff come on the show—a huge marketing boost for any substance abuse treatment facility. Some of the treatment centers featured on the Dr. Phil program have been found to provide inadequate and neglectful care, such as failing to supervise adolescents who run away or continue to abuse substances.

SOURCES: Allen, E., & Armstrong, D. (2017, December 31). Dr. Phil: Rescuer or reckless showman? *The Boston Globe*, part 1, A1, A6; Allen, E., & Armstrong, D. (2018, January 1). Dr. Phil's marketing clout boosts addiction centers, new venture. *The Boston Globe*, part 2, A1, A6.

The change in classification of substance abuse in the *DSM-5* has had repercussions for substance abuse treatment. Many substance abuse clinicians objected to collapsing substance abuse and substance dependence into one category titled *substance use and addictive disorders*. The distinction between abuse and dependence was very helpful in determining the type of treatment needed. For example, substance abusers are likely to need a lower level of intervention than those with substance dependence, in which there is physical addiction to substances (Mignon, 2015). Those with physical addiction are more likely to need detoxification from substances and perhaps an inpatient rehabilitation program.

While substance use disorder can be the sole diagnosis for an individual, it can also correlate with a number of mental health disorders. The substance use disorders most likely to be associated with mental health problems are anxiety disorders, depression, ADHD, bipolar disorder, and borderline personality disorder (Mignon, 2015). For example, it is estimated that 15% to 45% of adults with ADHD have an alcohol or drug use disorder (Ohlmeier et al., 2007).

Through the years, there has been a shift from treating substance use disorders before mental health disorders, and more of an effort to treat them simultaneously (Watkins, Hunter, Burnam, Pincus, & Nicholson, 2005). It has not been an easy melding of treatment approaches, as substance abuse programs and public mental health systems were independent of each other into the 1990s, and some continue to be independent today (Drake et al., 2001). Even today, some mental health treatment programs will not accept patients who are abusing substances, and some substance abuse treatment programs will not accept patients with mental health diagnoses (Becker, 2017).

It is more difficult to diagnose mental health problems when a substance use disorder is present. The reasoning is that an individual should be abstinent to determine whether substance abuse is the primary problem or whether it is secondary to mental illness (Mignon, 2015). Determining which disorder came first is especially difficult in individuals with anxiety disorders and depression. There is evidence that individuals use alcohol and drugs to reduce their anxiety, which in turn can lead to greater substance use (Spanagel, 2009). As depression is common among those persons with substance use disorder, it can be difficult to ascertain whether the substance use resulted from depression or the depression resulted from substance use. However, over time, both the substance use and depression can worsen (Mignon, 2015). Certainly, with the opioid addiction epidemic of recent years, these issues have become even more complex and challenging.

Evidence suggests, perhaps unsurprisingly, that a reduction in substance abuse is correlated with improved mental health (McGaffin, Deane, Kelly, & Ciarrochi, 2015). This confirms the importance of screening individuals for substance abuse. Screening for substance use disorders in mental health settings can help ensure that clients receive the appropriate type of treatment (Bartoli et al., 2016). Screening for mental health disorders in addiction programs is also very useful. Drake and Green (2015) point out that while there is a rich literature on the correlations between mental health disorders and substance use disorders, this does not necessarily lead to improved interventions for those individuals with both disorders.

Social work ethics require that client needs are of paramount importance in every treatment setting. Tips for the Field 5.1 describes themes and strategies for supporting clients with mental disorders.

TIPS FOR THE FIELD 5.1

DIGGING DEEPER INTO STRATEGIES: HELPFUL THEMES FOR SUPPORTING CLIENTS WITH MENTAL DISORDERS

There is agreement that social workers and other mental health professionals must create a trusting relationship and an environment that is both welcoming and supportive for their clients. After an initial appointment, the social worker can create optimism for clients by sharing that other clients with similar problems recover from mental illness. A clean and attractive physical space is also conducive to a client feeling comfortable. A qualitative study of interviews with mental health clients found there were seven themes and strategies that clients found helpful to their recovery (Lietz, LaCasse, Hayes, & Cheung, 2014). These can serve as important general guidelines for social workers working with the mentally ill.

1. *Establish safety.* This includes physical and emotional safety, especially for those clients who are hospitalized. One respondent reported that she bolted from the facility after an upsetting exchange with a nurse ordering her to move to a different part of the room, only to be recaptured. Another spoke of being restrained by five male staff members although she weighed only 104 pounds (Lietz et al., 2014, pp. 171–172). Respondents overall confirmed that staff making them feel safe was critical to their recovery process.

2. *Facilitate self-determination.* Social workers must encourage clients to participate in formulating their own treatment plan. In fact, some respondents reported they were being told what to do by professionals such as psychiatrists, especially when they were in an involuntary hospital situation. One woman was told, "Look, you're court ordered, I know more about this than you do. I'm the expert; this is what you're going to do" (p. 172). Understandably, this woman felt demeaned and diminished by this doctor. Others felt that they were listened to and felt good about participating in developing their treatment plan.

3. *Offer an individualized and humanizing approach.* Respondents said they appreciated efforts to address their specific needs rather than offering the same services and approaches to everyone. One woman's negative experience was that she felt shamed by her doctor for trying to seek advice about sexual intimacy. Respondents who had positive experiences appreciated their therapists and psychiatrists who were good listeners, were sincere, and treated them with respect.

4. *Foster hope.* Respondents reported that when their service providers expressed hope for their future, their motivation improved. Conversely, when their providers did not seem optimistic, clients were discouraged from trying to improve their lives. A doctor told one client, "'You get to never work again', that felt hopeless to me" (p. 175). With an emphasis on the chronicity of some major mental disorders such as schizophrenia, it is understandable that individuals are upset by the message that they will not get well.

5. *Validate experiences, including a trauma history.* Respondents appreciated their therapists engaging with them around their past trauma experiences. One woman who had been sexually abused as a child by her stepfather appreciated when her therapist stated, "I'm so sorry this happened to you. You did not deserve that" (p. 176). Another woman felt disrespected when her psychiatrist, who was from another country, stated, "In this country you guys make too much a big deal over sexual abuse. There was probably nothing that happened, and if it did, you over-exaggerate it. You have weak genes" (p. 176). When therapists validate the concerns of clients, there is a positive response; however, without validation, clients can feel retraumatized.

6. *Promote positive thought patterns and esteem.* Respondents reported that they were able to change and improve their patterns of thinking to healthier thoughts through either cognitive behavioral therapy or dialectical behavior therapy. One woman stated, "I would have to say my [DBT] therapist is the one who made the biggest

difference in my life, because she got me to see things from a completely different perspective than I had learned growing up" (p. 177).

7. *Ground services in shared experiences.* Active participation in peer-run services such as self-help groups is very important. One woman who lost her peer support group due to budget cuts felt this as a big loss: "I was getting peer support. Like a mentor who would come out, somebody holding me accountable. ... I really miss that" (p. 178). For those who had the opportunity to serve as peer mentors, they appreciated helping others as well as themselves.

SOURCE: Lietz, C. A., Lacasse, J. R., Hayes, M. J., & Cheung, J. (2014). The role of services in mental health recovery: A qualitative examination of service experiences among individuals diagnosed with serious mental illness. *Journal of the Society for Social Work and Research, 5*(2), 161–188.

Although social workers are well positioned to ensure that clients in programs get appropriate treatment, historically they have not contributed to policy making to ensure that profits of private corporations are monitored and restricted. This is an area in which far more social work influence is needed.

▌ SUMMARY AND CONCLUSION

Classification of mental disorders is a very complex process, as illustrated by the *DSM* revisions over many years. Social workers are mindful of the conflicts of interest and financial incentives of pharmaceutical companies, which have a strong impact on mental disorder classification and mental health treatment. With their very strong *Code of Ethics*, social workers are particularly sensitive to the exploitation of others in pursuit of profit and fame. Social workers should have greater input into revisions of the *DSM-5*. They should also work to reduce consequences for clients when the profit motive becomes paramount for pharmaceutical companies and treatment providers.

In the diagnostic process, social workers must ensure that a diagnosis helps to serve the needs of the clients by suggesting appropriate courses of treatment. Involuntary psychiatric hospitalization should be used only when those with a mental disorder are in need of medical stabilization services and to protect the patients and others from harm. Those with co-occurring mental health and substance use disorders need to be treated by professionals with expertise in both areas. And always, clients must be given opportunities to participate in their own treatment plan, including determining their own goals.

▓ DISCUSSION QUESTIONS/TOPICS

1. Why is it important to have an accurate diagnosis for an individual experiencing mental health problems?

2. Discuss the political factors that came to bear on the *DSM-5* when it was published in 2013.

3. What are the strengths and weaknesses of the *DSM-5*?

4. Describe the challenges to providing excellent mental healthcare within an inpatient psychiatric hospital.

5. Describe some circumstances in which involuntary psychiatric hospitalization may be necessary.

6. Why do you think that organizations such as UHS can continue to operate despite numerous complaints of very-low-quality mental health services?

7. In what ways is CBT helpful to patients with mental disorders?

8. Describe the relationship between substance use disorders and mental illness.

9. Discuss the importance of the relationship between the therapist and the client.

10. Discuss your own ideas for improving services to clients who have both a mental health disorder and a substance use disorder.

▓ REFERENCES

American Psychiatric Association. (2013). *Diagnostic and statistical manual of mental disorders* (5th ed.). Arlington, VA: Author.

American Psychiatric Association. (2018). *DSM history*. Retrieved from https://www.psychiatry.org/psychiatrists/practice/dsm/history-of-the-dsm

Ardito, R. B., & Rabellino, D. (2011). Therapeutic alliance and outcome of psychotherapy: Historical excursus, measurements, and prospects for research. *Frontiers in Psychology, 2*, 270. doi:10.3389/fpsyg.2011.00270

Aultman, J. M. (2016). Psychiatric diagnostic uncertainty: Challenges to patient-centered care. *AMA Journal of Ethics, 18*(6), 579–586.

Azam, M., Qureshi, M., & Kinnair, D. (2016). *Psychiatry: A clinical handbook*. Banbury, UK: Scion Publishing.

Barsky, A. (2015, Summer). *DSM-5 and the ethics of diagnosis. The New Social Worker*. Retrieved from http://www.socialworker.com/feature-articles/ethics-articles/dsm-5-and-ethics-of-diagnosis

Bartholomew, T., & Kensler, D. (2010). Illness management and recovery in state psychiatric hospitals. *American Journal of Psychiatric Rehabilitation, 13*, 105–123. doi:10.1080/15487761003756977

Bartoli, F., Crocamo, C., Biagi, E., Di Carlo, F., Parma, F., Madeddu, F., … Carra, G. (2016). Clinical utility of a single-item test for *DSM-5* alcohol use disorder among outpatients with anxiety and depressive disorders. *Drug and Alcohol Dependence, 165*, 283–287. doi:10.1016/j.drugalcdep.2016.06.003

Becker, D. (2017, May 8). Patients see gaps in treating both a mental health and substance use disorder. *WBUR CommonHealth*. Retrieved from http://www.wbur.org/commonhealth/2017/05/08/mental-health-substance-use-dual-diagnosis

Blashfield, R. K., Keeley, J. W., Flanagan, E. H., & Miles, S. R. (2014). The cycle of classification: *DSM-I* through *DSM-5*. *Annual Review of Clinical Psychology, 10*, 25–51. doi:10.1146/annurev-clnpsy-032813-153639

Centers for Disease Control and Prevention. (2018, June). *CDC's national vital statistics system, Vital Signs*. Retrieved from https://www.cdc.gov/vitalsigns/suicide/infographic.html

Citizens Commission on Human Rights International. (2017, June 5). *Universal Health Services psychiatric hospital chain under Department of Defense & FBI investigation*. Retrieved from https://www.cchrint.org/2017/06/05/uhs-under-investigation

Cosgrove, L. (2010, November–December). Diagnosing conflict-of-interest disorder. *American Association of University Professors*. Retrieved from https://www.aaup.org/article/diagnosing-conflict-interest-disorder

Cosgrove, L., & Krimsky, S. (2012). A comparison of *DSM-IV* and *DSM-5* panel members' financial associations with industry: A pernicious problem persists. *PLoS Medicine, 9*(3), e1001190. doi:10.1371/journal.pmed.1001190

Csipke, E., Williams, P., Rose, D., Koeser, L., McCrone, P., Wykes, T., & Craig, T. (2016). Following the Francis Report: Investigating patient experience of mental health in-patient care. *British Journal of Psychiatry, 209*(1), 35–39. doi:10.1192/bjp.bp.115.171124

Drake, R. E., Goldman, H. H., Leff, H. S., Lehman, A. F., Dixon, L., Mueser, K. T., & Torrey, W. C. (2001). Implementing evidence-based practices in routine mental health service settings. *Psychiatric Services, 53*(1), 45–50.

Drake, R. E., & Green, A. I. (2015). A call for creativity in dual diagnosis research (editorial). *Journal of Dual Diagnosis, 11*(2), 93–96. doi:10.1080/15504263.2015.1027125

Epstein, R., Ho, M., Hyun, S., Le, C., Robertson, R. E., & Stout, D. (2017). A *DSM-5*–based online mental health referral inventory: A large-scale validation study. *Journal of Technology in Human Services, 35*(3), 231–246. doi:10.1080/15228835.2017.1356800

Framingham, J. (2018, May 18). Schizophrenia: The challenges of taking medication. *PsychCentral*. Retrieved from https://psychcentral.com/lib/schizophrenia-the-challenges-of-taking-medication

Greenberg, G. (2013). *The book of woe: The DSM and the unmaking of psychiatry*. New York, NY: Blue Rider Press.

Hayward, M., & Moran, P. (2008). Comorbidity of personality disorders and mental illness. *Psychiatry, 7*(3), 102–104. doi:10.1016/j.mppsy.2008.01.010

Kendell, R. E. (2002). The distinction between personality disorder and mental illness. *British Journal of Psychiatry, 180*, 110–115. doi:10.1192/bjp.180.2.110

Kingdom, D., & Price, J. (2009). Cognitive-behavioral therapy in severe mental illness. *Psychiatric Times, 26*(4), 52. Retrieved from http://go.galegroup.com/ps/retrieve.do?tabID=T002&resultListType

Kowalczyk, L. (2018, September 7). Clinic sues for Medicaid payments. *The Boston Globe*, B10, B16

Krebs, M., Leopold, K., Hinzpeter, A., & Schaefer, M. (2006). Current schizophrenia drugs: Efficacy and side effects. *Expert Opinion on Pharmacotherapy, 7*(8), 1005–1016. doi:10.1517/14656566.7.8.1005

Kredlow, M. A., Szuhany, K. L., Lo, S., Xie, H., Gottlieb, J. D., Rosenberg, S. D., & Mueser, K. T. (2017). Cognitive behavioral therapy for posttraumatic stress disorder in individuals with severe mental illness and borderline personality disorder. *Psychiatry Research, 249*, 86–93. doi:10.1016/j.psychres.2016.12.045

Lauveng, A., Tveiten, S., Ekeland, T.-J., & Ruuud, T. (2015). Same diagnosis, different lives: A qualitative study of adults with severe mental illness, in treatment and education. *Psychosis, 7*(4), 336–347. doi:10.1080/17522439.2015.1024715

Lieberman, J. A., with Ogas, O. (2015). *Shrinks: The untold story of psychiatry.* New York, NY: Back Bay Books.

Marco, J. H., Garcia-Palacios, A., & Botella, C. (2013). Dialectical behavioral therapy for oppositional defiant disorder in adolescents: A case series. *Psicothema, 25*(2), 158–163. doi:10.7334/psicothema2012.119

Martin, B. (2018, April 4). In-depth: Cognitive behavioral therapy. *Psych Central.* Retrieved from https://psychcentral.com/lib/in-depth-cognitive-behavioral-therapy

McCauley, E. M., Berk, M. S., Asarnow, J. R., Adrian, M., Cohen, J., Korslund, K., … Linehan, M. M. (2018). Efficacy of dialectical behavior therapy for adolescents at high risk for suicide: A randomized clinical trial. *JAMA Psychiatry, 75*(8), 777–785. doi:10.1001/jamapsychiatry.2018.1109

McGaffin, B. J., Deane, F. P., Kelly, P. J., & Ciarrochi, J. (2015). Flourishing, languishing and moderate mental health: Prevalence and change in mental health recovery from drug and alcohol problems. *Addiction Research & Theory, 23*(5), 351–360. doi:10.3109/16066359.2015.1019346

Mental Health America. (2015, March 7). *Position statement 22: Involuntary mental health treatment.* Retrieved from http://www.mentalhealthamerica.net/positions/involuntary-treatment

Mignon, S. I. (2015). *Substance abuse treatment: Options, challenges and effectiveness.* New York, NY: Springer Publishing Company.

National Alliance on Mental Illness. (2018). *Psychotherapy.* Retrieved from https://www.nami.org/Learn-More/Treatment/Psychotherapy

Ohlmeier, M. D., Peters, K., Kordon, A., Seifert, J., Te Wildt, B., Wiese, B., … Schneider, U. (2007). Nicotine and alcohol dependence in patients with comorbid attention-deficit/hyperactivity disorder (ADHD). *Alcohol and Alcoholism, 42*(6), 539–543. doi:10.1093/alcalc/agm069

Osborne, C. (2018, March 15). *The impact of 2018 ICD-10 codes on mental, behavioral, and neurodevelopmental disorders.* Retrieved from http://5starconsultants.net/author/cindy-osborne

Phillips, M. L., & Kupfer, D. J. (2013). Bipolar disorder diagnosis: Challenges and future directions. *Lancet, 381*(9878), 1663–1671. doi:10.1016/S0140-6736(13)60989-7

Pomerantz, A., Cole, B. H., Watts, B. V., & Weeks, W. B. (2008). Improving efficiency and access to mental health care: Combining integrated care and advanced access. *General Hospital Psychiatry, 30*, 546–551. doi:10.1016/j.genhosppsych.2008.09004

Probst, B. (2012). Diagnosing, diagnoses, and the *DSM* in clinical social work. *Families in Society: The Journal of Contemporary Human Services, 93*(4), 255–263. doi:10.1606/1044-3894.4235

Probst, B. (2013). "Walking the tightrope:" Clinical social workers' use of diagnostic and environmental perspectives. *Clinical Social Work Journal, 41*, 184–191. doi:10.1007/s10615-012-0394-1

Reardon, C. (2014). *DSM-5*: Debate, soul searching, changes. *Social Work Today, 14*(3), 10.

Reddy, M. S., & Vijay, M. S. (2017). Empirical reality of dialectical behavioral therapy in borderline personality. *Indian Journal of Psychological Medicine, 39*(2), 105–108. doi:10.4103/IJPSYM.IJPSYM_132_17

Salzman-Erikson, M., & Soderqvist, C. (2017). Being subject to restriction, limitations and disciplining: A thematic analysis of individuals' experiences in psychiatric intensive care. *Issues in Mental Health Nursing, 38*(7), 540–548. doi:10.1080/01612840.2017.1299265

Schmidt, C. W. (2007). Environmental connections: A deeper look into mental illness. *Environmental Health Perspectives, 115*(8), A404–A410. doi:10.1289/ehp.115-a404

Spanagel, R. (2009). Alcoholism: A systems approach from molecular physiology to addictive behavior. *Physiological Reviews, 89*(2), 640–705. doi:10.1152/physrev.00013.2008

Thomas, J. (2016, February 29). The challenge of accurately diagnosing bipolar disorder. *Health*. Retrieved from https://www.health.com/health/condition-article/0,,20275016,00.html

Universal Health Services. (2018). *Universal Health Services*. Retrieved from https://www.uhsinc.com/about-uhs

Watkins, K. E., Hunter, S. B., Burnam, M. A., Pincus, H. A., & Nicholson, G. (2005). Review of treatment recommendations for persons with a co-occurring affective or anxiety and substance use disorder. *Psychiatric Services, 56*(8), 913–926. doi:10.1176/appi.ps.56.8.913

Whitaker, R. (2015). *Anatomy of an epidemic: Magic bullets, psychiatric drugs, and the astonishing rise of mental illness in America*. New York, NY: Broadway Books. (Original work published 2010).

World Health Organization. (2018). *ICD-11 is here!* Retrieved from http://www.who.int/classifications/icd/en

CHAPTER 6

SOCIAL WORK AND PSYCHIATRY: PSYCHOTROPIC MEDICATIONS AND BRAIN STIMULATION TECHNIQUES

LEARNING OUTCOMES

- Analyze the relationship between the fields of psychiatry and social work.
- Demonstrate an understanding of the historical development of psychotropic medications.
- Discuss attitudes, both positive and negative, toward the use of psychotropic medications in children.
- Describe the role of primary care physicians in prescribing psychotropic medications.
- Examine the uses of neuromodulation techniques, including electroconvulsive therapy (ECT) and transcranial magnetic stimulation (TMS).

INTRODUCTION

Social work and psychiatry have a long history, as described briefly in Chapter 2, A Short History of Mental Health Policy and Treatment in the United States. Yet it is an uneasy relationship with a considerable power and status differential. Although their compensation can be on the lower end of other physician specialists, psychiatrists have relatively high status in American society and considerable earning power. Psychiatry salaries in the United States average between $241,000 and $270,000 (Merrit Hawkins, 2017). Social work salaries average between

$43,000 and $52,000 (Indeed, 2018; Social Work Salary—PayScale, 2018). We wish the same status and compensation of psychiatrists could be accorded to social workers.

This chapter examines the development of psychiatry and its relationship to social work. It examines the increase in medication use for the treatment of mental disorders, and the medications most likely to be prescribed for specific mental illnesses. It reviews the role of primary care physicians as the predominant prescribers of psychotropic medications, and the role of social workers in working with clients regarding their medications. The chapter also examines neuromodulation techniques such as ECT and TMS. Finally, the chapter examines the role of pharmaceutical companies as well as their enormous profits.

As physician specialists in the treatment of mental illness, psychiatrists in the past have provided both psychotherapy and medication. Today, psychiatrists are often referred to as psychopharmacologists because they specialize in prescribing psychotropic medications. This shift from treating patients with therapy and medication did not come about by accident. Over time, the role of the psychiatrist has changed from therapy plus medication to a heavy reliance on prescribing medication. With medication appointments typically 15 to 20 minutes in length, psychiatrists are able to treat many more patients in a day than if they were also providing psychotherapy, which is typically 50 to 60 minutes per session. This translates into the ability to earn considerably more money. Dr. Daniel Carlat, a professor of psychiatry and author of the 2010 book *Unhinged: The Trouble With Psychiatry*, stated, "There is a huge financial incentive for psychiatrists to prescribe instead of doing psychotherapy. You can make two, three, four times as much money being a prescriber than a therapist" (Smith, 2012, p. 2).

Today there are many options for treatment of mental illness that include medication in inpatient or outpatient settings, and individual and group psychotherapy. A treatment plan should be devised according to the results of screening and assessing for mental health disorders. Social workers are well aware of the importance of the biopsychosocial approach in evaluating client problems and needs. When a patient is assessed, this includes whether the individual has a previous history of mental illness. Before formulating a treatment plan, an examination of the individual's current physical and mental health status is essential. When it comes to treatment of mental disorders, biological approaches include pharmacological therapy (the use of medication) and neuromodulation techniques such as TMS and ECT (Azam, Qureshi, & Kinnair, 2016). Psychological approaches emphasize different types of individual and group psychotherapy. Social approaches to the treatment of mental disorders include self-help and other support groups and can include referrals to social service agencies for financial assistance and housing needs (Azam et al., 2016).

DEVELOPMENT OF PSYCHIATRIC MEDICATIONS

Early psychiatric medications were developed in the 1940s and the 1950s. These early medications showed usefulness in the treatment of depression, anxiety, bipolar disorder, and schizophrenia. For example, chlorpromazine (Thorazine) was discovered in 1950 and became available in 1955. This antipsychotic drug was prescribed to many patients with schizophrenia and other psychotic disorders in state mental hospitals (Whitaker, 2005). Haloperidol (Haldol) was discovered in 1958 and was approved by the Food and Drug Administration (FDA) in 1967 as an antipsychotic. The introduction of these medications bolstered the status of psychiatrists as the experts in prescribing them and solidified the place of psychiatry within medicine (Preskorn, 2008). During the same time period, the seeds were sown for the search to understand the brain mechanisms leading to mental disorders.

The use of all kinds of psychiatric drugs has increased in recent years. The kindest explanation is a desire to help patients; however, that is only part of the story. In truth, there is considerable money to be made. *Psychotropic* medications are defined as those drugs that impact feelings, motions, and behaviors. *Antipsychotic* medication is a type of psychotropic medication that is given to those with severe mental illness such as schizophrenia or bipolar disorder. There is still some lack of clarity on how to categorize some types of medications for the treatment of specific mental illnesses. Typically medications are categorized according to the specific mental health diagnoses they are designed to treat. However, some medications are categorized based on "pharmacological activity and mechanism of action" (Sadock, Sadock, & Ruiz, 2017, p. viii). For example, some antidepressants are prescribed for anxiety disorders, and some antianxiety medications are used to treat depression and bipolar disorder. A thorough discussion of types of medications with examples is well beyond the purview of this text; therefore, only a few will be mentioned here.

Once the domain of psychiatrists, psychotropic medications are now readily obtained from primary care physicians and even pediatricians. With much greater availability comes the concern that primary care physicians may not have the necessary knowledge, training, or experience to prescribe medications for mental disorders. For children, careful monitoring of the types and dosages of medication is of critical importance (Huefner et al., 2017).

Antidepressants

Antidepressants can help address symptoms of sadness, fatigue, difficulty concentrating, and inability to function. Typically, antidepressants are not physically addictive. Yet, because there are so many from which a provider can choose, it can take time and patience to determine which is the most helpful. It remains unclear why some people respond better to one antidepressant than to another, and patients often need to take a specific medication for at least 4 to 6 weeks to determine if it is helpful.

Older medications, such as the monoamine oxidase inhibitors (MAOIs) and tricyclic antidepressants (TCAs) developed in the 1950s, were the first approved medications for the treatment of depression (Hillhouse & Porter, 2015). Their side effects include weight gain, diarrhea, insomnia, and sexual dysfunction (National Institute of Mental Health, 2016; Sadock et al., 2017). MAOIs can still be useful and may work best for some individuals who do not have a good response to the newer antidepressants.

Selective serotonin reuptake inhibitors (SSRIs) were developed in the 1960s in response to the view that serotonin played an important role in depression (Hillhouse & Porter, 2015). Fluoxetine (Prozac), the first SSRI to become available in the United States, received much media attention and support from clinicians, who saw dramatic improvements from depression in their patients (Whitaker, 2005). SSRIs had fewer side effects and reduced complaints of dry mouth and constipation (Sadock et al., 2017). In addition to fluoxetine, other SSRIs that are readily recognizable by name are paroxetine (Paxil), citalopram (Celexa), sertraline (Zoloft), and escitalopram (Lexapro). Overall, these SSRIs are considered equal in the treatment of depression, but some treat additional disorders such as panic disorder and social anxiety disorder, which can accompany depression (Sadock et al., 2017).

Newer drugs for depression treatment include selective serotonin–norepinephrine reuptake inhibitors (SNRIs), which were developed in the 1990s (Hillhouse & Porter, 2015). Currently four are approved by the FDA: venlafaxine (Effexor), desvenlafaxine succinate (Pristiq), duloxetine (Cymbalta), and levomilnacipran (Fetzima) (Sadock et al., 2017). Overall, while SNRIs may be considered more effective than SSRIs, the differences have been described as "relatively modest" (Hillhouse & Porter, 2015).

It is estimated that between 75% and 80% of antidepressants are prescribed by primary care physicians (Mojtabai & Olfson, 2011; Simon et al., 2014). Of concern is that antidepressants can be prescribed with no mental health diagnosis documented in the patient's medical record. This occurs more often with primary care doctors than with psychiatrists.

In a large study to evaluate the effectiveness of antidepressants, patients with major depression treated at 41 clinical sites were followed for a period of 7 years (National Institute of Mental Health, 2006). The treatment plan consisted of a maximum of four levels or steps, if needed. Specifically, depressed patients were given the opportunity, if they did not respond to a low level of medication, to continue on to more intensive medication interventions. In Level 1, all were initially prescribed citalopram (Celexa) for 12 to 14 weeks. Those who did not have a good response (they did not get substantial relief and/or experienced unpleasant side effects) had the opportunity to move to Level 2. These participants could switch to another antidepressant or add another medication to the Celexa. Level 3 participants were those who did not get relief in Level 2 and were switched to a different medication or assigned additional medications. Participants in Level 4 were those who had treatment-resistant depression and were switched to other medications (National Institute of Mental Health, 2006). This study yielded many important results, only a few of which are described here. Approximately half of the participants achieved good success in relieving depression and were symptom free by Level 2. By the completion of the study, and over the course of the four levels, approximately 70% of the participants became symptom free.

This important work illustrates that it can take considerable time and effort to find the appropriate medication and appropriate dosage to treat depression (National Institute of Mental Health, 2006). It is important for individuals with depression to understand that the process of getting relief may take months or longer. While it can be difficult to remain hopeful, it is important to continue the quest. Unfortunately, it may also be the case that antidepressants do not work or may cause more problems for the individual if the person has been misdiagnosed. For example, someone who has bipolar disorder and is treated with antidepressants may experience more symptoms of mental illness (Aiken, 2017).

Antidepressants and Suicide

With almost all medications, there are side effects, and those that can accompany antidepressant use can be extremely serious. Concerns about a possible relationship between antidepressant medication and suicide came to the forefront in 1990 (Gibbons & Mann, 2014). However, FDA hearings conducted in 1991 failed to produce evidence confirming this relationship. After a meta-analysis, in 2004 the FDA issued a "black box" warning for use of antidepressants in those persons younger than age 18. Another meta-analysis in 2006 resulted in the FDA extending the "black box" warning to those persons ages 18 through 24 (Gibbons &

Mann, 2014). Newer antidepressants developed in the early 2000s pose less risk of suicide than do the older antidepressants (Simon, Savarino, Operskalski, & Wang, 2006).

Paxil

Paxil, an SSRI, is associated with a significant risk of suicide for individuals older than the age of 25 (Silverman, 2017). The FDA did eventually require a warning label on Paxil for children and young adults. Unfortunately, no warning is required by the FDA for those older than the age of 25. In Chicago, a federal jury determined that such a warning on the package of the generic medication could have prevented the suicide of a 57-year-old man. The former FDA chief, Dr. David Kessler, agreed.

In 2006, GlaxoSmithKline, the maker of Paxil, offered to place the warning on the label for adults older than 25. However, the FDA preferred a warning limited to children and emerging adults for all drugs classified as SSRIs. The FDA recommended a supplemental warning and a review of the situation, but this did not occur. The man who took his life in Chicago had been taking a generic version of Paxil made by the company Mylan. Glaxo was part of the lawsuit because Mylan had to use the Glaxo label—companies that make generics are not allowed by the FDA to change the labeling unless the change is made to the brand-name drug. It is relatively rare for courts to hold the makers of brand-name drugs responsible for problems associated with taking the generic. However, in this case, the court found Glaxo at fault and the company was ordered to pay $3 million to the man's widow (Silverman, 2017).

There is a mixed picture about the effectiveness of antidepressants. In reality, antidepressants are not as effective as some people believe (Smith, 2012). A meta-analysis of studies on antidepressant use found SSRIs were not more effective than placebo (Moncrieff & Kirsch, 2005). They were not more effective in more severely depressed patients, nor were they shown to reduce suicides. A meta-analysis of clinical trials submitted to the FDA for four antidepressants found that the medications were not necessarily better than giving patients a placebo and that there was only a small benefit for those most severely depressed (Kirsch et al., 2008).

Recently ketamine has been heralded as a drug that can help those who do not respond to antidepressant medication (Oaklander, 2017). Long known as a "club drug," Special-K, that causes hallucinations, ketamine is now being prescribed for depression. In a study of mice, ketamine blocked the stress that often underlies depression. This use is now being expanded to the treatment of humans (Brachman et al., 2016; Itkowitz, 2017). Ketamine eases depression quickly, unlike antidepressants that can take many weeks to show results, and is the only psychedelic drug that is legally available in the United States (Oaklander, 2017). While not FDA approved for depression, it is approved as an anesthetic, so doctors are able to prescribe it for other conditions they believe will respond to the drug. Janssen (part of Johnson & Johnson) has developed a version called esketamine that can be administered through the nose. Sanacora et al. (2017) found research on ketamine used to treat depression typically has small participant sample sizes and has limited information on safety, and there is no long-term research on the effects. Thus, at this time, there is limited information on ketamine use upon which to develop evidence-based practices. However, that has not stopped the spread of clinics across the country offering ketamine at costs of between $350 and $1,000 per infusion (Thielking, 2018). Some clinics are clearly focused only on profits, do not employ psychiatrists, and do not even require that patients have a current mental health provider.

Antianxiety Medications

Antianxiety medications, also known as anxiolytics, are used to treat generalized anxiety disorder and panic disorder. They can reduce feelings of agitation and help with insomnia. Benzodiazepines are generally effective in the treatment of anxiety disorders in 70% to 75% of patients (Sadock et al., 2017). The first antianxiety medication was chlordiazepoxide (Librium), which was introduced in 1959; it was followed by diazepam (Valium) in 1963. Individuals typically take these drugs as needed rather than taking them consistently. Buspirone is typically effective for 60% to 80% of patients, although there is evidence that if individuals do not achieve a positive response to benzodiazepines, they are not likely to respond to buspirone. Antianxiety medications are also utilized with patients who have co-occurring disorders such as anxiety and another psychiatric disorder (Sadock et al., 2017).

Mood Stabilizers

Mood-stabilizing drugs are typically used to treat bipolar disorder, which is characterized by extreme shifts in mood from mania to depression. Lithium was the first medication to be developed in 1950 for the treatment of what was then called "manic-depressive" disorder and was for many years the only FDA-approved treatment (Sadock et al., 2017). Lamotrigine (Lamictal) was developed in the mid-1990s to treat epileptic seizures but in the early 2000s became a treatment for bipolar disorder; it can lengthen the time between episodes of mania and depression. Another medication for bipolar is divalproex sodium (Depakote), which is also used to treat seizure disorders and prevent migraine headaches.

Individuals with bipolar disorder are often expected by their prescribers to remain on their mood-stabilizing medications for the long term.

Antipsychotic Medications

Antipsychotic medications are typically used to treat psychotic disorders such as schizophrenia and are also used to treat bipolar disorder. Olanzapine (Zyprexa), risperidone (Risperdal), aripiprazole (Abilify), and quetiapine (Seroquel) are prescribed for schizophrenia and bipolar disorder, and patients can expect to be maintained on such medications over the long term (Sadock et al., 2017).

Antipsychotic medications for persons with schizophrenia show effectiveness in early treatment, but recent evidence regarding the longer-term effects of antipsychotics is concerning (Littrell, 2014). Wunderink, Nieboer, Wiersma, Sytema, and Nienhus (2013) found that at the 7-year follow-up mark, 40.4% of patients who were off medication were functioning well, had good relationships with others, and were able to work. Only 17.6% of those who were maintained on medication were functioning well (Wunderink et al., 2013). Another study followed schizophrenic patients over a 20-year period and found that 87% of those not on medication were doing well (as measured by IQ tests and evaluation of abstract reasoning abilities) as compared to 17% of those on medication (Harrow, Jobe, & Faull, 2012). That antipsychotic medication can make patients worse over the long term is a very serious problem confronting the mental health system today. More longitudinal research is essential to determine the best treatments for schizophrenic patients over a long period of time (Harrow & Jobe, 2013).

In November 2013, Janssen Pharmaceuticals consented to pay $2.2 billion for deceptive marketing of Risperdal and other drugs. The U.S. Department of Justice showed that antipsychotics had not been proven safe and that Janssen was not truthful about side effects and was paying physicians to both prescribe and promote these drugs (Consumer Reports, 2013). All of this speaks to the importance of evidence-based practices to ensure the safety of patients taking psychotropic medications.

▓ PSYCHOTROPIC MEDICATIONS AND CHILDREN

According to a national survey, prescriptions of psychiatric medications to 2- to 5-year-olds reached their highest number between 2002 and 2005, but then leveled off between 2006 and 2009 (Cincinnati Children's Hospital Medical Center, 2013). Overall, there was a decline in medication use—from 43% of children who had a behavioral/mental health diagnosis in the period 1994 to 1997, down to 29% in 2006 to 2009

(Chirdkiatgumchai et al., 2013). Stimulants were the most heavily prescribed, typically for the treatment of attention deficit hyperactivity disorder (ADHD). The FDA warnings in the 2000s can account for some of
the reductions in prescriptions. The national survey also found disparities in psychotropic medication use, such that white children, boys, and
children who did not have private health insurance were more likely to
be prescribed psychotropic medications. Chirdkiatgumchai et al. (2013)
concluded their report with a call for further research to examine the
reasons for these disparities and to find ways to ensure that pediatricians and others treating very young children utilize the most current
diagnostic and clinical practice guidelines.

There is concern that antipsychotics are overprescribed to children,
especially since the long-term effects remain unknown (Consumer
Reports, 2013). Side effects can include weight gain, high cholesterol,
and type 2 diabetes. A professor from Tufts University Medical School
stated, "What's not known about the long-term effects is very troubling.
The younger you go, the more you can affect the developing brain"
(Consumer Reports, 2013, p. 1). The American Psychiatric Association
(2010) guidelines state that antipsychotic medications should not be
prescribed unless the child has schizophrenia or a severe tic disorder, or
unless other treatments have not been helpful.

One example of controversial use of antipsychotic medication
involved a 5-month-old boy who began to have seizures. By the age of 18
months, he was prescribed Risperdal, an antipsychotic medication, after
medication for epilepsy failed to control his behavior (Schwarz, 2015).
He behaved aggressively, pushed other children, and broke toys. After 4
months, his mother stopped giving him Risperdal, stating, "Everything
became worse" (Schwarz, 2015, p. 5). Is this an example of inappropriate
prescribing of psychotropic medication to young children?

Children and adolescents with mental health issues and behavioral
problems are likely to be treated with psychotropic medications. Children in the foster care system have less access to mental health services
than other children but can be prescribed these medications with little
oversight (Mignon, 2017a; Ruff, Aguilar, & Clausen, 2016). In a sample
of youth admitted to residential treatment for mental health problems,
44% were taking multiple (an average of 3.2) psychotropic medications
(Huefner et al., 2017). In addition to concerns over the impact of psychotropic medications on brain development, there is concern for the
mixing of these drugs, despite the lack of research evidence to support
these practices. These prescribing practices for children should be monitored and evaluated (Huefner et al., 2017). See Case Example 6.1 for
an example of inappropriate prescribing of psychotropic medication to
children and youth.

CASE EXAMPLE 6.1

THE STORY OF ROCHELLE: FROM AN ABUSIVE CHILDHOOD AND THE FOSTER SYSTEM TO A MASTER'S DEGREE IN SOCIAL WORK

Rochelle is a young woman who endured years of physical and sexual abuse as a child. She made a suicide attempt at the age of 13. She described feeling relief when child protection social workers removed her from her home in Los Angeles. But in foster care Rochelle experienced many placements and was diagnosed with a range of mental illnesses, including bipolar disorder, schizoaffective disorder, posttraumatic stress disorder, major depression, generalized anxiety, and bulimia. She said, "They attach all these labels to you in foster care, but the bottom line is I come from a home where physical and sexual abuse were my daily norm, where I lived in fear every day, where I felt responsible to protect my younger sister from the abuse."

Rochelle then became too old for foster care and lived on the streets until she was invited to live with a friend's family. At that time she was on 10 different prescribed medications. With the help of a therapist, Rochelle realized that not only had she been deprived of a loving and safe family home, but the foster care system had clearly exacerbated her problems. Rochelle's therapist said she was "horribly diagnosed." Regarding the prescribed medications, the therapist stated, "My professional answer is I think that was overboard. My personal answer is: Big Pharma and Wall Street. There's big money in keeping these kids drugged, and I think it's a travesty." By 2014, Rochelle was off all psychotropic medication, enrolled in an MSW program, and working with troubled children.

SOURCE: de Sa, K. (2014, August 24). Drugging our kids: Children in California's foster care system are prescribed unproven, risky medications at alarming rates. *The Mercury News*. Retrieved from http://extras.mercurynews.com/druggedkids

Some experts think that the lack of child psychiatrists may be a factor in pediatricians prescribing psychotropic medications (Schwarz, 2015). One physician who directs a program to train health providers to work with families with children who have behavioral problems had this to say: "There are behavioral ways of working with the problems rather than medication. What is generating such fear and anger and withdrawal in the child? What is frustrating or causing stress in the parent? These are the things that have to be explored. But that takes time and money" (Schwarz, 2015, p. 5). Thus, it is simpler to medicate a child's symptoms than to deal with the underlying issues.

To ensure the appropriate use of antipsychotic medications for children and adolescents, Consumer Reports (2013) recommends a thorough medical checkup as the starting point, followed by the development of a treatment plan. This can include a neurological evaluation and assessment of whether the child has sustained head trauma. For those who are taking antipsychotic medication, it should be started at a very low dose and gradually increased, if needed. Most importantly, the child must be monitored closely, especially for side effects and to see if medication can be tapered off and stopped after 6 to 9 months. At any point in the process, a second medical opinion can be helpful (Consumer Reports, 2013). Parents who are satisfied with their children's experiences on psychotropic medications tend to feel well informed about the medications and the side effects (Hacker et al., 2011).

These recommendations for children and adolescents should apply to adults as well. It is important to remember that medication treatment can and should be used along with some form of psychotherapy. See Case Example 6.2 for a description of an innovative program for patients and families struggling with psychotic disorders.

CASE EXAMPLE 6.2

OPEN DIALOGUE: PSYCHOTHERAPY EMPHASIZING OPEN COMMUNICATION BETWEEN STAFF AND PATIENTS

Open Dialogue is a patient-centered form of psychotherapy for individuals with psychotic disorders, based upon a program that was developed in Finland by psychologist Jaakko Seikkula in the 1990s. Dr. Seikkula partnered with social worker and family therapist Dr. Mary Olson to create the Open Dialogue Institute in 2002. Its focus is on respectful treatment to cultivate strong communication between staff and patients and offer assistance according to patient and family preferences (Rosen & Stoklosa, 2016). Clear and open communication is essential, and medical discussions among physicians and therapists should include both the patient and family. The idea is to create a space where professionals can share and reflect upon their own views and inner dialogue. The program can be utilized with those persons on psychotropic medications as well as those not on medications.

The Open Dialogue program is being used in the inpatient unit at McLean Hospital for those individuals with schizophrenia and bipolar disorder. McLean is a top-rated psychiatric hospital in Belmont, Massachusetts, where staff has implemented new practices without additional financial costs or increased staff time. Anecdotal evidence showed that patients appreciated that professionals who discussed their illness and care in their presence fostered a trusting relationship. Psychiatrists, social workers, and nurses found that the Open Dialogue approach restructured their schedules and duties to become more efficient, reduced the number of involuntary admissions to voluntary admissions, and reduced the need to use physical restraints (Rosen & Stoklosa, 2016).

The Institute for Dialogic Practice offers trainings to professionals in the United States as well as clinical services to individuals and families in its New York office. Treatment focusing on the whole person can be utilized in family and group therapy as well (Institute for Dialogic Practice, 2018).

SOURCES: Institute for Dialogic Practice. (2018). Retrieved from http://www .dialogicpractice.net; Rosen, K., & Stoklosa, J. (2016). Finland in Boston? Applying open dialogue ideals on a psychotic disorders inpatient teaching unit. *Psychiatric Services, 67*(12), 1283–1285. doi:10.1176/appi.ps.201600340

WHO SHOULD PRESCRIBE PSYCHOTROPIC MEDICATIONS?

For many years, primary care physicians have been the principal prescribers of psychotropic medications. A national survey published in 1988 found that primary care physicians prescribed greater numbers of psychotropic medications than psychiatrists in every class of medications except for lithium (for bipolar disorder) (Beardsley, Gardocki, Larson, & Hidalgo, 1988). Primary care physicians prescribed antianxiety medications most often, while psychiatrists were more likely to prescribe antidepressants. In addition, psychiatrists were more likely to determine and record a mental health diagnosis than were primary care physicians (Beardsley et al., 1988).

In a survey of 539 patients seen in primary care offices who were screened for anxiety disorders, 47.3% who screened positive were not being treated for this condition (Weisberg, Dyck, Culpepper, & Keller, 2007). Of those being treated with medication, 41% obtained prescriptions from their primary care doctors and 40.2% from a psychiatrist; the remaining patients had prescriptions from a specialist or took another family member's medication.

Access to psychiatrists is a huge problem. Primary care physicians can be gatekeepers to psychiatrists through a complex system of requiring referrals from the primary care provider (Weisberg et al., 2007). The insufficient number of psychiatrists has important consequences. Some have said the lack of a sufficient number of psychiatrists is the most serious in all medical specialties (Levine, 2018). Merrit Hawkins (2017), a physician recruitment company, found that psychiatry is the second most sought-after medical specialty. The shortage of psychiatrists is especially felt in rural areas (Consumer Reports, 2013).

The prescribing of psychotropic medications by primary care physicians extends to pediatricians as well. Recently, more pediatricians have been prescribing antipsychotics to children, with a 25% increase in prescriptions occurring between 2006 and 2013 (Consumer Reports, 2013). Parents of children and adolescents with less severe mental health problems may seek care from primary care doctors—families can see this as a way to avoid stigma and perhaps the financial costs of seeing a psychiatrist. If primary care physicians are going to prescribe, they should be able to make accurate diagnoses and also be trained in psychopharmacology (Patel et al., 2006).

Psychiatric nurse practitioners can be very helpful in filling the void in psychiatric care. Nurse practitioner prescribers are regulated through state laws that vary regarding the prescribing role of nurses. In some states, there must be physician involvement and oversight; in other states, nurse practitioners can practice independently in diagnosing mental disorders and prescribing psychotropic medications (American Medical Association, 2017). In a review of 23 studies, Van Ruth, Mistiaen, and Francke (2007) found that the overall quality of care and general prescribing practices provided by nurses were similar to or better than the care provided by physicians. Patients were just as satisfied with care by nurses as with care by doctors in general medical practice. Little research is available on the effects of nurse practitioners treating psychiatric patients, but initial findings are positive. One recent study found psychiatric nurse practitioners made important contributions to the treatment of mental health patients taking medications, especially in public mental health services (Chapman, Phoenix, Hahn, & Strod, 2018). Another recent study found that psychiatric nurse practitioners prescribing psychotropic medications helped to promote patient self-reports of positive mental health and reduced suicide (Alexander & Schnell, 2018). Obstacles to expanding the use of psychiatric nurse practitioners in mental health include bureaucratic issues, lack of formal job descriptions, lack of clarity about appropriate boundaries and supervision, and recruitment and retention of nurses (Chapman et al., 2018). Overall, expanding nurse practitioner services to underserved populations can be beneficial.

OLDER ADULTS, NURSING HOMES, AND PSYCHOTROPIC MEDICATIONS

Antidepressants are the psychotropic medications most often prescribed to older adults (Mignon, 2017b). Cognitive decline and co-occurring disorders can make antidepressants less effective in this age group, and typically a lower dose should be tried initially (Frank, 2014; Tedeschini et al., 2011).

While older adults are more vulnerable to the side effects of psychotropic medications, these drugs continue to be used in nursing homes to manage troublesome patient behaviors (Lindsey, 2009). A survey of general practitioner physicians found psychotropic mediations were given to nursing home patients to cope with a lack of adequate nursing and other staff and were used as a substitute for behavioral interventions with patients with dementia (Cousins, Bereznicki, Cooling, & Peterson, 2017). Thus psychotropic drugs can be used to compensate for inadequate staffing within nursing homes.

See Case Example 6.3 for a description of an elderly man who died as a result of taking psychotropic medications.

CASE EXAMPLE 6.3

BOBBY GLENN TWEED: THE CASE OF AN ELDERLY MAN WHO DIED IN A NURSING HOME

Bobby Glenn Tweed was 78 years old when he was admitted to a nursing home in Tennessee in January 2013. With a diagnosis of Alzheimer's disease, Mr. Tweed was administered Depakote, Seroquel, and Geodon, all powerful psychotropic medications, without the permission of his family. He was dead by the middle of November.

In January 2014, Mr. Tweed's only daughter, Robin Tweed Keller, sued the Life Care Center of Greeneville nursing home and several physicians. The lawsuit alleged that the medications prescribed for Mr. Tweed were inappropriate and associated with a greater likelihood of death in elderly patients. The suit alleged that these drugs were administered to make Mr. Tweed "a more docile, compliant and passive patient" (Warren, 2015). Mr. Tweed's family settled a wrongful death suit with the nursing home in 2017, the terms of which are confidential.

SOURCES: American Association of Retired Persons. (2017, April 10). *Deadly drugs misused in US nursing facilities.* Retrieved from https://www.aarp.org/health/drugs-supplements/info-2017/wrongful-death-lawsuit-nursing-home-fd.html; Warren, L. (2015, January 16). Life Care of Greeneville named in wrongful death lawsuit. *The Greeneville Sun.* Retrieved from https://www.greenevillesun.com/news/local_news/life-care-of-greeneville-named-in-wrongful-death-lawsuit/article_97f1bacb-8675-5b1f-bf0c-a1808446269f.html

Psychiatric medications can be extremely powerful, and therefore it is critical for patients and their families to have a solid understanding of the reasons they are taking them, the potential benefits, and the side effects. While some individuals have an excellent response to medications, especially in the short term, much remains to be learned about the long-term effects. Some who oppose psychiatric drugs trace the increase in mental illness over the years to the beginning of the use of these drugs in the mid-1950s. For example, Whitaker (2005) stated that since 1955, "there has been an astonishing rise in the incidence of severe mental illness" (p. 23) in the United States. Whitaker concluded, "Psychiatric drugs perturb normal neurotransmitter function, and while that perturbation may curb symptoms over a short term, over the long run it increases the likelihood that a person will become chronically ill, or ill with new and more severe symptoms" (p. 33). It is important to remember that a variety of readily available and additional tools such as different forms of exercise, diet, and alternative treatments can have a positive impact on symptoms of psychiatric disorders.

SOCIAL WORKERS AND MEDICATION

Social workers cannot prescribe any kind of medication to their clients. This is outside the scope of social work practice, and that situation is not expected to change in the foreseeable future. The prescribing of medications is restricted to physicians and some nurses. However, this does not mean that social workers should not be knowledgeable about their clients' medications. Indeed, it is very important that social workers are well informed. Buccino (2006) advocated for psychotherapy as an initial treatment: "Social work's role should not be antimedication, but to actively promote alternatives to medications given their cost, risk of adverse events in children and adults, and marginal effectiveness" (pp. 188–189).

Since the 1960s, social workers have been encouraged to learn about medications prescribed for their clients (Bentley, Walsh, & Farmer, 2005). While social workers do not typically advocate for specific medications, some experts argue that social workers should play a role in medication discussions with their clients. Further, social work education should provide curricula specifically on psychopharmacology (Bentley et al., 2005). In the 1980s, it was argued that antipsychotic medication should not be the exclusive province of physicians and that social workers had an important role as an "advocate-consultant" (Gerhart & Brooks, 1983, p. 458). Certainly this is a reminder that "on an ongoing basis, the social worker provides for the overall well-being of the patient" (p. 458). During the 1990s, some experts argued that social workers should address with clients their feelings and concerns about taking medications. In their national survey of 994 social workers, Bentley et al. (2005) found that 96% of the respondents said social workers should discuss their clients' feelings toward taking medication and 75.8% said it is appropriate to help clients in their decision-making by reviewing with them the pros and cons of taking medication.

Attitudes of social workers toward psychotropic medication use in children and adolescents are correlated with professional background and experience. The training and theoretical background of social workers, the setting in which treatment is provided, and the type and severity of the behavior of clients are important factors (Moses & Kirk, 2006). In a national survey of 563 social workers, 52.4% of the respondents agreed that medication should be used as a last resort, rather than as an initial intervention; moreover, if needed, such medication should be used in conjunction with psychotherapy (Moses & Kirk, 2006). Social workers who were more likely to be supportive of medication use were men in direct clinical practice, often in school settings, with experience working with medicated youth. This group of social workers considered themselves more knowledgeable about psychotropic medications than did other social workers. Older social workers, who had not dealt with medication use during their education and training, were more concerned about the potential harm of medications to children and adolescents (Moses & Kirk, 2006).

Bentley et al. (2005) found some social work respondents requested more policies and guidelines on addressing medications with clients, the ethical and legal issues involved, and when it is appropriate to refer clients for a medication evaluation. This would entail developing stronger relationships between social workers and prescribers. Social workers can help clients prepare for medical appointments by developing a list of questions for physician and nurse practitioner prescribers. And in the process, clients can become stronger self-advocates (Bentley et al., 2005). See Tips for the Field 6.1 for recommendations for social workers to assist clients with medication issues.

TIPS FOR THE FIELD 6.1

DIGGING DEEPER INTO PSYCHOTROPIC MEDICATIONS: WHAT SOCIAL WORKERS CAN DO TO ASSIST CLIENTS REGARDING THEIR MEDICATIONS

1. Social workers must keep abreast of research developments on psychotropic medications. This can be achieved by attending professional conferences and earning continuing education units (CEUs) required to maintain a state social work license.

2. Develop professional relationships and stronger collaborations with psychiatrists, primary care physicians, and nurse prescribers.

3. Review the client's medical record, if available. Be knowledgeable regarding all psychotropic drugs clients have taken in the past and their perspectives on how they responded to those medications.

4. Keep a current list of all medications that the client is taking in the social work record.

5. Be mindful of the fact that knowing the correct medication dosage is as important as knowing the medication.

6. Acquire knowledge of potential side effects of medications and alert medication prescribers when a client experiences side effects.

7. Record the client's answers to questions about symptoms and responses to specific medications to create a record over a period of time and establish any patterns.

8. Social workers in nursing homes can help to monitor patient behavior and the use of psychotropic medications.

NEUROMODULATION: BRAIN STIMULATION TECHNIQUES

Brain stimulation techniques began to be developed in the 1950s and 1960s. Robert Heath of Tulane University was one psychiatrist whose controversial work consisted of placing electrodes in the brains of schizophrenic patients and using electrical stimulation (Frank, 2018). Heath, considered a pioneer in biological psychiatry, believed that defects in the brain were the cause of mental illness. Although he was heralded by some as an important innovator in the treatment of mental illness, others thought his work was quackery and inappropriate because he failed to design controlled studies to evaluate the effectiveness of his work (Frank, 2018). This work was a precursor to what today are known as neuromodulation techniques.

Electroconvulsive Therapy

ECT, described in Chapter 2, A Short History of Mental Health Policy and Treatment in the United States, and also known as shock treatment, has a long history that includes negative views by the public. Today ECT is considered a very effective treatment for chronic depression and is offered at some of the most prestigious institutions for the treatment of physical and mental illness, such as the Mayo Clinic (in Minnesota, Florida, and Arizona) and McLean Hospital (Massachusetts). Research shows that ECT can help patients who have not responded to psychotropic medications and is considered "the fastest and most effective available therapy" (Sadock et al., 2017, p. 659). Side effects include headaches, nausea, dry mouth, fatigue, and short-term memory loss (Kerner

& Prudic, 2014). ECT has been recommended specifically for patients with schizophrenia who have not had success with antipsychotic medications (Dokucu, 2015). It is also considered the most effective treatment with the shortest response time for older adults who have depression or bipolar disorder (Kerner & Prudic, 2014).

Magnetic seizure therapy (MST), which is similar to ECT, is a therapy that induces seizures but is designed to use a more localized current of electricity than can be achieved with ECT (Kerner & Prudic, 2014; Sadock et al., 2017). As with ECT, MST is given while the patient is under anesthesia along with a muscle relaxant. A recent small study found MST to be effective in patients with treatment-resistant schizophrenia (Tang et al., 2018). MST is in the early stages of clinical trials, and much more needs to be known about this therapy, including the determination of eligible patients, proper positioning of the coils, and proper electrical current dosage (Sadock et al., 2017).

Transcranial magnetic stimulation (TMS) was approved by the FDA in 2008 specifically for those individuals with major depressive disorder who did not achieve relief after taking at least one antidepressant (Oaklander, 2017). It is typically an outpatient procedure. A magnetic coil is held against the scalp to stimulate nerve cells, and patients remain awake during the procedure. Few side effects are reported, although some individuals may experience minor skin irritation or headache (Sadock et al., 2017). On average, 36 treatments are administered over a period of 4 to 6 weeks.

While still in the early stages of clinical research, TMS has been shown to be effective in reducing cravings for alcohol in persons with alcohol dependence (Mishra, Nizamie, Das, & Praharaj, 2010). It has also shown promise in treating schizophrenia that is resistant to medication (Dokucu, 2015). In a very small study of TMS in 10 veterans with both major depression and posttraumatic stress disorder, improvement was noted in both disorders (Philip, Ridout, Albright, Sanchez, & Carpenter, 2016). A review of clinical trials concluded that TMS seems to work best for individuals with depression of less than 3 years' duration, who were unsuccessful with taking between one and four different antidepressants, and who do not have psychoses (Janicak & Dokucu, 2015). There are likely to be considerably more research studies conducted, and published, on the effectiveness of TMS.

Social workers can play an active role in clinics and hospitals that offer neuromodulation treatments. They can help with the screening process to determine whether prospective clients have diagnoses that are likely to be improved by neuromodulation. For example, in some clinics, clients receive the diagnosis of major depressive disorder to qualify for insurance coverage for the treatment when, in fact, they do not have major depressive disorder. Social workers can help reduce the likelihood that clients are inappropriately treated with neuromodulation techniques when the treatment is not indicated for their specific diagnosis. Of course, social workers also provide short-term support for clients as well as referrals for various community resources.

■ PHARMACEUTICAL COMPANIES: PILLS AND PROFITS

The significant profits of pharmaceutical companies, and the rising costs to insurers and consumers, have opened up drug companies to greater scrutiny in recent years (Huskamp, 2006). Marketing strategies of the drug industry aimed at physicians and the public through direct advertising have been very fruitful, if at times unethical (Smith, 2012; Whitaker, 2010/2015). From 1996 to 2005, the drug industry tripled its spending on marketing, including a fivefold increase in direct-to-consumer advertising (Smith, 2012). Pharmaceutical companies justify the high prices charged for their products by claiming they provide the funds for research and development of the medications. Consumer advocates want to see both prices and profits controlled to ensure that medications are available at affordable prices (Huskamp, 2006).

Recent evidence points to a reduction in drug industry profits. Some supposedly "new drugs" are basically variations of existing drugs. Given the considerable time and financial investment needed to develop new psychiatric drugs, large companies such as Novartis, AstraZeneca, and GlaxoSmithKline have reduced their efforts to develop psychotropic medications (Sanders, 2013). Less expensive versions of some drugs known as generics can be sold by other companies after a period of years has elapsed for the developing drug company; this has cut into big pharmaceutical companies' profits. One psychiatrist involved in developing psychiatric medications acknowledged "not a single drug designed to treat psychiatric illness in a novel way has reached patients in more than 30 years" (Sanders, 2013, p. 27). See Robert Whitaker's *Anatomy of an Epidemic: Magic Bullets, Psychiatric Drugs, and the Astonishing Rise of Mental Illness in America* (2010/2015) for a fuller description of how drug companies manipulate information about their drugs and entice physicians to prescribe them.

■ SUMMARY AND CONCLUSION

It is essential that social workers and psychiatrists cooperate in providing mental healthcare. With an abundance of mental health diagnoses and many medications to treat them, it is often challenging to accurately diagnose patients and find medications that will be helpful. This puts pressure on patients and families to monitor and figure out whether the medications are useful. Social workers play an important role in assisting clients and families to become knowledgeable about psychotropic medications so that they can make more informed decisions about taking these drugs. The prescribing of psychotropic medications to children and adolescents, especially as it concerns social work involvement, is a critically important issue.

Neuromodulation techniques for psychiatric illness such as ECT, MST, and TMS offer significant opportunities for social workers to screen, assess, and monitor the progress of patients receiving these treatments. Older adults in nursing homes are likely to be administered psychotropic medications to control their behavior as a way to cope with inadequate staffing. Lastly, steps must be taken to make pharmaceutical companies accountable for ensuring transparency about their products, and those products' side effects, as well as to rein in costs.

DISCUSSION QUESTIONS/TOPICS

1. Describe the relationship between psychiatry and social work.
2. Discuss the variety of ways that individuals can access psychotropic medications.
3. Discuss the relationship between antidepressants and suicide.
4. Do you think psychotropic medications should be prescribed to children younger than the age of 5? Why or why not?
5. How do the prescribing patterns of physicians reflect the interests of pharmaceutical companies?
6. Discuss how social workers can help ensure their clients are on the proper medications and taking the appropriate dosages.
7. Discuss the Open Dialogue approach to the treatment of patients with psychoses.
8. Discuss the reasons that psychotropic medications are prescribed to older adults living in nursing homes.
9. How can nursing homes better manage patients who have behavioral problems?
10. What are your own ideas for making pharmaceutical companies more accountable when they do not disclose the truth about side effects and efficacy of their medications?

REFERENCES

Aiken, C. (2017, November). Who gets worse on an antidepressant? Six patients to watch for. *Psychiatric Times*. Retrieved from http://images.ubmmedica.com/psychiatrictimes/pdfs//2017/PT_PDF_Aiken_Bipolar_Nov2017.pdf

Alexander, D., & Schnell, M. (2018, July 3, revised). *Just what the nurse practitioner ordered: Independent prescriptive authority and population mental health*. Chicago, IL: Federal Reserve Bank of Chicago.

American Medical Association. (2017). State law chart: Nurse practitioner prescriptive authority. *Advocacy Resource Center*. Retrieved from https://www.ama-assn.org/sites/ama-assn.org/files/corp/media-browser/specialty%20group/arc/ama-chart-np-prescriptive-authority.pdf

American Psychiatric Association. (2010). *Practice guideline for the treatment of schizophrenia* (2nd ed.). Retrieved from https://psychiatryonline.org/pb/assets/raw/sitewide/practice_guidelines/guidelines/schizophrenia.pdf

Azam, M., Qureshi, M., & Kinnair, D. (2016). *Psychiatry: A clinical handbook*. Banbury, UK: Scion Publishing.

Beardsley, R. S., Gardocki, G. J., Larson, D. B., & Hidalgo, J. (1988). Prescribing of psychotropic medication by primary care physicians and psychiatrists. *Archives of General Psychiatry, 45*(12), 1117–1119. doi:10.1001/archpsyc.1988.01800360065009

Bentley, K. J., Walsh, J., & Farmer, R. L. (2005). Social work roles and activities regarding psychiatric medication: Results of a national survey. *Social Work, 50*(4), 295–303.

Brachman, R. A., McGowan, J. D., Perusini, J. N., Lim, S. C., Pham, T. H., Faye, C., … Denny, C. A. (2016). Ketamine as a prophylactic against stress-induced depressive-like behavior. *Biological Psychiatry, 79*(9), 776–786. doi:10.1016/j.biopsych.2015.04.022

Buccino, D. L. (2006). Social work's role in psychiatric medication. *Social Work, 51*(2), 188–189.

Chapman, S. A., Phoenix, B. J., Hahn, T. E., & Strod, D. D. (2018). Utilization and economic contribution of psychiatric mental health nurse practitioners in public behavioral health services. *American Journal of Preventive Medicine, 54*(6, suppl 3), S243–S249. doi:10.1016/j.amepre.2018.01.045

Chirdkiatgumchai, V., Xiao, H., Fedstrom, B. K., Adams, R. E., Epstein, J. N., Shah, S. S., … Froehlich, T. E. (2013). National trends in psychotropic medication use in young children: 1994–2009. *Pediatrics, 132*(4), 615–623. doi:10.1542/peds.2013-1546

Cincinnati Children's Hospital Medical Center. (2013, September). Psychotropic medication use in young children leveling off. *Science Daily, 30*. Retrieved from https://www.sciencedaily.com/releases/2013/09/130930093851.htm

Consumer Reports. (2013, December). *Are too many kids taking antipsychotics?* Retrieved from https://www.consumerreports.org/cro/2013/12/are-too-many-kids-taking-antipsychotic-drugs/index.htm

Cousins, J. M., Bereznicki, L. R. E., Cooling, N. B., & Peterson, G. M. (2017). Prescribing psychotropic medication for nursing home residents with dementia: A general practitioner survey. *Clinical Interventions in Aging, 12*, 1573–1578. doi:10.2147/CIA.S146613

Dokucu, M. E. (2015). Neuromodulation treatments for schizophrenia. *Current Treatment Options in Psychiatry, 2*(3), 339–348. doi:10.1007/s40501-015-005-4

Frank, C. (2014). Pharmacologic treatment of depression in the elderly. *Canadian Family Physician, 60*(2), 121–126.

Frank, L. (2018). *The pleasure shock: The rise of deep brain stimulation and its forgotten inventor*. New York, NY: Dutton.

Gerhart, U. C., & Brooks, A. D. (1983). The social work practitioner and antipsychotic medications. *Social Work, 28*(6), 454–460. doi:10.1093/sw/28.6.454

Gibbons, R. D., & Mann, J. J. (2014, December 31). The relationship between antidepressant initiation and suicide risk. *Psychiatric Times, 31*(12). Retrieved from http://www.psychiatrictimes.com/special-reports/relationship-between-antidepressant-initiation-and-suicide-risk

Hacker, K., Friedman, E., Tendulkar, S. A., Melvin, P., Jerz, M., & Lambert, L. (2011). Using a community participatory research approach to understand satisfaction with psychopharmacology among families of children with psychiatric co-morbidities. *Child & Adolescent Social Work Journal, 28*, 63–78. doi:10.1007/s10560-010-0220-y

Harrow, M., & Jobe, T. H. (2013). Does long-term treatment of schizophrenia with antipsychotic medications facilitate recovery? *Schizophrenia Bulletin, 39*(5), 962–965. doi:10.1093/schbul/sbt034

Harrow, M., Jobe, T. H., & Faull, R. N. (2012). Do all schizophrenia patients need antipsychotic treatment continuously throughout their lifetime? A 20-year longitudinal study. *Psychological Medicine, 42*(10), 2145–2155. doi:10.1017/S0033291712000220

Hillhouse, T. M., & Porter, J. H. (2015). A brief history of the development of antidepressant drugs: From monoamines to glutamate. *Experimental and Clinical Psychopharmacology, 23*(1), 1–21. doi:10.1037/a0038550

Huefner, J. C., Smith, G. L., Ringle, J. L., Stevens, A. L., Mason, W. A., & Parra, G. R. (2017). Patterns of psychotropic medication at admission for youth in residential care. *Journal of Child and Family Studies, 26*, 317–328. doi:10.1007/s10826-016-0548-9

Huskamp, H. A. (2006). Prices, profits, and innovation: Examining criticisms of the value of new psychotropic drugs. *Health Affairs, 25*(3), 635–646. doi:10.1377/hlthaff.25.3.635

Indeed. (2018). *Social worker salaries in the United States*. Retrieved from https://www.indeed.com/salaries/Social-Worker-Salaries

Itkowitz, C. (2017, April 26). Her drug aims to prevent mental illness: Scientist could be on the cusp of a breakthrough. *The Boston Globe*, A6.

Janicak, P. G., & Dokucu, M. E. (2015). Transcranial magnetic stimulation for the treatment of major depression. *Neuropsychiatric Disease and Treatment, 11*, 1549–1560. doi:10.2147/NDT.S67477

Kerner, N., & Prudic, J. (2014). Current electroconvulsive therapy practice and research in the geriatric population. *Neuropsychiatry, 4*(1), 33–54. doi:10.2217/npy.14.3

Kirsch, I., Deacon, B. J., Huedo-Medina, T. B., Scoboria, A., Moore, T. J., & Johnson, B. T. (2008). Initial severity and antidepressant benefits: A meta-analysis of data submitted to the Food and Drug Administration. *PLoS Medicine, 5*(2), e45. doi:10.1371/journal.pmed.0050045

Levine, D. (2018, May 25). What's the answer to the shortage of mental health care providers? *US News & World Report*. Retrieved from https://health.usnews.com/health-care/patient-advice/articles/2018-05-25/whats-the-answer-to-the-shortage-of-mental-health-care-providers

Lindsey, P. L. (2009). Psychotropic medication use among older adults: What all nurses need to know. *Journal of Gerontological Nursing, 35*(9), 28–38. doi:10.3928/00989134-20090731-01

Littrell, J. (2014). Will the treatment protocols for schizophrenia be changing soon? *Social Work in Mental Health, 12*(4), 365–385. doi:10.1080/15332985 .2014.894487

Merrit Hawkins. (2017). *2017 review of physician and advanced practitioner recruiting incentives.* Dallas, TX: Author.

Mignon, S. I. (2017a). *Child welfare in the United States: Challenges, policy, and practice.* New York, NY: Springer Publishing Company.

Mignon, S. I. (2017b). Aging and depression. *Annals of Psychiatry and Mental Health, 5*(5), 1113–1116. Retrieved from https://www.jscimedcentral.com/ Psychiatry/psychiatry-5-1113.pdf

Mishra, B. R., Nizamie, S. H., Das, B., & Praharaj, S. K. (2010). Efficacy of repetitive transcranial magnetic stimulation in alcohol dependence: A sham-controlled study. *Addiction, 105*(1), 49–55. doi:10.1111/.1360 -0443.2009.02777.x

Mojtabai, R., & Olfson, M. (2011). Proportion of antidepressants prescribed without a psychiatric diagnosis is growing. *Health Affairs, 30*, 1434–1442. doi:10.1377/hlthaff.2010.1024

Moncrieff, J., & Kirsch, I. (2005). Efficacy of antidepressants in adults. *British Medical Journal, 331*(7509), 155–157. doi:10.1136/bmj.331.7509.155

Moses, T., & Kirk, S. A. (2006). Social workers' attitudes about psychotropic drug treatment with youths. *Social Work, 51*(3), 211–222.

National Institute of Mental Health. (2006, November). Questions and answers about the NIMH Sequenced Treatment Alternatives to Relieve Depression (STAR*D) study—all medication levels. *National Institute of Mental Health.* Retrieved from https://www.nimh.nih.gov/funding/clinical -research/practical/stard/index.shtml

National Institute of Mental Health. (2016). *Mental health medications.* Retrieved from https://www.nimh.nih.gov/health/topics/mental-health -medications/index.shtml

Oaklander, M. (2017, August 7). The *anti* antidepressant. *Time*, 40–45.

Patel, N. C., Crismon, M. L., Hoagwood, K., Johnsrud, M. T., Rascati, K. L., & Wilson, J. P. (2006). Physician specialty associated with antipsychotic prescribing for youths in the Texas Medicaid program. *Medical Care, 44*(1), 87–106.

Philip, N. S., Ridout, S. J., Albright, S. E., Sanchez, G., & Carpenter, L. L. (2016). 5-Hz transcranial magnetic stimulation for comorbid posttraumatic stress disorder and major depression. *Journal of Traumatic Stress, 29*(1), 93–96. doi:10.1002/jts.22065

Preskorn, S. H. (2008). The development and use of modern psychotherapeutic medications. *Psychiatric Times, 25*(5). Retrieved from http://www.psychiatrictimes.com/schizophrenia/development-and-use -modern-psychotherapeutic-medications

Ruff, S. C., Aguilar, R. M., & Clausen, J. M. (2016). An exploratory study of mental health interventions with infants and young children in foster care. *Journal of Family Social Work, 19*(3), 184–198. doi:10.1080/10522158.2016 .1181128

Sadock, B. J., Sadock, V. A., & Ruiz, P. (2017). *Concise textbook of clinical psychiatry* (4th ed.). Philadelphia, PA: Wolters Kluwer.

Sanacora, G., Frye, M. A., McDonald, W., Mathew, S. J., Turner, M. S., Schatzberg, A. F., … American Psychiatric Association Council of Research Task Force on Novel Biomarkers and Treatments. (2017). A consensus statement on the use of ketamine in the treatment of mood disorders. *JAMA Psychiatry, 74*(4), 399–405. doi:10.1001/jamapsychiatry.2017.0080

Sanders, L. (2013). No new meds: With drug firms in retreat, the pipeline for new psychiatric medications dries up. *Science News, 183*(4), 26–29. doi:10.1002/scin.5591830422

Schwarz, A. (2015, December 10). Still in a crib, yet being given antipsychotics. *The New York Times*. Retrieved from https://www.nytimes.com/2015/12/11/us/psychiatric-drugs-are-being-prescribed-to-infants.html

Silverman, E. (2017, May 2). Paxil and suicide: The FDA should require a warning. *The Boston Globe*, C1, C6.

Simon, G. E., Savarino, J., Operskalski, B., & Wang, P. S. (2006). Suicide risk during antidepressant treatment. *American Journal of Psychiatry, 163*(1), 41–47. doi:10.1176/appi.ajp.163.1.41

Simon, G. E., Steward, C., Beck, A., Ahmedani, B., Coleman, K. J., Whitebird, R., … Hunkeler, E. M. (2014). National prevalence of receipt of antidepressant prescriptions by persons without a psychiatric diagnosis. *Psychiatric Services, 65*(7), 944–946. doi:10.1176/appi.ps.201300371

Smith, B. L. (2012). Inappropriate prescribing: Research shows that all too often, Americans are taking medications that may not work or may be inappropriate for their mental health problems. *American Psychological Association, Monitor on Psychology, 43*(6). Retrieved from http://www.apa.org/monitor/2012/06/prescribing.aspx

Social Worker Salary—PayScale. (2018). Retrieved from https://www.payscale.com/research/US/Job=Social_Worker/Salary

Tang, V. M., Blumberger, D. M., McClintock, S. M., Kaster, T. S., Rajji, T. K., Downar, J., … Daskalakis, Z. J. (2018). Magnetic seizure therapy in treatment-resistant schizophrenia. *Frontiers in Psychiatry, 16*(8), 310. doi:10.3389/fpsyt.2017.00310.

Tedeschini, R., Levkovitz, Y., Ioveno, N., Ameral, V. E., Nelson, J. C., & Papakostas, G. I. (2011). Efficacy of anti-depressant for late-life depression: A meta-analysis and meta-regression of placebo-controlled randomized trials. *Journal of Clinical Psychiatry, 72*, 1660–1668. doi:10.4088/JCP.10r06531

Thielking, M. (2018, October 1). Ketamine's promise sometimes turns to hype. *The Boston Globe*, B7, B9.

Van Ruth, L. M., Mistiaen, P., & Francke, A. L. (2007). Effects of nurse prescribing of medication: A systematic review. *Internet Journal of Healthcare Administration, 5*(2). Retrieved from http://ispub.com/IJHCA/5/2/3312

Weisberg, R. B., Dyck, I., Culpepper, L., & Keller, M. B. (2007). Psychiatric treatment in primary care patients with anxiety disorders: A comparison of care received from primary care providers and psychiatrists. *American Journal of Psychiatry, 164*(2), 276–282. doi:10.1176/appi.ajp.164.2.276

Whitaker, R. (2005). Anatomy of an epidemic: Psychiatric drugs and the astonishing rise of mental illness in America. *Ethical Human Psychology and Psychiatry, 7*(1), 23–35.

Whitaker, R. (2015). *Anatomy of an epidemic: Magic bullets, psychiatric drugs, and the astonishing rise of mental illness in America.* New York, NY: Broadway Books. (Original work published 2010).

Wunderink, L., Nieboer, R. M., Wiersma, D., Sytema, S., & Nienhuis, F. J. (2013). Recovery in remitted first-episode psychosis at 7 years of follow-up of an early dose reduction/discontinuation or maintenance treatment strategy: Long-term follow-up of a 2-year randomized clinical trial. *JAMA Psychiatry, 70*(9), 913–920. doi:10.1001/jamapsychiatry.2013.19

CHAPTER 7

GENDER, RACE, ETHNICITY, AND THE MENTAL HEALTH SYSTEM

LEARNING OUTCOMES

- Evaluate the role of gender, culture, race, and ethnicity within the mental health system.
- Describe the reasons women are more likely than men to seek mental healthcare.
- Analyze the racial and ethnic disparities in access to mental healthcare in the United States.
- Examine the barriers to mental health treatment of sexual and gender minorities.
- Demonstrate an understanding of the mental health needs of refugees and immigrants.

INTRODUCTION

Racial and ethnic diversity within the United States offers rich cultural differences that enhance life experiences and perspectives. This wealth of diversity underscores the importance of individuals and groups having a framework of strong mental health (Department of Health and Human Services, 2001). Mental disorders are found around the globe in all cultures and racial and ethnic groups and are not unique to certain countries (Department of Health and Human Services, 2001).

This chapter addresses the roles of sex, gender, culture, race, and ethnicity in the field of mental health. It reviews gender and cultural differences in perceptions of mental health disorders, perceptions of treatment, and ease of access to treatment. It examines disparities and obstacles to treatment. While cultural differences must be acknowledged and respected, mental health treatment should be tailored to each unique individual (Department of Health and Human Services, 2001).

Sociologists remind us that *race* and *ethnicity* are terms that are socially constructed and that individuals within these categories may or may not identify with specific racial and ethnic categories (Takeuchi & Williams, 2003). Race and ethnicity impact social, health, and economic realities for individuals and groups. According to the Institute of Medicine, racial and ethnic disparities in healthcare occur in a historical context, and within the context of contemporary social and economic inequality (Nelson, 2003).

The cultural backgrounds of those with mental illness have a significant impact on how mental health disorders may manifest. Factors include an individual's reactions to stressors, the coping mechanisms used, and the availability of social supports. Culture influences whether individuals will seek mental healthcare, and if so, the symptoms that they choose to discuss with professionals, as well as the type of care they seek (Roberts, Alegria, Roberts, & Chen, 2005; Satcher, 2001).

The term *disparity* addresses inconsistencies, discrepancies, inequalities, and gaps in care. According to the Institute of Medicine, "unequal treatment" focuses on the differences in the quality of healthcare and is not due to the specific healthcare needs or preferences of individuals from specific racial and/or ethnic groups (McGuire & Miranda, 2008; Smedley, Stith, & Nelson, 2003). Disparities are based on unequal access to quality mental health services, unequal access to health insurance, and discriminatory practices by providers. Low-quality mental healthcare can refer to services provided by those without adequate education, training, or licensing and without quality clinical supervision. Improving the overall quality of all types of healthcare can contribute to the reduction in disparities (McGuire & Miranda, 2008).

Essential to positive mental health is a secure sense of belonging as well as feeling comfortable within the society in which one lives (Meyers, 2006). In many respects, these factors are essential for all racial and ethnic groups. It is difficult, and often inappropriate, to generalize about members of specific races and ethnicities, yet we must learn more about members of groups to ascertain their perceptions of mental health problems, their willingness to seek help, and whether there are limitations to access to care based upon race and ethnicity.

During the Trump presidency, racial and ethnic issues have been thrust onto the international stage, where political efforts are being made to undermine diversity within the United States and to severely limit immigration to the United States. This includes efforts to deport immigrants in America back to their home countries. See Case Example 7.1 for examples of the Trump administration's efforts to remove Temporary Protected Status (TPS) from thousands of people living legally in the United States.

CASE EXAMPLE 7.1

TEMPORARY PROTECTED STATUS HOLDERS IN THE UNITED STATES FACE DEPORTATION

The following are several examples of immigrants with children facing deportation from the United States.

Ronde is an 11-year-old U.S. citizen living in Florida with her parents. While on the surface this may sound like a good life, Ronde lives with the stress and anxiety of not knowing what will happen to her family in the very near future. Ronde's parents are from Haiti, one of the six countries where those living in the United States are losing Temporary Protected Status (TPS). Ronde's parents will likely be forced to return to Haiti. Ronde is fearful of having to live in Haiti, a country she has never known. Alternatively, she is fearful of remaining behind in Florida and perhaps having to enter a foster home.

Mazan, who came to the United States from Sudan as a baby, is a 20-year-old student at the University of Southern Maine studying biology and biochemistry and planning to become a pediatrician. But Mazan, his mother, and two siblings may be forced to return to Sudan in the very near future due to the loss of their TPS.

Elba is a 71-year-old grandmother who worked low-wage jobs in the United States for almost 20 years. She lives with her daughter and two grandchildren, who are U.S. citizens. Elba is fearful of being forced to return to Nicaragua due to losing her TPS status. In her younger days, she had been an active supporter of the Contras, who fought to overthrow the socialist Sandinista government, and endured harassment and threats to her life. Elba stated, "What would I do there? At my age, there will be no jobs. My life there is going to be dangerous. Anybody can kill me for not accepting the injustices of the government" (Gomez, 2018, p. 2A).

The Trump administration has ended TPS for those from Sudan, Nepal, Honduras, Salvador, Nicaragua, and Haiti. This has affected more than 310,000 immigrants who came from other countries to live and work legally in the United States, some for more than 20 years. The Center for Migration Studies estimates that there are 273,000 children born to these immigrants in the United States and who are U.S. citizens themselves. In general, these families must decide whether to (a) remain in the United States and become undocumented immigrants facing deportation; (b) return to their country of origin with their children; or (c) return to their country of origin and leave their children behind in the United States.

What impact are these circumstances likely to have on these immigrant parents and their children? What mental health problems are likely to develop for these immigrants and their children?

SOURCE: Gomez, A. (2018, October 16). Decision of a lifetime: More than 310,000 Temporary Protected Status holders, who are documented residents, ordered to leave the USA. *USA Today*, 1A, 2A.

▨ SEX/GENDER DIFFERENCES IN MENTAL HEALTH ISSUES

Sex and gender issues are significant contributing factors to mental health as well as overall health. *Sex* refers to biological characteristics of an individual, while *gender* refers to the social roles related to an individual's sex or personal identity. According to the World Health Organization (WHO, n.d.), gender "influences the power and control men and women have over the determinants of their mental health, including their socioeconomic position, roles, rank and social status, access to resources and treatment in society" (p. 4).

Since the 1970s, it has been debated whether women have higher rates of mental illness compared to men, due to their societal sex roles as well as the impact of marriage on the mental health of men and women. Gove (1972, 1980, 1987) found evidence that women have higher rates of mental illness than men do, and observed that this can be associated with unrewarding and stressful roles in society, including roles as wives. More recently, with a focus on marriage, research shows that being married can extend benefits to both men and women (Simon, 2002). Certainly, sex roles in society are just one factor that may impact the mental health of women and men. One thing they share is that both women and men with severe mental illness are at much higher risk of violent victimization (Khalifeh & Dean, 2010).

While it continues to be debated whether women are more likely to have mental health problems, there are differences between men and women in the types of mental health problems they experience. Recently Gulland (2016) found that women have higher rates of mental illness compared to men, rates that are especially high among young women. Poor teenagers who experience their first pregnancy before the age of 19 have higher rates of anxiety disorders, behavioral disorders, and posttraumatic stress disorder (Tabet, Flick, Cook, Xian, & Chang, 2016).

Overall, women are known to have higher rates of depression and anxiety, while men have higher rates of conduct disorders and substance use disorders (Busfield, 2014). To explain these differences, researchers theorize that women are more likely to internalize their feelings, while men are more likely to externalize feelings (Eaton et al., 2012; Simon, 2002; Wirth & Bodenhausen, 2009). These differences can be associated with the dissimilar socialization experiences of males and females.

There are also sex differences in willingness to seek treatment for mental disorders, with women being more likely than men to seek assistance. Generally, men are less likely to express emotion and weakness than women and that correlates with their lower level of seeking mental health treatment (Wendt & Shafer, 2016). This reality impacts not only the lives of men themselves but also the lives of their spouses and children.

Minority women living in poverty are more likely to suffer from depression, yet are less likely to seek treatment (Grote, Zuckoff, Swartz, Bledsoe, & Geibel, 2007). As discussed previously, barriers to mental healthcare include high costs, lack of insurance, loss of income from time off work, lack of transportation, inconvenient hours provided by community agencies, and lack of child care. Having to keep appointments along with many other life challenges can make receiving mental healthcare feel like an additional problem (Grote et al., 2007). Considering that depression brings with it loss of energy, social isolation, feelings of being overwhelmed, and lack of concentration, it is not surprising that getting mental health help can sometimes feel impossible.

Stigma can add to the problems of women with mental health issues and to judgment by others of the ways some women choose to receive help. In an article on women and antidepressants, feminist writer Andrea Nicki asked the question, "If one fully acknowledges and accepts one's sufferings as understandable responses to an ever-challenging patriarchal culture, why should there be shame in using pharmaceutical tools to help alleviate them?" (2007, p. 59).

The impact of gender on mental illness is a reminder that mental illness is more than a chemical imbalance or disease of the brain (WHO, n.d.). As pointed out, mental illness greatly impacts family members. Most women who have severe mental illness do become mothers and are in need of supports (Dolman, Jones, & Howard, 2013). In a review of the literature by Dolman et al. (2013), 22 of 23 studies noted that women experienced problems in their interactions with medical staff. Additional issues included waiting for medical appointments, medical staff turnover, and the need for child-care assistance. Understanding the needs of pregnant women and mothers with mental illness can lead to the development of better professional interventions. As an "underresearched area of healthcare," much more remains to be learned about this topic (Dolman et al., 2013, p. 173).

Improvements to mental health services are possible when social workers see patients during primary care appointments. Social workers can then make referrals to community agencies and even make follow-up calls with reminders of appointments (Grote et al., 2007). Women should also be offered the choice of female or male mental health providers.

■ ETHNIC DISPARITIES IN MENTAL HEALTHCARE

For many years, minority populations in the United States have consistently had less access to mental healthcare and have received lower-quality mental healthcare (De Luca, Blosnich, Hentschel, King, & Amen, 2016).

These disparities have been a focus of research only since the 1990s. Interest in these issues increased after the U.S. Department of Health and Human Services report (2001) on the mental health of racial and ethnic minorities concluded there are, in fact, significant health disparities (Marrast, Himmelstein, & Woolhandler, 2016; Naddy & Ayon, 2015).

The obstacles to mental healthcare for racial and ethnic minorities have included financial barriers, the stigma of mental illness, and the lack of cohesiveness of mental health services (Department of Health and Human Services, 2001). A wide range of possible explanations have been offered. Less access to mental healthcare can correlate with lack of insurance coverage, where individuals and families do not have the ability to pay on their own. One national study found that lack of health insurance or the costs associated with mental health services is the reason most cited for not accessing mental health services by *all* racial and ethnic groups (Substance Abuse and Mental Health Services Administration [SAMHSA], 2015). Another reason is that racial and ethnic minorities can live in areas with fewer health and mental health resources. In its landmark report, the U.S. government acknowledged that "racial and ethnic minorities in the United States face a social and economic environment of inequality that includes greater exposure to racism and discrimination, violence, and poverty, all of which take a toll on mental health" (Department of Health and Human Services, 2001, p. 5). Inadequate research translates into ignorance about disorders and related mental health needs of racial and ethnic minorities.

One national study offered additional reasons for racial and ethnic minorities not using mental health services beyond the financial issues (SAMHSA, 2015). Some respondents preferred to handle their mental health problems on their own. Some respondents expressed concern over the stigma of mental health problems and the desire to prevent neighbors from finding out their struggles. These concerns also included fears that services may not be confidential and the potential consequences if employers learned of their help-seeking (SAMHSA, 2015). Other respondents were fearful of being committed to a mental hospital or being expected to take medications, both of which they did not want. Other barriers included lack of knowledge of how to access mental healthcare, lack of transportation, lack of time to obtain assistance, and the perception that services would not actually be helpful (SAMHSA, 2015).

Quality mental health services should be available for individuals specifically based on sex/gender, age, race, and ethnicity (Department of Health and Human Services, 2001). Research has established that the various racial and ethnic groups differ in their use of mental health services, as discussed in the sections on specific races and ethnicities later in this chapter (SAMHSA, 2015). Racial and ethnic minorities are more likely than whites to believe that race and ethnicity are important in the experience of mental health treatment (Meyer & Zane, 2013). Greater racial and ethnic diversity in the armed forces and among veterans means that mental health issues can become more complicated (De Luca et al., 2016).

A national study that examined data from 2008 to 2012 found that the use of mental health services was highest, at 17.1%, for adults who reported two or more races. The group that had the next highest utilization within the past year was white adults, at 16.6%. Native American adults followed at 15.6%, African American adults at 8.6%, Hispanic adults at 7.3%, and Asian American adults at 4.9% for utilization of mental health services (SAMHSA, 2015). In this sample, psychotropic medication use was highest among white adults, at 14.4%, and next highest among adults of two or more races, at 14.1% within the past year. The proportion of Native American adults taking psychotropic medications within the previous year was 13.6%, followed by African Americans at 6.5%, Hispanics at 5.7%, and Asian American adults at 3.1% (SAMHSA, 2015). When race and ethnicity were not acknowledged and addressed in mental health treatment, clients expressed less satisfaction with the services they received (Meyer & Zane, 2013).

CHILDREN/ADOLESCENTS AND RACE AND ETHNICITY

Culture also has a bearing on whether parents recognize mental health problems in their children, and their explanations of their children's behavior. White parents are more likely to report mental health problems in their adolescent children than are parents of African American and Latino children (Roberts et al., 2005). This may be related to a higher threshold of problem behaviors in minority children or bias against reporting problems due to concern for stigma. More authoritarian parenting styles may discourage minority youth from disclosing mental health concerns. Another possible explanation is that minority parents may see the mental health problems of their children as a result of their own poor parenting and may think problems should be resolved within the family and not by outsiders (Roberts et al., 2005).

Adolescents who experience racial/ethnic discrimination are at increased risk of victimization, depression, and suicidal thoughts (Tobler et al., 2012). Black and Hispanic children can be labeled as troublesome at school or pulled into the juvenile justice system, but that path infrequently leads to them receiving mental health services (Marrast et al., 2016). In a national study, white children and young adults received significantly more mental health and substance abuse treatment services than did black and Hispanic children and youth, after controlling for severity of mental health impairment, income, and health insurance

(Marrast et al., 2016). The low rates of mental healthcare may be associated with a tendency to seek less formal sources of counseling such as from family or clergy. It may also be that primary care health providers fail to recognize the need for mental health treatment and, therefore, do not refer these patients for help.

The lack of mental health services is juxtaposed against the high rates of involvement in the juvenile justice system, where correctional facilities house many mentally ill, as discussed in Chapter 8, Social Work, Mental Illness, and the Criminal Justice System. In a recent study of 377 juveniles who were arrested, white juveniles received more mental health and substance abuse treatment than did minority juveniles (Lopez & Nuno, 2018). Minority youth in the study were less likely to think they needed mental healthcare.

Attention has been given to matching clients and therapists according to race/ethnicity under the assumption that clients will have a more positive treatment experience in an environment freer of cultural mistrust and racism. However, rather than promoting self-disclosure among adolescents about substance use in clinical assessment, racial matching seemed to inhibit adolescents in their self-disclosure (Ureche, Smith, David, & Tabb, 2016). While the reasons for this outcome are unclear, Ureche et al. (2016) suggest that white therapists in the study may have been especially skilled in working with minority adolescents. Alternatively, it may be the result of "in-group stereotyping" in which respondents were careful to avoid negative views of those from the same group (Ureche et al., 2016).

Overall, racial and ethnic minorities are less likely than whites to receive optimal care for depression and anxiety (McGuire & Miranda, 2008). Efforts to reduce racial and ethnic disparities in psychiatric care and primary care services have not been particularly effective, and the quest for innovative and more effective approaches must continue (McGuire & Miranda, 2008). See Tips for the Field 7.1 for the strategic plan for research developed by the National Institute of Mental Health.

TIPS FOR THE FIELD 7.1

THE NATIONAL INSTITUTE OF MENTAL HEALTH'S STRATEGIC PLAN FOR RESEARCH

The National Institute of Mental Health acknowledges gender, racial, and ethnic disparities in healthcare in the United States. It also acknowledges the responsibility to support research to identify and alleviate mental healthcare disparities. Studies of these diverse groups add to knowledge of mental health risks, can improve access to mental health services, and can point the way toward improved prevention and treatment efforts. Importantly, all these efforts lead to greater effectiveness of treatment interventions. The following are brief descriptions of the strategic objectives of the National Institute of Mental Health as they relate to gender, race, and ethnicity.

Strategic objective #1: Define the mechanisms of complex behaviors.

This first objective focuses on expanding and improving the science behind understanding mental disorders. This includes examining the biological mechanisms that underlie mental processes. It also includes how these mechanisms may differ according to sex, gender, age, race, and ethnicity.

Strategic objective #2: Chart mental illness trajectories to determine when, where, and how to intervene.

This second objective focuses on distinguishing typical brain development from atypical brain development, with a focus on early intervention to prevent mental disorders. For example, it emphasizes the need to recognize the signs and symptoms of mental disorders that differ according to gender, race, and ethnicity.

Strategic objective #3: Strive for prevention and cures.

This third objective focuses on the need to develop and expand more effective prevention and treatment interventions. These interventions must be tested within community service agencies. Interventions must also be tested not only in heterogeneous groups, but also in smaller groups that, for example, include specific racial and ethnic participants.

Strategic objective #4: Strengthen the public health impact of National Institute of Mental Health (NIMH)–supported research.

This fourth objective focuses on research to improve the quality of mental health services and develop new evidence-based practices. It includes developing research and clinical partnerships that can improve the implementation of mental health services. Innovative delivery of services can include partnering with insurance companies and other payers to determine research needs, expanding team-based mental healthcare, and ensuring that patient treatment data and feedback can be utilized to improve mental healthcare. Regarding gender, race, and ethnicity, the focus is on what can be done to develop and expand the delivery system to improve mental health outcomes.

SOURCE: National Institute of Mental Health. (2015). *The National Institute of Mental Health strategic plan for research.* Retrieved from https://www.nimh.nih.gov/about/strategic-planning-reports/index.shtml

AFRICAN AMERICANS

African Americans have a long history of racial discrimination that includes atrocious treatment for mental illness in insane asylums. In 1868, the Central State Lunatic Asylum for the Colored Insane opened in Petersburg, Virginia. It was the first asylum established specifically for African Americans with mental disorders (Jones, 2017). In 1870, the Eastern Asylum for the Colored Insane opened in North Carolina (Jackson, 2002). If the conditions in public asylums were horrendous for whites, they were even worse for African American patients. Given the backdrop of racism, it is not surprising that, even today, African Americans prefer to avoid mental health services. Some describe this as persistent "institutional racism" that favors putting African Americans in prison over providing the mental health services they need (Leonard, 2012).

African Americans have lower rates of depression and higher rates of schizophrenia compared to whites (American Psychological Association, 2018; McGuire & Miranda, 2008). However, it remains unclear whether higher rates of schizophrenia represent actual numbers of cases, or misdiagnoses by mental health professionals (King, 2015; National Alliance on Mental Illness, 2018a).

The stigma attached to mental illness is felt by all racial and ethnic groups; however, it may be experienced more strongly by African Americans (Campbell & Mowbray, 2012). This stigma is likely associated with research findings that indicate African Americans are less likely to utilize mental health services than are whites (Masuda, Anderson, & Edmonds, 2012). Since African Americans are less likely to have health insurance than whites, this can be a significant deterrent to seeking professional help (Kirby & Kaneda, 2010).

African Americans sometimes prefer to seek assistance from family members, friends, or clergy, and they can view psychotherapists as insensitive to their life experiences. Church attendance and deep spiritual beliefs are the mainstays of support for many of these individuals (King, 2015; National Alliance on Mental Illness, 2018a). Some African Americans believe that mental health problems can get better on their own without treatment (Ward, Wiltshire, Detry, & Brown, 2013). Regarding gender differences, there is evidence that African American women are more open to seeking mental health services than are African American men (Ward et al., 2013).

This pattern of not seeking professional assistance extends to college students as well. One study found that older African American college students and those who had previously sought mental health services were more likely to seek assistance than were younger students or those without any experience with mental health help-seeking (Masuda et al., 2012).

While research on African American mental illness has been increasing, much more needs to be understood about the barriers to treatment for African Americans as well as the services offered by white practitioners (Ward et al., 2013). White therapists sometimes avoid discussions with clients about race and ethnicity due to their own discomfort (Copeland, 2006). For adolescent African Americans, it can be especially difficult to accept that their therapists understand them, care about them, and want to see them succeed.

Cultural misinterpretations and communication problems must be identified and addressed for African Americans to increase their use of mental health services (Copeland, 2006). Education and training of African Americans to serve as mental health professionals can also help encourage better service usage (American Psychological Association, 2018). Finally, partnerships between faith organizations and mental health services can be very helpful to African Americans in need of treatment for mental disorders (Ward et al., 2013).

LATINO/HISPANIC AMERICANS

Latino Americans are not a homogeneous group, and therefore it is challenging to make generalizations about their mental health issues (Guarnaccia, Martinez, & Acosta, 2005; Naddy & Ayon, 2015). With considerable diversity across Latino populations from more than 20 countries, many factors can come into play, such as different cultural and political traditions, diverse reasons for leaving their birth countries, and varied immigration statuses in the United States (Acosta, 2008). Mexican Americans are the largest group of Latinos living in the United States (Guarnaccia et al., 2005).

Often Latinos tend not to talk about mental health concerns, may not recognize symptoms of mental health problems, and may not know where to seek help. Further, if they do not speak English well, communication with healthcare professionals can be challenging (Hinojosa, Knapp, & Woodworth, 2015; National Alliance on Mental Illness, 2018b).

In the largest study of diverse Latino groups, depression and anxiety rates were highest among Puerto Ricans (Wassertheil-Smoller et al., 2014). Rates of depression ranged from a low of 22.3% for Mexican Americans to a high of 38% for Puerto Ricans. Undertreatment of depression and lower use of antidepressants in Latino populations are likely associated with lack of health insurance (Naddy & Ayon, 2015; Wassertheil-Smoller et al., 2014). For Mexican Americans, limited access to mental health services is associated with job pressure and low wages, the high cost of mental healthcare, and U.S. immigration status (Guarnaccia et al., 2005). Puerto Ricans have the lowest socioeconomic status of Latinos, which can be related to their higher rates of depression (Guarnaccia et al., 2005).

Research shows that in Latino families, children with mental illness are less likely to follow the recommended treatment regimen, thereby increasing family strain (Hinojosa et al., 2015). In a survey of 268 parents who responded that their children received professional mental health interventions such as counseling or medication within the prior

12 months, 171 parents were white and only 97 were Latino (Hinojosa et al., 2015). Family strain was related to stress associated with the child's mental illness, resources available to the family such as family supports and health of the parent(s), parental perceptions of the quality of the treatment, and involvement in their child's treatment (Hinojosa et al., 2015). Parental perceptions of a child's mental health treatment had the strongest impact on the level of family strain. It is critical that mental health professionals involve parents in their child's treatment by seeking their input and closely monitoring their level of satisfaction.

In a study of older Latino adults living in Massachusetts, greater levels of depression were found in those who lived alone and those with significant health problems (Falcon & Tucker, 2000). Puerto Rican and Dominican older adults had higher rates of depression associated with chronic health problems.

More research is required to better understand the mental health problems of Latino populations, including the reasons why Puerto Ricans have higher rates of depression compared to other Latino groups (Falcon & Tucker, 2000). In addition, a better understanding is needed of both protective and risk factors for all Latino groups (Guarnaccia et al., 2005). This knowledge is essential to develop appropriate treatment responses, including matching Latino clients with Latino therapists, if that is the preference of clients. Outreach efforts by social workers and other mental health professionals can better inform Latinos about available services and how to access them. Further, engaging with leaders of Latino communities can support these efforts (Acosta, 2008).

ASIAN AMERICANS

As with Latino Americans, there is significant diversity in Asian American groups regarding culture and religious beliefs. Asian Americans encompass 43 ethnic groups and speak more than 100 different languages, with Chinese Americans accounting for approximately one fourth of the Asian American population (Kramer, Kwong, Lee, & Chung, 2002). Asian American groups are unified by a cultural concern for "saving face" and avoiding shame and stigma for the family.

Asian Americans have lower rates of mental disorders than whites and also seek mental health treatment less often (Meyers, 2006; National Alliance on Mental Illness, 2003). They are known to have the lowest rates of alcohol and drug problems (Mignon, 2015). Asians are far more likely to present with physical problems rather than emotional problems. A staff member from the Asian Counseling and Referral Services in Seattle, Washington, estimated that approximately half of appointments with primary care physicians are related to mental/emotional problems (Peng, 2008).

Due to acculturation, Asians born in the United States may have more mental health problems than those immigrating to the United States from Asian countries (Meyers, 2006). Those who perceive that their social status is low and have experienced prejudice and discrimination can be at higher risk for mental health problems. Asian American children have been taught to not show emotion, to be grateful for what they have, and to try not to be a burden to others. Intense parental pressure to succeed in the United States can affect Asian American children and adolescents. A typical example is an adolescent boy who experienced anxiety and depression associated with feelings of low self-esteem. He had excellent grades in school, but that was not sufficient—his parents expected him to achieve perfect grades. His symptoms of depression and anxiety were attributed by his parents to being lazy and not working hard enough, and his parents felt he should be "stronger" and succeed in his studies and in life (SAMHSA, 2017).

Asian American women are known to have high rates of depression (National Alliance on Mental Illness, 2003). In a study of Asian American women who were children of immigrants, very high rates of depression and a history of suicidality were found. Among this sample of 701 women, 43% were currently experiencing moderate-to-severe depression or had a history of suicidal ideation and/or attempts (Augsberger, Yeung, Dougher, & Hahm, 2015). Among the women at high risk, 60% sought no mental health treatment. Underutilization of mental health services was attributed to stigmatizing attitudes within the family, stigma within the Asian community, and lack of culturally sensitive mental health services (Augsberger et al., 2015).

Barriers to treatment for Asian Americans include language, difficulty with accessing mental healthcare, and dissatisfaction with the care they receive (Meyers, 2006). Little is known about Asian Americans' use of psychotropic medications, as few studies have addressed this topic (Naddy & Ayon, 2015).

Asian Americans are likely to respond more positively when mental health services are offered within primary care settings. In an ideal situation, patients are screened using a depression tool and can then see a therapist (ideally, a culturally sensitive therapist) on the same primary care visit (Augsberger et al., 2015). Helpful interventions will focus on supporting family harmony and recognizing the value of hard work and education (Kramer et al., 2002). Recent efforts to combat mental health stigma within Asian American communities are harnessing the power of Asian American women. For example, Kristina Wong, a Chinese American, became a comedian and performance artist. She focuses her material and humor on mental health issues among Asian Americans (Chen, 2018). After a struggle with anxiety and depression, Emily Wu Troung, a

Tawainese American, became a spokesperson for the National Alliance on Mental Illness and for Recovery International, seeking to raise awareness of mental illness and the importance of treatment. Other efforts are directed toward establishing more mental health services modeled after the Yu-Ai Kai Senior Center for Japanese Americans. Located in San Jose, California, Yu Ai Kai offers older adults a more emotionally comfortable environment, where they are not required to directly discuss their feelings (Chen, 2018).

NATIVE AMERICANS

With more than 500 different federally recognized tribes, Native Americans are not a homogeneous society. Native American risk factors for depression and other mental illnesses include historical trauma inflicted on Native Americans, living in poverty, family violence, substance abuse, and prejudice and discrimination (Mays, 2015). Native Americans have especially high rates of co-occurring disorders such as alcohol abuse together with other substance abuse and diabetes (Mignon, 2015; Urban Indian Health Institute, 2012). Historically, much more clinical and research attention has been given to the substance use disorders of Native Americans, rather than to their mental health disorders (Department of Health and Human Services, 2001).

Mindful of their history of exploitation, Native Americans may have an inherent mistrust of government services and white providers of health services (Department of Health and Human Services, 2001). They may perceive that they are misdiagnosed and assigned labels they do not want to accept, such as bipolar disorder. These labels can impact their self-esteem and undercut their Native identity (University of California [UC] Davis Center for Reducing Health Disparities [CRHD], 2009). One Native American community leader put mental illness in this context: "I am dealing with people who have been disenfranchised and their mental illness originates in the system around them, the environment, the surrounding historical trauma. They are not crazy, they are people responding to trauma in their life" (CRHD, 2009, p. 6).

Native American youth are at especially high risk for depression and suicide, with 40% having more than one psychiatric disorder (Mays, 2015). Risk factors include shame and stigma, untreated depression, increased exposure to suicidal behavior, family history of suicide, and lack of mental health services.

Prevention efforts are essential for Native Americans and should focus on the entire community. Community cultural events can strengthen Native identity and pride as well as lead to healthy role models (CRHD, 2009). For example, the UC Davis CRHD project (2009) is building partnerships as part of an important effort for the community and policy makers to learn about, respond to, and provide services to facilitate mental health in Native communities. The CRHD's wide-ranging efforts also focus on improving access, detection, and mental health treatment within primary care settings. Tips for the Field 7.2 identifies themes in preventing and treating mental illness among Native Americans.

TIPS FOR THE FIELD 7.2

NATIVE AMERICAN THEMES FOR MENTAL ILLNESS PREVENTION AND TREATMENT

In a review of the literature on depression among Native Americans, the Urban Indian Health Institute devised eight themes to expand and improve mental healthcare for Native Americans on reservations and in urban settings.

Theme #1: Prevention and treatment efforts should focus on the family and the community, not just the individual. Mental health education needs to be provided to youth and families as well as all members of Native American communities. Interventions must be devised and accepted by Native Americans themselves, with research being conducted to evaluate the effectiveness of these interventions.

Theme #2: Traditional Native knowledge of health and spirituality should be incorporated into prevention and treatment efforts, based upon the individual's cultural identity and level of acculturation. Traditional practitioners and Native American elders must be involved in providing care, with an emphasis being placed on life balance and harmony. This can include healing ceremonies, prayer, the use of sacred plants, Native American crafts, and drumming.

Theme #3: Prevention and treatment efforts should focus on skill building, such as improving communication, coping with stress, and managing conflict with others. Youth mentoring by Native American elders can assist with problem solving, employment and educational advice, and management of finances. Storytelling is a critical mechanism for passing on individual and cultural wisdom.

Theme #4: Screening for mental illness should be included in primary care medical settings as well as schools, and should include referrals to community providers. Screening and early intervention can ensure that mental illness is discovered and treated at an earlier and less severe point. Mental health screenings in schools offer the opportunity for children and adolescents to receive assistance from within the school system. The Indian Health Service supports the change from receiving mental health services within mental health centers to accessing mental healthcare within primary care medical settings.

Theme #5: Develop ways to ensure the cultural competency of mental health and other health providers. Mental health providers need to be educated and trained in cultural competency. Additionally, the number of Native American mental health providers must be increased. Expansion of mental health certifications and licenses to traditional Native American healers to acknowledge their expertise could increase treatment options by allowing for health insurance billing.

Theme #6: Focus on developing a deeper and more flexible relationship between the mental health provider and the client. With a strong emphasis on Native American community, mental health providers need to develop a trust with the community and can become a part of the community. Some advocate for a Native American model of wellness to bring mind, body, and spirit into balance. Models of therapy such as cognitive behavioral therapy can be adapted to include Native teachings and approaches.

Theme #7: Make environmental and structural changes that support a healthy lifestyle and reduce socioeconomic and health disparities. The focus must be on not just the interaction between individual clients and other people, but also the environment itself. This means working to reduce poverty, especially on Native American reservations, and understanding and promoting employment and educational opportunities.

Theme #8: Utilize advocacy skills to change policy and systems to better support economic opportunities and improved health. Social determinants of health and mental health such as socioeconomic status, education, and discrimination must be addressed through advocacy efforts. This includes seeking increased federal, state, and foundation funding to address Native American mental health. It includes bolstering research that can be used to prove the effectiveness of treatment approaches and be accepted as evidence-based practices.

SOURCE: Urban Indian Health Institute, Seattle Indian Health Board. (2012). *Addressing depression among American Indians and Alaska Natives: A literature review.* Seattle, WA: Author.

■ SEXUAL MINORITY AND GENDER NONCONFORMITY

There are increased mental disorder risk factors for sexual minority and gender minority individuals, including high rates of social rejection and violent victimization. *Sexual minorities* include persons who are lesbian, gay, or bisexual, and *gender minorities* are those who are transgender or gender nonconforming (Wofford, 2017). Individuals' cultural backgrounds can have a negative impact on their acceptance of their sexual identity (SAMHSA, 2017). Some sexual minorities believe that they must lead double lives and not "come out" to their families. Those with different gender identity expressions have often been considered as having mental disorders in the past, with the *Diagnostic and Statistical Manual of Mental Disorders* (*DSM*) removing homosexuality as a mental disorder only in 1974. The *DSM-5* (American Psychiatric Association, 2013) describes *gender dysphoria* as "a marked incongruence between one's experienced/expressed gender and assigned gender" (p. 452). Although the issue is still controversial, one should not assume that having a different gender identity is in and of itself a mental disorder. However, prejudice and discrimination within American society have a negative impact on self-esteem, and they do increase the risk for mental illness.

Risk factors for mental problems for children and adolescents include bullying, violent victimization, substance abuse, quitting high school, and homelessness. These risk factors make youth far more vulnerable to mental health problems. Not surprisingly, mental health problems often are associated with academic problems. However, since the emphasis has been on the provision of services, little attention has been paid to monitoring the progress of students and obtaining feedback on the services from clients, as well as giving feedback to students on their progress (Borntrager & Lyon, 2015).

Schools should do more to address the issues of sexual minority and gender-nonconforming adolescent students by providing school-based mental health services (Wofford, 2017). Mental health services within schools can also reduce racial and ethnic disparities in the provision of services (Lyon, Ludwig, Vander Stoep, Gudmundsen, & McCauley, 2013). While outcomes appear to be promising, school-based services are not without problems. The biggest issue is how to safeguard confidentiality when students can observe other students taken from classes or entering the office of a social worker or other clinical provider. The issue of funding can also be challenging when trying to add mental health services. Within this context, school social workers help to reduce discrimination against students by participating in the establishment of system-wide school policies to protect their rights (Wofford, 2017).

Medical and mental health professionals may also exhibit discrimination toward sexual and gender minorities. This will only serve to heighten the distress of the individual client (Mizock & Fleming, 2011; Schreiber, 2016). Overall, lack of acceptance of sexual and gender minorities creates barriers to appropriate mental healthcare (Robles et al., 2016). More research is required to create appropriate mental health services for sexual and gender minorities. Recent efforts by the Trump administration to curb the rights of sexual and gender minorities can only serve to exacerbate problems.

▮ REFUGEES AND IMMIGRANTS AND MENTAL HEALTH ISSUES

Being forced to flee one's home for safety reasons, poverty, isolation, and fear of the future are all factors that contribute to mental and physical stress for refugees and immigrants. Today we see increasingly desperate individuals and families forced to leave their countries to seek safety for themselves and their children. The Trump administration has promoted policies that ensure discrimination, separate families, and leave families without any sense of permanency in their lives. The impact of policy changes and restrictions by the Trump administration, as well as the disturbing news coverage about these changes, have strong bearing on increased stress. Not surprisingly, this leaves refugee and immigrant adults and children at high risk of developing mental disorders (Fortuna & Porche, 2013). A study of U.S. Latino parents with adolescents found that those facing immigration issues were coping with high levels of psychological stress (Roche, Vaquera, White, & Rivera, 2018). One study of undocumented Mexican immigrants found that 23% of the sample had mental disorders, with depression and anxiety being the most prevalent (Garcini et al., 2017).

Challenges in addressing the mental health problems of refugees and immigrants extend beyond their stressful personal experiences, to include those who are providing health and mental healthcare. Different languages and cultures can make it difficult to recognize, assess, and treat mental disorders of refugees and immigrants (Kirmayer et al., 2011). Increased efforts must be made to recognize the problems of refugees and immigrants and will help overcome their limited access to mental healthcare (Chantler, 2012; Fortuna & Porche, 2013). Social workers specializing in mental health must be part of the effort to challenge the U.S. government's treatment of immigrants and refugees, and they should work in coordination with legal advocates (Chantler, 2012). Social workers can also work toward a specialty by developing evidence-based practices in the treatment of mental disorders of refugees and immigrants.

Social workers have much experience and expertise in the various ways to reduce mental health disparities for all racial and ethnic groups. Tips for the Field 7.3 highlights the contributions social workers can make to reduce mental health disparities.

TIPS FOR THE FIELD 7.3

DIGGING DEEPER INTO POLICY: WAYS SOCIAL WORKERS CAN HELP REDUCE MENTAL HEALTH DISPARITIES

1. Promote diversity within all roles in the mental health workforce and provide improved and more culturally appropriate treatment through expanded education and training of clinicians.

2. Ensure the availability of interpreter services for patients and families.

3. Provide written educational materials to patients and families regarding mental health diagnosis and treatment.

4. Expand evidence-based clinical strategies for addressing issues related to race and ethnic minority status for those with mental illness.

5. Along with other mental health clinicians, seek innovations in managing, coping with, and overcoming prejudice and discrimination in American society.

6. Work toward the adoption of universal mental health insurance coverage for all who live in the United States.

SOURCES: McGuire, T. G., & Miranda, J. (2008). Racial and ethnic disparities in mental health care: Evidence and policy implications. *Health Affairs (Millwood), 27*(2), 393–403. doi:10.1377/hithaff.27.2.393; Meyer, O. L., & Zane, N. (2013). The influence of race and ethnicity in clients' experiences of mental health treatment. *Journal of Community Psychology, 41*(7), 884–901. doi:10.1002/jcop.21580

SUMMARY AND CONCLUSION

Disparities in mental healthcare are a major issue. Overall, racial and ethnic minorities have less access to mental healthcare, are less likely to receive the care they need, and receive a lower quality of mental healthcare. Women are more likely to have depression and anxiety disorders, while men have more substance use disorders and behavioral disorders.

African Americans are more likely to rely on family, their religious beliefs, and their clergy for assistance with mental health issues. Latinos have strong families and are less likely to seek professional mental healthcare. Asian Americans are concerned with bringing shame on their families and are not likely to seek mental healthcare. Native Americans are more likely to engage in mental healthcare if that care includes their rich cultural traditions, including storytelling and close contact with Native American elders. Refugees and immigrants can have significant mental health issues that are only recently getting the professional attention they deserve. Sexual and gender minorities face many barriers to seeking mental health treatment, and much more research is needed to determine how to respond to their needs appropriately.

Providing culturally competent services, including linguistic services, and expanding mental health services to those groups can improve their willingness to seek help. Most important is to create spaces where clients feel accepted, safe, and satisfied with the services they receive. The current trend toward providing mental health services in primary care settings can help create that safe and comfortable environment. Overall, there is the need for social workers to develop a specialty in treating the mental health disorders of diverse racial and ethnic groups. And it is likely in the coming years, there will be a greater need for social workers to assist refugees and immigrants.

DISCUSSION QUESTIONS/TOPICS

1. Discuss gender differences in mental health disorders.
2. Discuss how cultural attitudes can impact the willingness of those with mental disorders to seek treatment.

3. Describe the challenges for youth with nonconforming gender identities.

4. Why is it difficult to generalize about the mental health issues of Latinos?

5. Discuss the importance of avoiding stigma and the consequences it can have for Asian Americans with mental disorders.

6. Describe the mental health issues of Native Americans.

7. What are the mental health challenges of immigrants to the United States amid today's political backlash against immigration?

8. What strategies of social workers can be helpful to reduce disparities in the provision of mental health services?

9. What national policies can be developed to reduce disparities in mental healthcare?

10. What roles can social workers have in ensuring the fairness of American national immigration policies?

■ REFERENCES

Acosta, H. (2008). *Do's and don'ts when working with Hispanics in mental health*. Mercerville, NJ: National Resource Center for Hispanic Mental Health. Retrieved from https://www.nrchmh.org/attachments/DoAnd Dont.pdf

American Psychiatric Association. (2013). *Diagnostic and statistical manual of mental disorders* (5th ed.). Arlington, VA: Author.

American Psychological Association. (2018). *African Americans have limited access to mental and behavioral health care*. Retrieved from https://www.apa .org/advocacy/civil-rights/diversity/african-american-health.aspx

Augsberger, A., Yeung, A., Dougher, M., & Hahm, H. C. (2015). Factors influencing the underutilization of mental health services among Asian American women with a history of depression and suicide. *BMC Health Services Research, 15*, 542. doi:10.1186/s12913-015-1191-7

Borntrager, C., & Lyon, A. R. (2015). Monitoring client progress and feedback in school-based mental health. *Cognitive Behavioral Practice, 22*(1), 74–86. doi:10.1016/j.cbpra.2014.03.007

Busfield, J. (2014, February). Gender and mental illness. *The Wiley Encyclopedia of Health, Illness, Behavior, and Society*. doi:10.1002/9781118410868.wbehibs253

Campbell, R. D., & Mowbray, O. (2016). The stigma of depression: Black American experiences. *Journal of Ethnic & Cultural Diversity in Social Work, 25*(4), 153–269. doi:10.1080/15313204.2016.118710

Chantler, J. K. (2012). Gender, asylum seekers and mental distress: Challenges for mental health social work. *British Journal of Social Work, 42*, 318–334. doi:10.1093/bjsw/bcr062

Chen, S. (2018, September 10). New generation of Asian-American women are fighting to normalize mental health treatment. *ABC News*. Retrieved from https://abcnews.go.com/GMA/Wellness/generation-asian-american -women-fighting-normalize-mental-health/story?id=57651825

Copeland, V. C. (2006). Disparities in mental health service utilization among low-income African American adolescents: Closing the gap by enhancing practitioner's competence. *Child and Adolescent Social Work Journal, 23*(4), 407–431. doi:10.1007/s10560-006-0061-x

De Luca, S. M., Blosnich, J. R., Hentschel, E. A. W., King, E., & Amen, S. (2016). Mental health care utilization: How race, ethnicity and veteran status are associated with seeking help. *Community Mental Health Journal, 54*, 174–179. doi:10.1007/s10597-015-9964-3

Department of Health and Human Services. (2001). *Mental health: Culture, race, and ethnicity. A supplement to mental health: A report of the Surgeon General,* 1999. Rockville, MD: U.S. Public Health Service, Substance Abuse and Mental health Services Administration.

Dolman, C., Jones, I., & Howard, H. M. (2013). Pre-conception to parenting: A systematic review and meta-synthesis of the qualitative literature on motherhood for women with severe mental illness. *Archives of Women's Mental Health, 16*, 173–196. doi:10.1007/s00737-013-0336-0

Eaton, N. R., Keyes, K. M., Krueger, R. F., Balsis, S., Skodol, A. E., Markon, K. E., … Hasin, D. S. (2012). An invariant dimensional liability model of gender difference in mental disorder prevalence: Evidence from a national sample. *Journal of Abnormal Psychology, 121*(1), 282–288. doi:10.1037/a0024780

Falcon, L. M., & Tucker, K. L (2000). Prevalence and correlates of depressive symptoms among Hispanic elders in Massachusetts. *Journal of Gerontology, 55B*(2), S108–S116. doi:10.1093/geronb/55.2.S108

Fortuna, L. R., & Porche, M. V. (2013). Clinical issues and challenges in treating undocumented immigrants. *Psychiatric Times, 31*(1). Retrieved from http://www.psychiatrictimes.com/special-reports/clinical-issues-and-challenges-treating-undocumented-immigrants

Garcini, L. M., Pena, J. M., Galvan, T., Fagundes, C. P., Malcarne, V., & Klonoff, E. A. (2017). Mental disorders among undocumented Mexican immigrants in high-risk neighborhoods: Prevalence, comorbidity, and vulnerabilities. *Journal of Consulting and Clinical Psychiatry, 85*(10), 927–936. doi:10.1037/ccp0000237

Gove, W. R. (1972). The relationship between sex roles, marital status and mental illness. *Social Forces, 51*, 34–44. doi:10.1093/sf/51.1.34

Gove, W. R. (1980). Mental illness and psychiatric treatment among women. *Psychology of Women Quarterly, 4*(3), 345–362. doi:10.1111/j.1471-6402.1980.tb01109.x

Gove, W. R. (1987). Book review of *Women and Mental Health Policy,* ed. by Lenore E. Walker. *Contemporary Sociology, 16*(6), 876–877.

Grote, N. K., Zuckoff, A., Swartz, H., Bledsoe, S. E., & Geibel, S. (2007). Engaging women who are depressed and economically disadvantaged in mental health treatment. *Social Work, 52*(4), 295–308. doi:10.1093/sw/52.4.295

Guarnaccia, P. J., Martinez, I., & Acosta, H. (2005). Mental health in the Hispanic immigrant community: An overview. *Journal of Immigrant & Refugee Services, 3*(1/2), 21–45. doi:10.1300/J191v03n01_02

Gulland, A. (2016). Women have higher rates of mental disorders than men, NHS survey finds. *British Medical Journal, 354*, i5320. doi:10.1136/bmj.i5320

Hinojosa, M. S., Knapp, C., & Woodworth, L. (2015). Family strain among white and Latino parents of children with mental and behavioral health disorders. *Journal of Child and Family Studies, 24*(6), 1575–1581. doi:10.1007/s/10826-014-9961-0

Jackson, V. (2002). An early history: African American mental health. Excerpted from *In Our Own Voices: African American Stories of Oppression, Survival and Recovery in the Mental Health System*, 1–36, 4–8. Retrieved from https://academic.udayton.edu/health/01status/mental01.htm

Jones, J. (2017). Absurd reasons why blacks were admitted to the "Central State Lunatic Asylum for the Colored Insane." *Black Then: Discovering Our History*. Retrieved from https://blackthen.com/absurd-reasons-why-blacks-were-admitted-to-the-central-state-lunatic-asylum-for-the-colored-insane

Khalifeh, H., & Dean, K. (2010). Gender and violence against people with severe mental illness. *International Review of Psychiatry, 22*(5), 535–546. doi:10.3109/09540261.2010.506185

King, T. (2015, June 12). The truth about overcoming mental illness in the black community. *Atlantic Black Star*. Retrieved from https://atlanticblackstar.com/2015/06/12/mental-illness-black-community-schizophrenia-bipolar-disorder

Kirby, J. B., & Kaneda, T. (2010). Unhealthy and uninsured: Exploring racial differences in health and health insurance coverage using a life table approach. *Demography, 47*(4), 1035–1051. doi:10.1007/BF03213738

Kirmayer, L. J., Narasiah, L., Munoz, M., Rashid, M., Ryder, A. G., Guzder, J., ... Canadian Collaboration for Immigrant and Refugee Health. (2011). Common mental health problems in immigrants and refugees: General approach in primary care. *Canadian Medical Association Journal, 183*(12), E959–E967. doi:10.1503/cmaj.090292

Kramer, E. J., Kwong, K., Lee, E., & Chung, H. (2002). Cultural factors influencing the mental health of Asian Americans. *Western Journal of Medicine, 176*(4), 227–231.

Leonard, D. (2012, June 180). The criminalization of mental illness in black America. *Urban Cusp*. Retrieved from https://www.urbancusp.com/2012/06/the-criminalization-of-mental-illness-in-black-america

Lopez, V., & Nuno, L. (2018). Racial/ethnic differences in mental health and drug treatment among juvenile arrestees. *Journal of Crime and Justice, 41*(4), 398–409. doi:10.1080/0735648X.2018.1440249

Lyon, A., Ludwig, K., Vander Stoep, A., Gudmundsen, G., & McCauley, E. (2013). Patterns and predictors of mental health care utilization in schools and other service sectors among adolescents at risk for depression. *School Mental Health, 5*(3), 155–165. doi:10.1007/s12310-012-9097-6

Marrast, L., Himmelstein, D. U., & Woolhandler, S. (2016). Racial and ethnic differences in mental health care for children and young adults: A national study. *International Journal of Health Services, 46*(4), 810–824. doi:10.1177/0020731416662736

Masuda, A., Anderson, P. L., & Edmonds, J. (2012). Help-seeking attitudes, mental health stigma, and self-concealment among African American college students. *Journal of Black Studies, 43*(7), 773–786. doi:10.1177/0021934712445806

Mays, A. (2015). *Depression, mental health and Native American youth* [PowerPoint presentation]. Oakland, CA: Native American Health Center.

McGuire, T. G., & Miranda, J. (2008). Racial and ethnic disparities in mental health care: Evidence and policy implications. *Health Affairs (Millwood)*, *27*(2), 393–403. doi:10.1377/hithaff.27.2.393

Meyer, O. L., & Zane, N. (2013). The influence of race and ethnicity in clients' experiences of mental health treatment. *Journal of Community Psychology*, *41*(7), 884–901. doi:10.1002/jcop.21580

Meyers, L. (2006). *Asian-American mental health*. American Psychological Association. Retrieved from https://www.apa.org/monitor/feb06/health.aspx

Mignon, S. I. (2015). *Substance abuse treatment: Options, challenges, and effectiveness*. New York, NY: Springer Publishing Company.

Mizock, L., & Fleming, M. Z. (2011). Transgender and gender variant populations with mental illness: Implications for clinical care. *Professional Psychology: Research and Practice, 42*(2), 208–213. doi:10.1037/a0022522

Naddy, M. B. G., & Ayon, C. (2015). Predictors of psychotropic medication use in a nationally representative sample of Latino/Latina and Asian American Adults: Findings from the NLAAS. *Journal of the Society of Social Work and Research, 6*(1), 21–49. doi:10.1086/680150

National Alliance on Mental Illness. (2003). *Asian American and Pacific Island (AA/PI) community and mental health fact sheet*. Retrieved from http://www.naminys.org/images/uploads/pdfs/AsianAmericanCommunityMentalHealthFacts.pdf

National Alliance on Mental Illness. (2018a). *African American mental health*. Retrieved from https://www.nami.org/Find-Support/Diverse-Communitiies/African-Americans

National Alliance on Mental Illness. (2018b). *Latino mental health*. Retrieved from https://www.nami.org/Find-Support/Diverse-Communities/Latino-Mental-Health

Nelson, A. R. (2003). Unequal treatment: Report of the Institute of Medicine on racial and ethnic disparities in healthcare. *Annals of Thoracic Surgery, 76*, S1377–S1381. doi:10.1016/S0003-4975(03)01205-0

Nicki, A. (2007). Women and anti-depressants. *Off Our Backs, 37*(4), 57–59.

Peng, T. (2008, August 11). Mental illness may go untreated in Asian-Americans. *Newsweek*. Retrieved from https://www.newsweek.com/mental-illness-may-go-untreated-asian-americans-87613

Roberts, R. E., Alegria, M., Roberts, C. R., & Chen, I. G. (2005). Mental health problems of adolescents as reported by their caregivers: A comparison of European, African, and Latino Americans. *Journal of Behavioral Health Services Research, 32*(1), 1–13. doi:10.1007/BF02287324

Robles, R., Fresan, A., Vega-Ramirez, H., Cruz-Islas, J., Rodriguez-Perez, V., Dominguez-Martinez, T., & Reed, G. M. (2016). Removing transgender identity from the classification of mental disorders: A Mexican field study for ICD-11. *Lancet, 3*(9), 850–859. doi:10.1016/S2215-0366(16)30165-1

Roche, K. M., Vaquera, E., White, R. M. B., & Rivera, M. I. (2018). Impacts of immigration actions and news and the psychological distress of U.S. Latino parents raising adolescents. *Journal of Adolescent Health, 62*(5), 525–531. doi:10.1016/j.jadohealth.2018.01.004

Satcher, D. (2001). *Mental health: Culture, race, and ethnicity—A supplement to Mental Health: A Report of the Surgeon General*. Washington, DC: U.S. Department of Health and Human Services.

Schreiber, K. (2016, December 6). Why transgender people experience more mental health issues. *Psychology Today*. Retrieved from https://www .psychologytoday.com/us/blog/the-truth-about-exercise-addiction/201612/ why-transgender-people-experience-more-mental-health

Simon, R. W. (2002). Revisiting the relationships among gender, marital status, and mental health. *American Journal of Sociology, 107*(4), 1065–1096. doi:10.1086/339225

Smedley, B., Stith, A. Y., & Nelson, A. R. (2003). *Unequal treatment: Confronting racial and ethnic disparities in health care.* Institute of Medicine Committee on Understanding and Eliminating Racial and Ethnic Disparities in Health Care. Washington, DC: National Academies Press.

Substance Abuse and Mental Health Services Administration. (2015). *Racial/ethnic differences in mental health service use among adults.* HHS Publication No. SMA-15-4906. Rockville, MD: Author.

Substance Abuse and Mental Health Services Administration. (2017). *Advancing best practices in behavioral health for Asian American, Native Hawaiian and Pacific Islander boys and men.* HHS Publication No. (SMA) 17-5032. Rockville, MD: Author.

Tabet, M., Flick, L. H., Cook, C. A. L., Xian, H., & Chang, J. J. (2016). Age at first birth and psychiatric disorders in low-income pregnant women. *Journal of Women's Health, 25*(8), 810–817. doi:10.1089/jwh.2015.5236

Takeuchi, D. T., & Williams, D. R. (2003). Race, ethnicity and mental health: Introduction to the special issue. *Journal of Health and Social Behavior, 44*(3), 233–236.

Tobler, A. L., Maldonado-Molina, M. M., Staras, S. A., O'Mara, R. J., Livingston, M. D., & Komro, K. A. (2012). Perceived racial/ethnic discrimination, problem behaviors, and mental health among minority urban youth. *Ethnicity and Health, 18*(4), 337–349. doi:10.1080/13557858.2 012.730609

University of California Davis Center for Reducing Health Disparities. (2009, March). *Building partnerships: Conversations with Native Americans about mental health needs and community strengths.* Sacramento, CA: Author.

Urban Indian Health Institute, Seattle Indian Health Board. (2012). *Addressing depression among American Indians and Alaska Natives: A literature review.* Seattle, WA: Author.

Ureche, D. J., Smith, D. C., Davis, J. P., & Tabb, K. M. (2016). Racial matching and adolescent self-disclosure of substance use and mental health symptoms. *Journal of Ethnicity in Substance Abuse, 15*(2), 176–188. doi:10.1 080/15332640.2015.1017784a

Ward, E., Wiltshire, J. C., Detry, M. A., & Brown, R. L. (2013). African American men and women's attitude toward mental illness, perceptions of stigma, and preferred coping behaviors. *Nursing Research, 62*(3), 185–194. doi:10.1097/NNR.0b013e31827bf533

Wassertheil-Smoller, S., Arrendondo, E. M., Cai, J. W., Castaneda, S. F., Choca, J. P., Gallo, L. C., … Zee, P. C. (2014). Depression, anxiety, antidepressant use, and cardiovascular disease among Hispanic men and women of different national backgrounds: Results from the Hispanic Community Health Study/Study of Latinos. *Annals of Epidemiology, 24*(11), 822–830. doi:10.1016/j.annepidem.2014.09.003

Wendt, D., & Shafer, K. (2016). Gender and attitudes about mental health help seeking: Results from national data. *Health & Social Work, 41*(1), e20–e28. doi:10.1093/hsw/hlv089

Wirth, J. H., & Bodenhausen, G. V. (2009). The role of gender in mental-illness stigma: A national experiment. *Psychological Science, 20*(2), 169–173. doi:10.1111/j.1467-9280.2009.02282.x

Wofford, N. C. (2017). Mental health service delivery to sexual minority and gender non-conforming students in school: A Winnicottian approach. *Child and Adolescent Social Work, 34*, 467–478. doi:10.1007/s10560-016-0482-0

World Health Organization. (n.d.). *Gender disparities in mental health.* Department of Mental Health and Substance Abuse. Retrieved from who .int/mental_health/media/en/242.pdf

CHAPTER 8

SOCIAL WORK, MENTAL ILLNESS, AND THE CRIMINAL JUSTICE SYSTEM

LEARNING OUTCOMES

- Define the relationship between violence and mental illness.

- Describe police responses to individuals with mental illness and demonstrate knowledge of the effects of crisis intervention training (CIT).

- Evaluate the effectiveness of specialty courts including drug courts and mental health courts.

- Discuss the treatment of mentally ill individuals in correctional facilities.

- Identify different roles that social workers can take on within the criminal justice system.

INTRODUCTION

It is well known that there is a close association between mental health problems and contact with the criminal justice system. However, the relationship is unclear and can be difficult to understand. While mental illness can be a factor in the commission of crime, many other factors are more likely to have a bearing on crime. A disproportionate number of those persons with mental illness do end up in the criminal justice system, but it is also true that "mental illness is not as directly related to criminal involvement or violence as is often assumed" (Mulvey & Schubert, 2017, p. 231).

This chapter reviews the responses to the mentally ill by the three major components of the criminal justice system: police, courts, and corrections. It examines the relationship between mental illness and violence as well as race and ethnicity as factors that determine services for the mentally ill within the criminal justice system. The chapter reviews police responses to the mentally ill with a focus on crisis intervention training (CIT) for officers. The mental health issues of those incarcerated in jails and prisons are described, with special attention being paid to issues of mentally ill women in the criminal justice system and concerns for their children. The chapter reviews specialty courts, particularly mental health courts that developed in the late 1990s. Finally, the chapter calls for expanded social work services for the mentally ill in all phases of the criminal justice system, including release to the community with parole or probation supervision.

What are the reasons that mentally ill individuals are found in the criminal justice system? A number of hypotheses have been offered but do not tell the whole story. For example, while deinstitutionalization in the 1950s brought many of the mentally ill back into communities, this alone cannot account for the numbers of mentally ill in correctional facilities (Lamb & Weinberger, 2017; Mulvey & Schubert, 2017). A second hypothesis is that the untreated mentally ill are repeatedly arrested and charged with crimes such as public nuisance and, over time, collect criminal charges that result in longer incarceration. This hypothesis is only partially correct (Mulvey & Schubert, 2017). A third hypothesis is that those with severe mental disorders receive longer sentences than individuals without mental health problems who commit similar crimes. This hypothesis has limited evidence and is likely associated with whether the individual has a co-occurring substance use disorder (Mulvey & Schubert, 2017). A fourth hypothesis is that when the mentally ill lack access to treatment, their symptoms may occur in public, grow worse, and bring about their arrest. There is not much support for this hypothesis, but there can certainly be greater numbers of the mentally ill in areas of high crime and greater police enforcement (Mulvey & Schubert, 2017). The homeless with mental illness are the subject of Chapter 9, No Place to Go.

The criminal justice system is where we see racial and ethnic discrimination most strongly. Racial and ethnic minorities have long been over-represented in the prison system, and this is the case for the mentally ill as well (Alexander, 2010; Cole et al., 2018; Grekin, Jemelka, & Trupin, 1994; Mignon, 2015). One huge factor that increased incarceration of those with mental illness was the harsher drug laws that were established in the 1980s. These laws required stiff sentences for use, possession, and sale of illegal drugs. Of course, this resulted in prison overcrowding owing to the war on drugs, very long mandatory prison sentences (e.g., 10–20 years), and countless negative impacts on families of color (Lamb & Weinberger, 2017; Mignon, 2015). Only in recent years have states been reconsidering the effects of the failed war on drugs, including acknowledging the negative impacts on people of color, and reducing lengthy prison sentences. As discussed in Chapter 5, Social Work and Mental Illness: Labels and Diagnoses, substance use and mental health disorders are separate problems but can co-occur, and both need treatment (Mignon, 2015).

Typically, the individuals who do come into contact with the criminal justice system do so because they commit criminal offenses, regardless of their mental health status. The mental health status of criminal offenders is not usually considered, at least not in the initial stages. This means that those committing serious criminal offenses are likely to be incarcerated without any attention being paid to the individual's mental health. Many academic careers have been built on studying the causes and consequences of criminal behavior. For example, social disorganization theories focus on poverty and the accompanying social and environmental problems as root causes of crime. Differential association theory holds that criminal behavior is learned from other criminals, just as law-abiding behavior is learned from those who do not violate the law. Conflict theory holds that the exploitation of the poor by the rich and powerful creates the conditions under which criminal behavior develops and thrives. Risk factors for criminal behavior include experience in which criminal activity yields benefits, an environment that accepts and even promotes crime, an attraction to impulsive or risk-taking behaviors, and attitudes and values that support criminal behavior (MacPhail &Verdun-Jones, 2013).

It is important to remember that individuals with serious mental illness are not a homogeneous group. The majority of those with mental disorders recognize their issues; participate in treatment, including taking medication; have jobs; and live fulfilling lives. Their risk for involvement in the criminal justice system is low. However, a smaller group do not accept that they have a mental illness, known as anosognosia. They neither participate in treatment nor take medication, may have a propensity for violence, and are more likely to be involved in criminal activity (Lamb & Weinberger, 2017).

■ VIOLENCE AND MENTAL ILLNESS

While there is a public perception that those with mental illness are dangerous, this is rarely the case. Severe mental illness such as schizophrenia does not predict violent or criminal behavior (Mulvey & Schubert, 2017). Additionally, symptoms of mental illness rarely precipitate crime even in cases where individuals experience psychotic episodes (Skeem, Kennealy, Peterson, & Appelbaum, 2015). In a study of 143 criminal offenders, 10% of crimes were associated with bipolar disorder, 4% were associated with psychosis, and 3% were associated with depression

(Peterson, Skeem, Kennealy, Bray, & Zvokovic, 2014). Factors more closely associated with crime are antisocial personality disorder and substance abuse, as discussed in the following sections (MacPhail & Verdun-Jones, 2013).

Those with mental illness are, in fact, more likely to be crime victims than perpetrators of crime (MacPhail & Verdun-Jones, 2013). In one review of adult violence victimization and perpetration, an average of 23.9% of individuals with mental disorders reported engaging in violent behavior and an average of 30.9% of those with mental disorders reported they had been victimized (Desmaris et al., 2014). Almost two thirds (63.5%) of violence occurred in residential treatment facilities.

Both the media and public opinion have a tendency to associate horrific crimes with mental disorders and to assume heinous crimes are committed because of mental illness. Our society prefers to think of mass murders and other violent crimes as attributable to mental disorders, rather than to bigotry that has been stoked by politics and the shaping of political careers. In reality, the United States has a long-established history of unwillingness to significantly reduce the types of guns available for purchase, and the consequences of that policy have been enormous. Not even the devastating massacre of 20 elementary school children and 6 adults in Sandy Hook, Connecticut, on December 14, 2012, could prompt a substantial change in gun control laws. Some states, such as Massachusetts, have chosen to take gun control more seriously than others and succeeded in reducing the availability of guns. Clearly, access to guns and other weapons has a powerful impact on the types of crimes committed. In the wake of the massacre of Jewish worshippers in their synagogue in Pittsburgh, Pennsylvania, on October 27, 2018, many are now asking whether President Trump's stand against illegal immigrants and his openly negative rhetoric geared toward certain racial and ethnic groups are fueling racial, ethnic, and religious intolerance. During his visit to Pittsburgh a few days after the shootings, Trump was met by thousands of protesters blaming him for inciting violence with his hate rhetoric (Robertson, Davis, & Gabriel, 2018). Protesters' signs read "Words Matter" and "President Hate Is Not Welcome in Our State" (p. A2). It is much easier to blame only the individual criminal offender, when in fact political and societal factors can and do encourage violent criminal activity.

In some extreme cases of violence, perpetrators with known mental disorders have not received the screening, assessment, and treatment they need. At this writing, Nikolas Cruz is accused of shooting and killing 14 students and 3 staff members at the Marjory Stoneman Douglas High School in Parkland, Florida, on February 14, 2018. An additional 17 people were wounded (Anderson, 2018). Cruz's mother had sought mental health treatment for him after becoming concerned that her son was depressed and possibly suicidal. (Parental pleas for mental health treatment are clear indicators of severe problems.) In September 2017, school officials and a sheriff's deputy had sought an involuntary inpatient mental health evaluation for Cruz. For reasons that are unclear at this time, this evaluation was never conducted. If Cruz had been hospitalized involuntarily before this high school tragedy, he would have been prevented from legally buying firearms. Cruz faces the death penalty for these heinous crimes (Anderson, 2018).

Antisocial Personality Disorder

If there is a mental health disorder associated with criminal activity, it is antisocial personality disorder, also known as sociopathy or psychopathy. According to the *Diagnostic and Statistical Manual of Mental Disorders*, Fifth Edition (*DSM-5*), antisocial personality disorder is characterized by a failure to conform to social norms and laws, including disregard for the rights of other people (American Psychiatric Association, 2013). The individual displays aggressive behaviors and is irresponsible, manipulative, and impulsive. The hallmark of antisocial personality disorder is the inability to feel remorse for negative and/or harmful behaviors. This translates to a wide range of behaviors that are unacceptable and dangerous. Antisocial personality disorder is known to be a difficult problem to treat, even more so when it co-occurs with substance abuse (Mignon, 2015). While between 0.2% and 3.3% of the population has antisocial personality disorder, rates of 70% and higher have been found in samples of persons with substance use disorder and those in criminal justice settings (American Psychiatric Association, 2013). One suggestion for reducing recidivism in the criminal justice system is to develop interventions that specifically address antisocial personality traits (Peterson et al., 2014).

There is a great need to better identify those individuals with mental illness who are at increased risk of criminal behavior. Yet mental illness, as discussed earlier, does not predict involvement in violence. In reality, age, substance use, and socioeconomic status are much better predictors of criminal involvement (Mulvey & Schubert, 2017). In fact, individuals living in poor crime-ridden environments are at greater risk for mental illness and/or crime victimization. Thus, it is very difficult to sort out the specific contributions of each issue to criminal activity. In a systematic review of the literature on offenders with substance use and mental health disorders, significant variation was found in treatment outcomes (Woodhouse et al., 2016). The lack of clarity on causes as well as how to obtain the best treatment results has to be further examined. Research must expand and improve this knowledge base, including adding more details on the mental health diagnoses of study participants (Woodhouse et al., 2016).

◼ POLICE

No one can deny the importance of police within a society. Police departments are literally the social service agencies available 24 hours a day and can be the first to come into contact with those individuals who have severe behavioral disorders. For the mentally ill who interact with the police, this contact is where and when police decide what to do: arrest and pull the individual into the criminal justice system or divert the individual to mental health resources (Watson, Morabito, Draine, & Ottati, 2008). See Case Example 8.1 for a police intervention with a mentally ill person that went terribly wrong.

CASE EXAMPLE 8.1

DONTRE HAMILTON KILLED BY THE POLICE IN 2014

Dontre Hamilton was a 31-year-old African American father with a history of schizophrenia and suicide attempts. He had previously worked as a roofer. Although police reports stated that Hamilton was homeless, he had been living in a mental health group home, where a social worker supervised his care. On the day of his death, Hamilton was frightened because he was hearing voices and was too afraid to stay at the group home, so he wandered into the Red Arrow Park in Milwaukee.

Hamilton was asleep in the park at about noon on April 30, 2014, when workers at Starbucks called the police to report that customers were scared by the sight of this sleeping man. Twice police officers had passed the sleeping Hamilton and found no reason to intervene. The white beat police officer Christopher Manney had no knowledge of the previous police response when he retrieved a voice mail message about Hamilton. Officer Manney then approached Hamilton lying on the ground and asked him to stand. During Manney's pat-down of him, Hamilton took the police officer's baton; Manney then shot him 14 times, killing him on the spot. Manney was fired 6 months after the shooting, not for excessive use of force but for not following departmental policy in the pat-down procedure. As a result, the Milwaukee Police Department participated in crisis intervention training, a mental health training program for police regarding their interactions with the mentally ill. In June 2017, Milwaukee Community Council officials approved a payment to the Hamilton family in the amount of $2.3 million.

SOURCES: Barton, G., & Luthern, A. (2017, April 12). Family of Dontre Hamilton, man fatally shot by police, prevails in early round. *Milwaukee Journal Sentinel*. Retrieved from https://www.jsonline.com/story/news/crime/2017/04/12/family-dontre-hamilton-milwaukee-man-fatally-shot-police-prevails-early-legal-round/100391404; Jenkins, A. (2017, June 1). Milwaukee approved a $2.3 million settlement for family of mentally ill man. *Time*. Retrieved from http://time.com/4800622/dontre-hamilton-christopher-manney-settlement; In Milwaukee, a $1.2 million police training misses the mark. *Milwaukee Journal Sentinel*. Retrieved from https://www.jsonline.com/story/news/investigations/2018/06/08/resentful-officers-dub-mental-health-program-hug-thug/680618002

Police are in an important position to assist those with mental disorders, and there are a number of strategies for police involvement with the mentally ill. An early effort to study police and mental health found that officers wanted access to background information such as whether the person had a history of violence or suicide attempts, and also wanted a mental health professional available to evaluate the individual (Gillig, Dumaine, Stammer, Hillard, & Grubb, 1990). Since the early 1990s, considerably more attention has been paid to the relationship between police and those with mental illness, as well as to appropriate ways to handle police interventions. One model calls for specially trained officers to respond to an incident. Another model is for mental health professionals to work with the police and provide consultation regarding interventions. A third model involves independent mental health crisis teams who cooperate with the police (Mulvey & Schubert, 2017). Each approach is designed to avoid dangerous confrontation, to diffuse the crisis situation, and to access mental health services. Unfortunately, for some individuals with mental illness, contact with the police may be their only opportunity to access treatment (Taheri, 2016).

Crisis intervention training (CIT) is the most widely used mental health and police training program. It was developed in Memphis, Tennessee, in 1987 in response to the shooting and killing of a mentally ill individual by police (Goldfarb, 2018). CIT developed as a collaboration among the Memphis Police Department, the National Alliance on Mental Illness, and other community partners (Taheri, 2016). The program consists of 40 hours of police training to provide an overview of mental illness, state and local laws, and local mental health resources. The collaborative efforts of law enforcement and mental health systems are the hallmark of CIT programs.

In a recent study, officers in Georgia who had completed a CIT program had significantly better knowledge, attitudes, and skills than officers who did not participate in such training (Compton et al., 2014a).

CIT-trained officers knew more about mental illness and treatments, acquired de-escalation skills, and made better referral decisions. They also made fewer arrests of mentally ill individuals and increased their transport and referrals to mental health services (Compton et al., 2014b). However, research evidence confirms that over time police officers' skills in handling individuals with mental illness decline, so they need to be maintained and renewed (Davidson, 2016).

It is hard to get a definitive picture of the effectiveness of CIT. Each police department tends to add its own flavor, and community resources are different, which adds to difficulties in assessing programs (Taheri, 2016). In a systematic review of the literature and meta-analysis, Taheri (2016) found that there is not sufficient evidence on whether police injuries are reduced, and there is only mixed evidence on whether CIT reduces police use of force.

On the positive side, research has found that officers who volunteer for the training, as well as those who are involuntary participants, are able to benefit from it (Davidson, 2016). CIT can also be adapted to corrections officers as well, and this holds promise for improving custodial staff responses to mentally ill inmates (Davidson, 2016). Going forward, CIT must progress to the point where police work with other agencies to define the roles of various professionals and to determine how best to coordinate services for the mentally ill (Mulvey & Schubert, 2017; Wood & Beierschmitt, 2014). Taheri (2016) concluded that overall CIT programs are "without sufficient evidence to their success" (p. 93).

In one Massachusetts model, a social worker works directly within a police department. The social worker can be a town employee or working through a contract between the town police department and a local mental health organization (Goldfarb, 2018). Social workers can accompany police officers to their crisis calls. They also can make referrals to community agencies and then follow up with the individual after the crisis has passed. These efforts demonstrate that social workers are increasingly invited to work with police officers and are making positive contributions to crisis mental health services.

Mental Health First Aid (2018) is an Australian mental health intervention program that was introduced to the United States in 2008. This 8-hour training program for the public, or anyone interested in providing initial help, focuses on understanding mental health and substance abuse issues. The website states that more than 1 million people in the United States have been trained so far. This type of training program can add to efforts to reduce the stigma of mental illness and has introduced key interventions to assist those with mental disorders.

COURTS

Mentally ill defendants present a huge problem for the court system, as little effort is made to determine whether defendants have a mental health disorder and/or a substance use disorder when they enter the system. Ideally, social workers in court clinics will screen and assess for substance abuse and mental illness prior to or as part of the arraignment process (Hardy-Fanta & Mignon, 2000). Uncovering a defendant's mental health and substance abuse problems at a very early point in the criminal justice process can bring a defendant into treatment at an earlier point, perhaps averting more severe problems.

In a study of mentally ill court defendants charged with homicide, 58% had at least one psychiatric diagnosis, while 47% percent had a substance use disorder (Martone et al., 2013). Thirty-seven percent of the sample had a history of prior psychiatric treatment, but only 8% had received treatment 3 months before committing the homicides. Clearly, these circumstances demonstrate the importance of prevention and early intervention.

Assisted outpatient treatment (AOT), also known as involuntary outpatient treatment, is a civil court procedure wherein a judge orders a person with mental illness to participate in a specific treatment plan. AOT often requires a commitment to take medication (Torrey, Kennard, Eslinger, Lamb, & Pavle, 2010). This intervention was established to reduce the need for involuntary psychiatric hospitalization and to give patients the opportunity to remain in the community with an individualized treatment plan (Lamb & Weinberger, 2017). Forty-six states have made AOT available, according to the Treatment Advocacy Center (2018). AOT is considered effective by the National Institute of Justice, as participants can have lower rates of rearrest and reduced violent behavior. One controversy over AOT is whether states should require administration of medication against the will of the client. Some states include the medication requirement as part of AOT, whereas others require a separate legal procedure. Many states have AOT laws, but they are "applied infrequently" (Lamb & Weinberger, 2017, p. 312). This can be due to lack of funding as well as legal concerns for due process and placing restraints on individual liberty.

Drug Courts

The first drug court was established in 1989 in Miami–Dade County in Florida, and approximately 3,000 drug court programs now operate today (Laurio, 2018; National Association of Drug Court Professionals,

2018). Drugs courts marked the beginning of specialty courts that now include mental health courts and veterans' courts, as described later in this chapter. Drug courts have had a dramatic impact on the criminal justice system by emphasizing treatment opportunities over punishment in a coordinated effort between courts and substance abuse treatment programs (Mignon, 2015).

Positive outcomes of drug courts include staying in treatment longer, reducing substance use and abuse, and reducing criminal activity. A review of 16 studies of drug court effectiveness found almost all showed reduced use of substances and concluded there were "moderately positive results" (Wittouck, Dekkers, De Ruyver, Vanderplasschen, & Vander Laenen, 2013, p. 2).

Mental Health Courts

Mental health courts were established in the late 1990s and are heralded as one of the most important innovations in criminal justice (Castellano, 2017). These courts are the embodiment of *therapeutic jurisprudence*: They have a focus on promoting mental and physical health while also incorporating public safety concerns (Lamb & Weinberger, 2017). Typically, judges with a special interest in those with mental illness volunteer for mental health courts under the assumption that mental health treatment can reduce criminal offending (Swartz, 2014). These judges help motivate clients, set boundaries for their behavior and treatment, and strive to achieve positive outcomes for individuals while ensuring due process under the law (Castellano, 2017).

Mental health courts that tend to work well consider factors beyond mental illness in their supervision of clients, such as environmental and social supports. One study found that those persons completing mental health court programs had a recidivism rate of 28.6%, whereas those not assigned to mental health courts had a recidivism rate of 32.6% (Campbell et al., 2015). Mental health court programs that connect clients with mental health services offer incentives to comply with requirements, which are associated with reduced recidivism. Not surprisingly, clients who complete the mental health court programs are more likely to have reduced recidivism (Campbell et al., 2015; Snedker, Beach, & Corcoran, 2017).

In a comparison of clients in mental health courts with those in AOT, clients in mental health courts felt more respected by the system, perceived less coercion, and had more positive feelings about their experiences than did those in AOT (Munetz, Ritter, Teller, & Bonfine, 2014).

Mental health courts are not necessarily less expensive than regular courts. In the first multisite study of mental health courts, known as the MacArthur Mental Health Court Study, comparing offenders in mental health courts with jailed offenders receiving psychiatric services and not enrolled in mental health courts revealed that costs were higher for those persons adjudicated in mental health courts (Steadman et al., 2014). Higher costs were associated with offenders who had co-occurring mental health and substance use disorders.

The growth in the number of mental health courts has occurred with little input from federal agencies and with little outcomes research (Swartz, 2014). It is hard to compare program outcomes due to the complexity of interventions and to figure out who benefits and under what circumstances. Honegger's (2015) review of mental health courts found that while popular, they are still an "emerging practice" (p. 478), whose differing methodologies make it difficult to assess and compare research findings. Therefore, while receiving much attention, evidence on the efficacy of mental health courts is not conclusive (Mulvey & Schubert, 2017).

Veterans Courts

The first veterans court opened in Buffalo, New York, in 2008 and was modeled on drug and mental health courts (National Center for State Courts, 2018). With more than 461 veterans' courts now in existence at this writing, they are a fast-growing specialty court (Tsai, Finley, Flatley, Kasprow, & Clark, 2018). Veterans courts deal with both mental illness and substance use disorders. Participants have the opportunity to avoid incarceration and may be eligible to have charges dropped if they complete the program. Veteran mentors can be important sources of support for clients within the veterans courts (National Center for State Courts, 2018).

In a national study of 7,931 veterans, individuals averaged 1 year as clients in the veterans court program (Tsai et al., 2018). Those with substance disorders were more likely to experience a new incarceration. Employment was the area where most participants faced major barriers. Those with a diagnosis of posttraumatic stress disorder and prior psychiatric hospitalizations were more likely to be receiving Veterans Administration benefits. As discussed previously, more attention must be given to the mental health needs of veterans, including supporting their efforts to obtain employment (Tsai et al., 2018).

CORRECTIONS

Exact numbers of jail and prison inmates with mental illness are unknown, with varying estimates depending on definitions of mental illness and research study designs. However, it is known that a disproportionate number of those with mental disorders are living in jails and prisons (MacPhail &Verdun-Jones, 2013). The quality of mental healthcare in correctional facilities is "barbarically low" (Mulvey & Schubert, 2017, p. 247). The Treatment Advocacy Center concluded, "It is thus fact, not hyperbole, that America's jails and prisons have become our new mental hospitals" (Torrey et al., 2010).

As with the general public, those who work with the mentally ill in the correctional systems tend to assume that mental illness is the cause of criminal behavior, while overlooking a myriad of other possible contributing factors, such as childhood abuse and trauma and past involvement with the juvenile justice system (Martin, Eljdupovic, McKenzie, & Colman, 2015; Skeem, Winter, Kennealy, Louden, & Tatar, 2014). One study showed that while those with mental illness are equally as likely to recidivate as were individuals without mental illness, those with mental illness were more likely to be reincarcerated (Skeem et al., 2014).

Once the mentally ill enter the criminal justice system through the police and courts, those with serious mental illness are more likely to remain incarcerated for longer periods of time and are less likely to have the opportunity for supervision within the community. Upon release, those with serious mental illness are more likely than others to violate parole restrictions (Mulvey & Schubert, 2017; Skeem et al., 2014). Case Example 8.2 describes the preventable death of Matthew Burns in a jail.

CASE EXAMPLE 8.2

MATTHEWS BURNS HANGED HIMSELF IN JAIL IN 2012

Matthew Burns was a 23-year-old man who hanged himself in a county jail in Tennessee in September 2012. He had been arrested 4 days earlier on a charge of bank robbery. Matthew had a history of childhood sexual abuse and mental illness, including diagnoses of bipolar disorder, depression, and substance abuse. He also had a history of suicide attempts and was on psychotropic medications. The nurse at the jail failed to recognize from his medication list that these were psychotropic medications. The medications should not have been abruptly withdrawn, because such an event can be associated with suicidal behavior. Despite three family telephone contacts with the jail to share his mental health history and express concern about possible suicidality, no consideration was given to Matthew's mental health status other than the nurse asking him if he was suicidal. His denial was deemed sufficient, and the nurse remained unaware of family phone calls to the facility.

Matthew's mother sued the Robertson County Jail in 2013 for $10 million in Nashville's United States District Court, claiming that the facility was indifferent to her son's needs and had inadequate policies to identify and evaluate suicidal inmates, which resulted in his death. At this writing, court mediation is being considered to resolve the legal case.

SOURCES: Leagle. (2017). *Burns v. Robertson County.* 192 F.Supp.3d 909 (2016). Retrieved from https://www.leagle.com/decision/infdco20160616799; Young, N. (2016, July 3). Mediation possible in Robertson county jail suicide lawsuit. *Tennessean.* Retrieved from https://www.tennessean.com/story/news/local/robertson/2016/07/03/ mediation-possible-robertson-county-jail-suicide-lawsuit/86161252

Effects of Solitary Confinement

The prison environment is likely to exacerbate the mental health problems of inmates and can reduce the chances of mental health recovery (Mulvey & Schubert, 2017). This can be the case especially when inmates are subjected to solitary confinement.

In Massachusetts in 2007, a lawsuit was brought by Prisoners' Legal Services and the Disability Law Center. An agreement was reached where the state committed to ending the practice of long-term stays in isolation for the seriously mentally ill (Cramer & Russell, 2017). Subsequently, two specialized mental health units within prisons were established but were not able to accommodate all inmates in need. Prison officials have since been accused of changing serious mental health diagnoses to less severe problems such as anxiety, essentially making seriously mentally ill inmates eligible for solitary confinement (Cramer & Russell, 2017).

In January 2018, inmates at the Bristol County Jail in Massachusetts filed a lawsuit against Sheriff Thomas Hodgson and other officials (Cramer, 2018). Sheriff Hodgson has had a long career that includes boasts of strong discipline and physical and emotional discomfort for his inmates. He achieved national attention when he offered President Trump the option of using Bristol County inmates to build the wall between the United States and Mexico. The lawsuit alleges that the Sheriff's Office does not assess the mental health backgrounds and current issues of inmates before imposing solitary confinement. Solitary or isolation typically means spending at least 23 hours a day locked up and alone. The lawsuit includes documentation that the suicide rate at the Bristol Country Jail is three times higher than the national average for jails. In 2016, there were four suicides at the jail, two of whom were inmates in solitary confinement. One inmate who is part of the lawsuit has a history of childhood victimization, suicide attempts, bipolar disorder, and posttraumatic stress disorder (PTSD) and spent almost 2 years in segregation (Cramer, 2018). Without a doubt, the time has come to require an end to solitary confinement for those with mental illness.

Mentally Ill Incarcerated Women

Women in jails and prisons usually have a host of problems that have resulted in their incarceration. This often includes low socioeconomic status, low educational level, low self-esteem, substance abuse, childhood and adult physical and sexual victimization, homelessness, and mental health problems (Fedock, Fries, & Kubiak, 2013; Hardy-Fanta & Mignon, 2000). Women who have been victims of intimate-partner violence can feel a very limited sense of power that contributes to their mental health problems (Minieri et al., 2014). Importantly, incarcerated women may not understand that their history of victimization has had an impact on their mental health (Minieri et al., 2014). One study of incarcerated women in New Zealand found that 90% had used substances prior to incarceration, 54% had experienced family violence, 58% had a history of mental health treatment, and 43% had a history of psychiatric hospitalization (Collier & Friedman, 2016). These large percentages emphasize the importance of appropriate treatment responses to women in need.

A comparison of incarcerated men and women found that women have higher rates of trauma, substance abuse, serious mental disorders, homelessness, and co-occurring disorders (Fedock et al., 2013). While incarcerated women have higher rates of mental disorders than incarcerated men do, they have lower rates of antisocial personality disorder (MacPhail & Verdun-Jones, 2013).

Jails and prisons are very stressful environments, but particularly for women, and this is associated with higher rates of depression and anxiety among incarcerated women (Mignon, 2016). It remains unclear how many women enter jail or prison with mental health problems and how many develop mental health problems as a result of their incarceration (Collier & Friedman, 2016).

Mental health screening and assessment are critical for women entering jails and prisons (Lynch et al., 2017). Screening should include whether a woman has a history of victimization (Minieri et al., 2014).

Women in jails and prisons should have the opportunity to get necessary mental health services to help prepare them to reenter the community. Even though a jail stay is typically short term and mental health services are more difficult to provide, issues can be identified and potential resources located during this period (Rose, LeBel, & Blakey, 2016). For women, trauma-informed care within correctional settings is essential (Lynch et al., 2017).

For women released from prison, mental health concerns are very likely to continue. Violent victimization, PTSD, and depression can predict substance abuse after release back into the community

(Lynch & Heath, 2017). This underscores the importance of providing simultaneous treatment for both mental health and substance use disorders.

There should be much concern for the well-being of children of incarcerated mothers. The issues affecting children, which typically stem from multiple family problems, can be both the cause and the consequence of parental incarceration. Historically, prison environments have done very little to assist incarcerated mothers to have visits from their children and to maintain connections through telephone calls and newer forms of technology (Mignon & Ransford, 2012). Regular contacts with children offer incarcerated women hope for the future and can support them and their use of mental health and other available programs while incarcerated. These experiences help mothers become better prepared for returning to their families and communities.

Children of incarcerated women have their own significant issues that need professional attention. Once again, we see the importance of stigma for individuals and families, especially where parental incarceration is involved. A study of children of incarcerated mothers in Arizona found that these children were more likely to receive mental health services if they were being cared for by their grandparents and/or the children were involved with the state or local child protection agency. Children of incarcerated Native American mothers and those exposed to violence were less likely to receive mental healthcare (Turanovic & Rodriguez, 2017).

Much more needs to be done to meet the mental health needs of children with mothers in the criminal justice system. This includes screening jail and prison inmates upon admission regarding where and with whom their children are living, and whether their children have identified mental health problems. To monitor and assist these children, improved collaboration between correctional institutions and social workers in child protection agencies is essential (Mignon, 2017; Mignon & Ransford, 2012; Turanovic & Rodriquez, 2017).

Overall, correctional facilities must offer appropriate services to the mentally ill to avoid their mental deterioration while incarcerated. Prisons should have specific mental health units for those who have severe symptoms, although these services are not often available (Mulvey & Schubert, 2017). The quality of staff, both professional and custodial, is a huge issue regardless of the setting, and staff can do much to create a supportive environment for prison inmates (To, Vanheule, De Smet, & Vandevelde, 2015). Peer support and role modeling can also be helpful (Mulvey & Schubert, 2017).

▧ THE PRISON TO COMMUNITY TRANSITION

It is important to remember that reducing the number of mentally ill persons in the criminal justice system does not typically mean that mental disorders are cured. Rather, symptoms need to be managed to achieve stability and to avoid future contacts with the system (Mulvey & Schubert, 2017). It is highly problematic to release incarcerated people with serious mental illness from the criminal justice system, only to have them then receive care from an inadequate community mental health system (Lamb & Weinberger, 2017). Offenders with mental disorders who are released from prison are at risk of poor health and negative social outcomes, and they are in great need of transitional services (Cutcher, Degenhardt, Alati, & Kinner, 2014). Unfortunately, it can be difficult to find social workers and other clinicians with interest and expertise in criminal justice populations (Lamb & Weinberger, 2017).

Overall, American society has done a poor job in assisting the incarcerated to return to the community. Typically, such individuals, when reentering the community, lack the essential social, medical, and employment supports that they need to help them succeed. Criminal risk assessments of individuals have received much research attention; however, the need extends beyond evaluation of offender characteristics, to include locating and expanding available services for newly released individuals. When the focus is solely on an offender's actions, this can be a setup for punitive responses (Denton, Foster, & Bland, 2017). Thus, lack of availability of the specific services needed by clients can be a strong contributor to recidivism, and a better understanding of community criminal justice and mental health supports is needed. For example, correctional facilities and programs may not provide an adequate amount of psychotropic medication prior to inmates' release, leading individuals to have to go off their medications before they get an appointment with a new provider (Mulvey & Schubert, 2017).

Interventions with the mentally ill tend to focus exclusively on their mental illness, when a more comprehensive approach is actually needed to reduce recidivism (Skeem, Manchak, & Peterson, 2011). While it is clear that additional mental health services are needed, an increase alone is not sufficient to reduce crime and violence (Mulvey & Schubert, 2017). There must be a close collaboration between social workers and staff within criminal justice agencies (Lamb & Weinberger, 2017). Social workers and other clinicians must possess the education, training, experience, and confidence level necessary to provide services to clients in all facets of the criminal justice system. See Tips for the Field 8.1 for a description of the many roles for social workers within the criminal justice field.

TIPS FOR THE FIELD 8.1

SOCIAL WORK ROLES IN THE CRIMINAL JUSTICE SYSTEM

There are many critical roles for social workers in all facets of the criminal justice system. Known as forensic social work, this includes any form of social work that involves contact with police, courts, and corrections. The following are examples of roles for social workers with clients in the criminal justice system:

1. Crisis intervention with the police.

2. Sentencing advocate—develop treatment plans after court adjudication.

3. Screen and assess court defendants for substance abuse and mental health problems.

4. Serve as a child welfare guardian ad litem, to ensure the needs of the child remain paramount in child abuse court investigations and proceedings.

5. Work in specialty courts such as drug courts and mental health courts to screen, assess, treat, and make referrals to community agencies.

6. Serve as an expert witness in child abuse and neglect court cases.

7. Provide clinical services in jails and prisons for those with substance abuse and/or mental health problems.

8. Provide victim advocacy, such as with victims of family violence seeking restraining orders or other court protections.

9. Collaborate with parole and probation officers to assist clients to transition back to the community after incarceration.

10. Serve as a mitigation specialist for death penalty cases, including work with the clients and families to uncover background information and evidence to mitigate against a sentence of capital punishment.

SOURCE: Laurio, A. (2018, June). Social work roles are many in the criminal justice system. *NASW News,* 8, 9, 11.

A study of parole officers illustrated that they have a significant impact on the mental health and substance abuse services that parolees can access (Thompson, Newell, & Carlson, 2016). Generally, parole officers felt that substance abuse treatment was more accessible to parolees than mental health treatment. Parole officers acknowledged the difficulty in identifying those individuals with mental illness, as it is a much more difficult task than identifying those with substance use disorders. The lack of mental health services for parolees was attributed primarily to lack of health insurance or private funds (Thompson et al., 2016).

Some of the parole officers stated that race had an impact on mental health issues (Thompson et al., 2016). For example, some said that African American parolees had an especially difficult time acknowledging mental health problems and did not want to be labeled. White parole officers had a hard time discussing issues of race and its impact on treatment. Parole officers of color found it less difficult to talk about race and more swiftly attributed barriers to treatment to race than did white officers. As discussed in Chapter 7, Gender, Race, Ethnicity, and the Mental Health System, there is a great need for culturally competent mental health services. Recent policy changes brought by the Affordable Care Act are important, including expanded access to mental healthcare (Thompson et al., 2016).

The work of Thompson et al. (2016) illustrates the difficulties associated with racist views and their impact on parolees and their treatment. Regardless of color, parole officers were troubled by parolees' claims of racism. The parole officers were not clear whether these were genuine concerns or whether racism was raised as an effort to get out of treatment. If parole officers are not sensitive to parolees' concerns and if there is no trust in mental health services providers or parole officers, treatment is less likely to be effective.

JUVENILE JUSTICE AND MENTAL ILLNESS

As for the adult justice system, the primary goal of the juvenile justice system is to maintain public safety (Espinoza, Sorensen, & Lopez, 2013). Unfortunately, the general health and mental health needs of juveniles can be overlooked when priority is given only to physical safety.

Mental health screening and assessment are crucial for juveniles at an early point of contact with the juvenile justice system and can help determine appropriate treatment options (Kempker, Schmidt, & Espinosa, 2017; Mallett, 2015). One study of 54 females in a juvenile facility found 80% had mental health or substance abuse issues, a clear call for screening and assessment (Kataoka et al., 2001). One such effort is the Massachusetts Youth Screening Instrument, which is designed to identify the mental health problems of juveniles ages 12 to 17 on probation, in diversion programs, or held in secure correctional institutions (National Youth Screening and Assessment Partners, 2018). Screening youth for a history of trauma is also of great importance (Espinoza et al., 2013).

Juvenile offenders can also be subject to solitary confinement, with significant consequences for their mental health. For example, an American Civil Liberties Union (ACLU) review of the use of solitary confinement with juveniles in Nebraska found some juveniles spent up to 90 days in isolation (Staff Editors, 2016). It is not surprising that mental health professionals find that solitary confinement "can destabilize a youth's mental condition, worsen anxiety and depression, and can lead to psychosis" (pp. 1, 14).

One study of 232 youth who were court-ordered to have a mental health assessment showed that they were not more likely to reoffend than those youth without mental health issues (McCormick, Peterson-Badali,

& Skilling, 2017). This was the case whether their mental health problems were addressed or not. Nevertheless, McCormick et al. (2017) suggest more research is needed on the mental health problems of juveniles and outcomes.

Research must continue on mental health disorders among youth in the juvenile justice system, placement decisions in secure or nonsecure settings, and the likelihood of juvenile reoffending. Mallett (2015) emphasized that while social workers and other mental health and child advocates have much experience in working with youth, when they work in the juvenile justice system these professionals are "sidelined" (p. 7), as the court takes over. This serves as an important reminder that social workers and others must continue their advocacy on behalf of children and adolescents.

See Tips for the Field 8.2 for proposals to expand and improve care for mentally ill offenders.

TIPS FOR THE FIELD 8.2

DIGGING DEEPER INTO POLICY: EXPANDING AND IMPROVING CARE FOR MENTALLY ILL CRIMINAL OFFENDERS

The following are proposals to provide improved care for the mentally ill in the criminal justice system.

Proposal #1: Service availability. Services for the incarcerated mentally ill must be significantly increased in jails and prisons. This can help prevent crises for individual inmates who challenge staff authority, as well as reduce problematic behaviors among inmates within the facility.

Proposal #2: Diversion from the system. Criminal offenders with serious mental disorders accused of less serious crimes should be diverted from the correctional system to mental health services.

Proposal #3: Training and education. All personnel in the criminal justice system, including police, court staff, and corrections officers, must be educated on mental disorders and effective ways to respond to those with mental illness.

Proposal #4: Collect data. Each component of the criminal justice system—police, courts, and corrections—should collect data on the mental health problems of individuals in their systems. Implementing the same or similar research designs can enhance efforts to offer the most appropriate services.

Proposal #5: Develop aftercare options. Criminal justice and mental health professionals should strive for better collaboration to improve continuity of services for those released, especially access to medications. Social workers and other mental health professionals must seek greater integration of services with probation and parole officers.

SOURCE: MacPhail, A., & Verdun-Jones, S. (2013, January). *Mental illness and the criminal justice system.* Paper delivered at Re-inventing Criminal Justice: The Fifth National Symposium. International Centre for Criminal Law Reform and Criminal Justice Policy, Montreal, Canada.

SUMMARY AND CONCLUSION

We must be able to identify those persons with mental illness at every stage in the criminal justice process. It is not sufficient to screen for mental health and substance use disorders; instead, efforts must broaden to include assessment and treatment. CIT for police officers is an important step in efforts to improve responses to the mentally ill in crisis situations. Courts have always dealt with mentally ill and substance-abusing offenders, and in recent years specialty courts have been developed that emphasize treatment over punishment. While there has been an increase in mental health and drug courts in recent years, all courts need to screen defendants for mental health and substance abuse problems.

Mental health services for jail and prison inmates are inadequate, and social workers can be part of plans to improve and increase these services. Solitary confinement should never be used with inmates with mental disorders. More services are needed to address the special health and mental health needs of incarcerated women. Youth with mental health problems in the juvenile justice system do not fare especially well. For all offenders, the transition from prison back to the community is very challenging, but reentry is especially difficult for the mentally ill. Therefore, community mental health systems need to do much more to assist those with mental disorders. Social work skills are needed within all components of the juvenile justice and criminal justice systems.

DISCUSSION QUESTIONS/TOPICS

1. What are the associations between crime and mental illness?
2. Why do many people think violent crimes are committed by the mentally ill?
3. What can courts do to determine if defendants have a mental health disorder and/or a substance use disorder?
4. Discuss the benefits of specialty courts, including mental health courts.
5. Discuss the importance of CIT for police officers.
6. What is the relationship between antisocial personality disorder and involvement in the criminal justice system?
7. Do you think mentally ill prison inmates should be subjected to solitary confinement? Why or why not?
8. What can be done to improve the mental health services available to incarcerated women?
9. What are your suggestions to address the mental health needs of children whose parents are incarcerated?
10. Suggest ways that social workers and probation and parole officers can work more closely to assist mentally ill offenders living in the community.

REFERENCES

Alexander, M. (2010). *The new Jim Crow: Mass incarceration in the age of colorblindness.* New York, NY: New Press.

American Psychiatric Association. (2013). *Diagnostic and statistical manual of mental disorders* (5th ed.). Arlington, VA: Author.

Anderson, C. (2018, March 19). Move made to commit Fla. suspect in 2016. *The Boston Globe*, A2.

Campbell, M. A., Canales, D. D., Weir, R., Totten, A. E., Macaulay, W. A., & Wershler, J. L. (2015). Multidimensional evaluation of a mental health court: Adherence to the risk–need–responsivity model. *Law and Human Behavior, 39*(5), 489–502. doi:10.1037/lhb0000135

Castellano, U. (2017). The politics of benchcraft: The role of judges in mental health courts. *Law & Social Inquiry, 42*(2), 398–422. doi:10.1111/lsi.12266

Cole, D. M., Thomas, D. M., Field, K., Wool, A., Lipiner, T., Massenberg, N., & Gutherie, B. J. (2018). The 21st Century Cures Act implications for the reduction of racial health disparities in the U.S. criminal justice system: A public health approach. *Journal of Racial and Ethnic Health Disparities, 5*(4), 885–893. doi:10.1007/s40615-017-0435-0

Collier, S., & Friedman, S. H. (2016). Mental illness among women referred for psychiatric services in a New Zealand women's prison. *Behavioral Sciences and the Law, 34*, 539–550. doi:10.1002/bsl.2238

Compton, M. T., Bakeman, R., Broussard, B., Hankerson-Dyson, D., Husbands, L., Krishan, S., … Watson, A. C. (2014a). The police-based crisis intervention team (CIT) model: I. Effects on officers' knowledge, attitudes, and skills. *Psychiatric Services, 65*(4), 517–522. doi:10.1176/appi.ps.201300107

Compton, M. T., Bakeman, R., Broussard, B., Hankerson-Dyson, D., Husbands, L., Krishan, S., … Watson, A. C. (2014b). The police-based crisis intervention team (CIT) model: II. Effects on level of force and resolution, referral and arrest. *Psychiatric Services, 65*(4), 523–529. doi:10.1176/appi.ps.201300108

Cramer, M. (2018, January 10). Mentally ill prisoners sue over solitary confinement. *The Boston Globe*, B1.

Cramer, M., & Russell, J. (2017). Advocates: Mentally ill inmates held in solitary isolation. *The Boston Globe*, A1, A5.

Cutcher, Z., Degenhardt, L., Alati, R., & Kinner, S. (2014). Poor health and social outcomes for ex-prisoners with a history of mental disorder: A longitudinal study. *Australian and New Zealand Journal of Public Health, 38*(5), 424–429. doi:10.1111/1753-6405.12207

Davidson, M. L. (2016). A criminal justice system-wide response to mental illness: Evaluating the effectiveness of the Memphis crisis intervention team training curriculum among law enforcement and correctional officers. *Criminal Justice Policy Review, 27*(1), 46–75. doi:10.1177/0887403414554997

Denton, M., Foster, M., & Bland, R. (2017). How the prison-to-community transition risk environment influences the experience of men with co-occurring mental health and substance use disorder. *Australian & New Zealand Journal of Criminology, 50*(1), 39–55. doi:10.1177/0004865815620703

Desmaris, S. L., Van Dorn, R. A., Johnson, K. L., Grimm, K. J., Douglas, K. S., & Swartz, M. S. (2014). Community violence perpetration and victimization among adults with mental illnesses. *American Journal of Public Health, 102*(12), 2342–2349. doi:10.2105/AJPH.2013.301680

Espinoza, E. M., Sorensen, J. R., & Lopez, M. A. (2013). Youth pathways to placement: The influence of gender, mental health need and trauma on confinement in the juvenile justice system. *Journal of Youth and Adolescence, 42*, 1824–1836. doi:10.1007/s10964-013-9981-x

Fedock, G., Fries, L., & Kubiak, S. P. (2013). Service needs for incarcerated adults: Exploring gender differences. *Journal of Offender Rehabilitation, 52*, 493–508. doi:10.1080/10509674.2012.759171

Gillig, P. M., Dumaine, M., Stammer, J. W., Hillard, J. R., & Grubb, P. (1990). What do police officers really want from the mental health system? *Psychiatric Services, 41*(6), 663–665. doi:10.1176/ps.41.6.663

Goldfarb, D. (2018, May/June). Are social workers the new face of community policing? *Social Work Voice*, 14–16.

Grekin, P. M., Jemelka, R., & Trupin, E. W. (1994). Racial differences in the criminalization of the mentally ill. *Bulletin of American Academy of Psychiatry and the Law, 22*(3), 411–420.

Hardy-Fanta, C., & Mignon, S. I. (2000). *Alternatives to incarceration for substance abusing female defendants/offenders in Massachusetts 1996–1998.* Boston, MA: University of Massachusetts Boston, Center for Women in Politics and Public Policy.

Honegger, L. N. (2015). Does the evidence support the case for mental health courts? A review of the literature. *Law and Human Behavior, 39*(5), 478–488. doi:10.1037/lhb0000141

Kataoka, S. H., Zima, B. T., Dupre, D. A., Moreno, K. A., Yang, X., & McCracken, J. T. (2001). Mental health problems and service use among female juvenile offenders: Their relationship to criminal history. *Journal of the American Academy of Child and Adolescent Psychiatry, 40*(5), 549–555. doi:10.1097/00004583-200105000-00014

Kempker, S. M., Schmidt, A. T., & Espinosa, E. M. (2017). Understanding the influence of mental health diagnosis and gender on placement decisions for justice-involved youth. *Journal of Youth and Adolescence, 46*, 1562–1581. doi:10.1007/s10964-016-0572-5

Lamb, H. R., & Weinberger, L. E. (2017). Understanding and treating offenders with serious mental illness in public sector mental health. *Behavioral Sciences and the Law, 35*, 303–318. doi:10.1002/bsl.2292

Laurio, A. (2018, June). Social work roles are many in the criminal justice system. *NASW News*, 8, 9, 11.

Lynch, S. M., Dehart, D. D., Belknap, J., Green, B. L., Dass-Brailsford, P., Johnson, K. M., & Wong, M. M. (2017). An examination of the associations among victimization, mental health, and offending in women. *Criminal Justice and Behavior, 44*(6), 796–814. doi:10.1177/0093854817704452

Lynch, S., & Heath, N. (2017). Predictors of incarcerated women's postrelease PTSD, depression, and substance-use problems. *Journal of Offender Rehabilitation, 56*(3), 157–172. doi:10.1080/10509674.2017 .1290007

MacPhail, A., & Verdun-Jones, S. (2013, January). *Mental illness and the criminal justice system.* Paper delivered at Re-inventing Criminal Justice:

The Fifth National Symposium. International Centre for Criminal Law Reform and Criminal Justice Policy, Montreal, Canada.

Mallett, C. A. (2015). The incarceration of seriously traumatised adolescents in the USA: Limited progress and significant harm. *Criminal Behavior and Mental Health, 25*, 1–9. doi:10.1002/cbm.1946

Martin, M. S., Eljdupovic, G., McKenzie, K., & Colman, I. (2015). Risk of violence by inmates with childhood trauma and mental health needs. *Law and Human Behavior, 39*(6), 614–622. doi:10.1037/lhb10000149

Martone, C. A., Mulvey, E. P., Yang, S., Nemoianu, A., Shugarman, R., & Soliman, L. (2013). Psychiatric characteristics of homicide defendants. *American Journal of Psychiatry, 170*(9), 994–1002. doi:10.1176/appi.ajp.2013.12060858

McCormick, S., Peterson-Badali, M., & Skilling, T. (2017). The role of mental health and specific responsivity in juvenile justice rehabilitation. *Law and Human Behavior, 41*(1), 55–67. doi:10.1037/lhb0000228

Mental Health First Aid. (2018). *What is Mental Health First Aid?* Retrieved from https://www.mentalhealthfirstaid.org/about

Mignon, S. I. (2015). *Substance abuse treatment: Options, challenges and effectiveness.* New York, NY: Springer Publishing Company.

Mignon, S. I. (2016). Health issues of incarcerated women in the United States. *Ciência & Saúde Coletiva, 21*(7), 2051–2060. doi:10.1590/1413-81232015217.05302016

Mignon, S. I. (2017). *Child welfare in the United States: Challenges, policy and practice.* New York, NY: Springer Publishing Company.

Mignon, S. I., & Ransford, P. (2012). Mothers in prison: Maintaining connections with children. *Social Work in Public Health, 27*(1–2), 69–88. doi:10.1080/19371918.2012.630965

Minieri, A. M., Staton-Tindall, M., Leukefeld, C., Clarke, J. G., Surratt, H. L., & Frisman, L. K. (2014). Relationship power as a mediator of intimate partner violence and mental health issues among incarcerated, substance-using women. *International Journal of Offender Therapy and Comparative Criminology, 58*(3), 303–319. doi:10.1177/0306624X12472017

Mulvey, E. P., & Schubert, C. A. (2017). *Mentally ill individuals in jails and prisons.* University of Chicago. Retrieved from https://www.equitasproject.org/wp-content/uploads/2017/09/Mulvey-2016-Mentally-Ill-Individuals-in-Prison-and-Jail.pdf

Munetz, M. R., Ritter, C., Teller, J. L., & Bonfine, N. (2014). Mental health court: Perceived coercion, procedural justice, and program impact. *Psychiatric Services, 65*(3), 352–358. doi:10.1176/appi.ps.002642012

National Association of Drug Court Professionals. (2018). *About NADCP.* Retrieved from https://www.nadcp.org/about

National Center for State Courts. (2018). Veterans courts resource guide. Retrieved from https://www.ncsc.org/Topics/Alternative-Dockets/Problem-Solving-Courts/Veterans-Court/Resource-Guide.aspx

National Youth Screening and Assessment Partners. (2018). *National Youth Screening and Assessment Partners.* Retrieved from http://www.nysap.us/Index.html

Peterson, J. K., Skeem, J., Kennealy, P. Bray, B., & Zvonkovic, A. (2014). How often and how consistently do symptoms directly precede criminal behavior among offenders with mental illness. *Law and Human Behavior, 38*(5), 439–449. doi:10.1037/lhb0000075

Robertson, C., Davis, J. H., & Gabriel, T. (2018, October 31). United in grief, Pittsburgh splits over Trump: President's visit lays bare deep national divide. *The Boston Globe,* A2.

Rose, S. J., LeBel, T. P., & Blakey, J. M. (2016). The health and mental health needs of incarcerated women. *Correctional Mental Health Report, 18*(1), 1–2, 4–14. Retrieved from https://www.civicresearchinstitute.com/online/article.php?pid=14&iid=1183

Skeem, J. K., Kennealy, P., Monahan, J., Peterson, J. K., & Applebaum, P. A. (2015). Psychosis uncommonly and inconsistently precedes violence among high risk individuals. *Clinical Psychological Science, 4*(1), 4–49. doi:10.1177/2167702615575879

Skeem, J. K., Manchak, S., & Peterson, J. K. (2011). Correctional policy for offenders with mental illness: Creating a new paradigm for recidivism reduction. *Law and Human Behavior, 35*(2), 110–126. doi:10.1007/s10979-010-9223-7

Skeem, J. L., Winter, E., Kennealy, P. J., Louden, J. E., & Tatar, J. R. II. (2014). Offenders with mental illness have criminogenic needs, too: Toward recidivism reduction. *Law and Human Behavior, 38*(3), 212–224. doi:10.1037/lhb0000054

Snedker, K. A., Beach, L. R., & Corcoran, K. E. (2017). Beyond the "revolving door"? Incentives and criminal recidivism in a mental health court. *Criminal Justice and Behavior, 44*(9), 1141–1162. doi:10.1177/0093854817708395

Staff Editors. (2016). Isolation of juveniles: Rarely a good idea; often excruciatingly bad. *Correctional Mental Health Report, 18*(1), 1, 14. Retrieved from https://www.civicresearchinstitute.com/online/article.php?pid=14&iid=1183

Steadman, H. J., Callahan, L., Robbins, P. C., Vesselinov, R., McGuire, T. G., & Morrissey, J. P. (2014). Criminal justice and behavioral healthcare costs of mental health court participants: A six-year study. *Psychiatric Services, 65*(9), 1100–1104. doi:10.1176/appi.ps.201300375

Swartz, M. S. (2014). How do mental health courts work? *Psychiatric Services, 65*(9), 1077–1083. doi:10.1176/appi.ps.650902

Taheri, S. A. (2016). Do crisis intervention teams reduce arrests and improve office safety? A systematic review and meta-analysis. *Criminal Justice Policy Review, 27*(1), 76–96. doi:10.1177/0887403414556289

Thompson, M., Newell, S., & Carlson, M. J. (2016). Race and access to mental health and substance abuse treatment in the criminal justice system. *Journal of Offender Rehabilitation, 55*(2), 69–94. doi:10.1080/10509674.2015.1112867

To, W. T., Vanheule, S., De Smet, S., & Vandevelde, S. (2015). The treatment perspectives of mentally ill offenders in medium- and high-secure forensic settings in Flanders. *International Journal of Offender Therapy and Comparative Criminology, 59*(14), 1605–1622. doi:10.1177/0306624X14566355

Torrey, E. F., Kennard, A. D., Eslinger, D., Lamb, R., & Pavle, J. (2010, May). *More mentally ill persons are in jails and prisons than hospitals: A survey of the states.* Treatment Advocacy Center. Retrieved from http://www.treatmentadvocacycenter.org/storage/documents/final_jails_v_hospitals_study.pdf

Treatment Advocacy Center. (2018). *Treatment Advocacy Center: Eliminating barriers to the treatment of mental illness.* Arlington, VA. Retrieved from http://www.treatmentadvocacycenter.org/?gclid=EAIaIQobChMIl_3Hzfau3 gIVD-DICh15XA8wEAAYASAAEgJ-ofD_BwE

Tsai, J., Finlay, A., Flatley, B., Kasprow, W. J., & Clark, S. (2018). A national study of veterans treatment court participants: Who benefits and who recidivates. *Administrative Policy and Mental Health, 45*(2), 236–244. doi:10.1007/s10488-017-0816-z

Turanovic, J. J., & Rodriguez, N. (2017). Mental health service needs in the prison boom: The case of children of incarcerated mothers. *Criminal Justice Policy Review, 28*(5), 415–436. doi:10.1177/0887403415591269

Watson, A. C., Morabito, M. S., Draine, J., & Ottati, V. (2008). Improving police response to persons with mental illness: A multi-level conceptualization of CIT. *International Journal of Law and Psychiatry, 31*(4), 359–368. doi:10.1016/j.ijlp.2008.06.004

Wittouck, C., Dekkers, A., De Ruyver, B., Vanderplasschen, W., & Vander Laenen, F. (2013). The impact of drug treatment courts on recovery: A systematic review. *Scientific World Journal, 2013*, 1–12. doi:10.1155/2013/493679

Wood, J., & Beierschmitt, L. (2014). Beyond police crisis intervention: Moving "upstream" to manage cases and places of mental health vulnerability. *International Journal of Law and Psychiatry, 37*(5), 439–447. doi:10.1016/j .ijlp.2014.02.016

Woodhouse, R., Neilson, M., Martyn-St James, M., Glanville, J., Hewitt, C., & Perry, A. E. (2016). Interventions for drug-using offenders with co-occurring mental health problems: A systematic review and economic appraisal. *Health and Justice, 4*, 10. doi:10.1186/s40352-016-0041-y

CHAPTER 9

NO PLACE TO GO: HOMELESSNESS AND MENTAL ILLNESS

INTRODUCTION

Mental illness can be both a cause and a consequence of homelessness. People with mental health problems are more likely to become homeless than those without mental disorders (National Coalition for the Homeless, 2009). Mental health problems make it difficult to access support services, engage with family and friendship supports, and overcome barriers to employment, putting individuals at risk for homelessness (Jackson, 2013). It is very difficult to distinguish the homeless with mental illness from the homeless without mental illness (Gittelman, 2005). The homeless are not a homogeneous group, and their needs for services can vary considerably beyond the need for a stable living environment (Polcin, 2016). The mentally ill most at risk of homelessness have serious mental illnesses such as schizophrenia and bipolar disorder (Martin,

2015). The homeless with both serious mental illness and substance use disorders are also exceptionally vulnerable (Sun, 2012).

This chapter examines the relationship between homelessness and mental illness and substance abuse. It examines the risk factors for homelessness as well as special groups such as homeless families, women and children, and veterans. It examines the recent rise of homelessness and related societal responses. The chapter discusses the role of homeless courts and the shelter system. Responses to homelessness include Housing First (HF) and Treatment First (TF) approaches. The National Alliance on Mental Illness (NAMI) policy recommendations are discussed, as are the recommendations of the National Alliance to End Homelessness. Finally, the role of social workers in reducing homelessness is addressed.

Rates of mental illness and substance abuse among the homeless are especially high (Henry, Watt, Rosenthal, & Shivji, 2017; Martens, 2001–2002). Numerous studies have found that between 18% and 25% of the homeless have mental illness of some kind (Harrison, 2015; Henry et al., 2017). In January 2017, according to the Department of Housing and Urban Development (HUD), approximately 20% of the homeless population had severe mental illness, and an additional 20% had a chronic substance use disorder (Henry et al., 2017). As indicated, it can be difficult to determine whether mental illness and substance abuse are the causes or the consequences of homelessness.

There are many risk factors for homelessness, including mental disorders, poverty, substance abuse, trauma history, death of family members, social isolation, disability, and low educational levels (Martens, 2001–2002; Padgett, Smith, Henwood, & Tiderington, 2012). A multitude of adverse events in childhood can set the stage for adverse events in adulthood (Padgett et al., 2012). Therefore, while homelessness is related to the individual characteristics of the homeless population, it is also related to societal structures and lack of opportunities (Aubry, Duhoux, Klodawsky, Ecker, & Hay, 2016). Unfortunately, most research on homelessness has focused on the characteristics of the homeless themselves. rather than on societal contributors to their homelessness and social and environmental solutions (Thompson, Pollio, Eyrich, Bradbury, & North, 2004).

Homelessness in the United States grew significantly in the 1980s, for the first time since the Great Depression in the 1930s (Bassuk, DeCandia, Beach, & Berman, 2014; Burt, 1992; Gittelman, 2005). Many factors contributed to the increase in homelessness during this time period. These factors, which exerted tremendous pressure on the poor, included (a) policies of the Reagan era, (b) reduced welfare benefits, (c) an increase in the cost of living, (d) decreased household income, (e) lack of affordable rental units, and (f) a decline in manufacturing jobs (Burt, 1992).

To provide information on the number of homeless persons in the United States, HUD conducts a survey of the homeless population, both those in shelters and those living on the streets, during January of each year (Henry et al., 2017). In January 2017, 553,742 individuals were homeless, with 65% in shelters and 35% living outside (Henry et al., 2017). Half of the homeless population in the United States in 2017 was found in California, New York, Florida, Texas, or Washington.

Some communities, such as Boston, strive to hide their homeless from public view. In other communities, such as Honolulu, Hawaii, the homeless are highly visible and sleep on pieces of cardboard on the streets. Public places such as bus and train stations, and public libraries, are locations where the homeless tend to congregate. Others live in abandoned properties, under bridges, and in tents on the outskirts of cities (Treatment Advocacy Center, 2016). In recent years, many large cities have started to consider the homeless population an "emergency." This does not necessarily translate into increased efforts to help the homeless, but rather a desire to make them less visible. For example, cities such as St. Petersburg, Florida, and Santa Cruz, California, have laws that prohibit sleeping outside on the streets (Treatment Advocacy Center, 2016). This criminalization of homelessness focuses on improving the lives of community members at the expense of those members of society most in need of assistance (Aykanian & Lee, 2016).

Life lived on the streets is extremely difficult. The homeless with mental illness are easy targets for criminals, and homeless young women are easy prey for sexual assault. In leading a marginalized life, the homeless struggle to meet their basic needs and may have to resort to unconventional methods to survive (Thompson et al., 2004). As discussed earlier, homeless people are at higher risk of becoming involved in the criminal justice system (Polcin, 2016). Some homeless must resort to foraging for food in garbage cans and dumpsters (Martin, 2015).

In their study of the homeless population in Melbourne, Australia, Chamberlain and Johnson (2011) found five common ways adults become homeless: (a) a housing crisis that follows severe financial problems such as job loss; (b) family breakdown that can be associated with violence and victimization within the family or when one adult partner chooses to leave the family; (c) substance abuse that becomes a major problem; (d) mental health problems that for individuals younger than the age of 25 can take the form of being forced to leave the family home due to behavioral problems, and for those 25 and older, becoming homeless when parents die and there is no one to provide for the mentally ill individual; and (e) the "youth-to-adult" pathway to homelessness for those older than 18 that is often attributed to aging out of foster home or other type of child protection services or to no longer being willing to accept the restrictions of living at home. In the Australia study, those with mental health problems often were homeless for long periods of time, had few social supports, and had few housing options (Chamberlain & Johnson, 2011).

Not surprisingly, homeless people must often rely on hospital emergency departments for their healthcare. One study found that mentally ill homeless persons seeking emergency department treatment had a 31.1% chance of being treated again in the emergency department within 30 days (Lam, Arora, & Menchine, 2016). It is evident that this "revolving door" is not helpful to homeless patients and is also a factor in driving up healthcare costs.

Homelessness is not often a topic debated by political candidates at the local, state, or national levels. In reality, not much political capital is expended on the homeless, nor do homeless individuals often participate in politics (Gittelman, 2005). The homeless are eligible to vote in all 50 states and often list a shelter or an outdoor location such as a park as their home address (Nonprofit Vote, 2018). Considering the difficulties of life as a homeless person, it is hard to imagine such an individual prioritizing voting in political elections.

SUBSTANCE ABUSE, CO-OCCURRING DISORDERS, AND HOMELESSNESS

Chapter 5, Social Work and Mental Illness: Labels and Diagnoses, described the difficulties associated with having both a mental illness and a substance use disorder. Homelessness adds to these complexities. In a qualitative study of 28 individuals with homelessness experiences, substance abuse problems were key to becoming homeless and exacerbated other problems (McNaughton, 2008). Substance abuse was described as a way to cope with social isolation while living on the margins of society, as a way to assimilate into the homeless culture, and as a way to cope with a trauma history. However, of the 19 of 28 respondents who obtained a home, most continued to have substance abuse problems (McNaughton, 2008).

In a large study of 4,291 homeless individuals in Melbourne, Australia, 43% had substance abuse problems (Johnson & Chamberlain, 2008). One third had substance problems before becoming homeless, and two thirds were homeless before they developed a substance problem. Younger individuals were more likely to develop a substance problem after becoming homeless.

In the late 1990s, the Substance Abuse and Mental Health Services Administration (SAMHSA) made housing a priority for the homeless with mental health and substance use disorders by funding a number of projects focused on permanent supportive housing (Rog et al., 2014).

In addition to a permanent home, supportive housing means that crisis intervention and other counseling services are available, as well as other community resources such as transportation. Supportive housing is affordable, with tenants typically paying only 30% of their monthly income for rent. It does not require participating in additional services; however, tenants may choose from among a range of services such as counseling or support services.

In their review of housing studies from 1995 to 2012, Rog et al. (2014) found the supportive housing model helped reduce visits to hospital emergency departments and hospitalizations, showed good client satisfaction, and increased time in stable housing. The effects of supportive housing for those with substance use disorders or co-occurring disorders have yet to be adequately studied. Improved methods for comparing different housing models for clients with mental health and substance use disorders are needed (Rog et al., 2014).

HOMELESS FAMILIES

Family violence, substance abuse, depression, and other mental health disorders all contribute to homelessness in families (Amerson, 2008). In 2017, among homeless families with children, 184,661 individuals within those families were homeless, a decline of 5% over the previous year (Henry et al., 2017). Thirty percent of homeless families with children were found in New York.

While having a home is certainly of critical importance, it does not guarantee that mental health status will improve. In a study of homeless families in the United Kingdom, 1 year after they were rehoused, mental health issues were still evident for mothers and their children (Vostanis, Gratten, & Cumella, 1998). Approximately 25% of mothers and 20% of children had ongoing mental health problems. Unfortunately, some 20 years later, health services for the homeless have not significantly improved, and there continues to be little collaboration and coordination among agencies serving the mentally ill homeless.

Homeless Women

Women are less likely than men to become homeless, and if they do, they have shorter periods of homelessness (Aubry et al., 2016). However, women and their children can pay a heavy price for their homelessness. Homeless women are at higher risk of physical injury and have less access to healthcare (American College of Obstetricians and Gynecologists, 2010, reaffirmed 2018). Homeless women have more exposure to trauma than other women; the stress associated with trauma contributes to both the social and economic problems of a family

(Bassuk et al., 2014). Trauma can also include leaving home at an early age due to family violence, which also puts women at greater risk of victimization in adulthood (Jasinski, Wesely, Mustaine, & Wright, 2005).

In interviews with women who were previously homeless, the women described a history of traumatic events, betrayal by others, anxiety about leaving treatment programs, concern for stigma, and wanting to have their own space (Padgett, Hawkins, Abrams, & Davis, 2010). Helpful clinical responses should include better training for those providing services to homeless women, therapy for trauma and feelings of betrayal, and a stronger focus on their current mental health symptoms rather than their prior history of mental health diagnoses. See Case Example 9.1 for the description of one homeless woman whose life ended in tragedy for herself and her family.

CASE EXAMPLE 9.1

A HOMELESS MOTHER'S LIFE AND DEATH

In 2017, San Diego, California, council member Lorrie Zapf, at a time when her city was establishing temporary housing for the homeless, chose to share the story of her mother's homelessness, mental illness, and substance use disorder. Lorrie's mother had a history of alcoholism and was divorced when Lorrie was 7 years old. Lorrie and her younger brother and sister were forced to live in various chaotic situations, including cheap motels. Lorrie and her siblings suffered from nightmares, fear, and confusion. The siblings were removed from their mother's custody when Lorrie was 11 and were split up in different foster homes. Lorrie felt lucky to be able to stay in one foster home, while her siblings were moved around to different placements. Lorrie's sister developed her own mental health and substance use disorders that she struggled with over the years.

While in her early 20s, Lorrie received the phone call she had always dreaded. Her homeless, toothless 44-year-old mother with kidney and liver problems was found along a highway in Los Angeles. She died in a hospital several days later. Sadly, Lorrie's sister endured a similarly tragic life of mental illness and substance abuse, eventually dying from cancer. Lorrie was left to struggle with feelings of resentment, guilt, and sadness, especially because earlier in her own life she had not understood her mother's illnesses. Sharing her mother's story came to be part of Lorrie's own healing.

SOURCE: Zapf, L. (2017, October 4). How I came to understand my homeless mother's mental illness. *The San Diego Union-Tribune*. Retrieved from https://www.sandiegouniontribune.com/opinion/commentary/sd-utbg-mental-illness-homelessness-20171004-story.html

Depression is the most common mental health disorder among homeless mothers, although it most often is unrecognized and untreated (Bassuk & Beardslee, 2014). Homeless mothers can be at very high risk for depression, with research finding between 45% and 85% of homeless mothers have depression, much higher than the 12% rate for all women (Bassuk et al., 2014). Depression makes parenting more difficult and is strongly associated with inadequate and poor parenting, as well as problems for the children. Children of depressed mothers are more likely to have poor mental and physical health and lower academic performance (Bassuk & Beardslee, 2014). Strong parenting skills can help reduce the impacts of homelessness on children (Perlman, Willard, Herbers, Cutuli, & Garg, 2014).

Children and Youth

Homeless youth younger than the age of 25, described as "unaccompanied youth," numbered 40,799 in January 2017. Eighty-eight percent were aged 18 to 24, and 55% of unaccompanied youth were not living in shelters (Henry et al., 2017). Unaccompanied youth were 62% male, 37% female, and 2% transgender. A recent study over a 1-year period found that 3% of 13- to 17-year-olds were homeless, either running away or ordered to leave their homes (Morton et al., 2018). Among those aged 18 to 25, 5.9% were homeless.

Effects of homelessness on children include anxiety, depression, attachment disorder, and behavioral problems (Smith, 2010). Children who are homeless are more often hungry and sick than other children and are worried about the future of their families (Bassuk et al., 2014). They are among the most needy children in American society, yet are mostly invisible to others. When children are exposed to early trauma, they become at risk for long-term effects that impact their adult lives (Bassuk et al., 2014). Services for homeless children and youth must focus on trauma-informed interventions (McKenzie-Mohr, Coates, & McLeod, 2012).

It is not surprising that homeless youth have high rates of mental illness (Perlman et al., 2014). Determining the prevalence of homelessness among children and youth as well as understanding their individual experiences must be priorities (Perlman et al., 2014). LGBT youth are at even higher risk of mental health problems than are heterosexual homeless youth. A study of LGBT youth in New York found that the majority were homeless due to family rejection of their gender identity, which led them to being kicked out of their homes (Forge & Ream, 2014). Clearly, the consequences for the future of homeless youth can be very damaging without appropriate interventions (Morton et al., 2018).

One helpful approach to providing supports to homeless families is the Parenting Through Change (PTC) program, which is aimed at developing and improving parenting skills (Bassuk et al., 2014). The focus is on problem-solving, monitoring, and setting limits with children, and positive involvement of parents in the lives of their children. Another approach to providing parenting help in shelters is strengths based; it encourages parents to become more sensitive to the needs of their children, especially understanding their thoughts and feelings (Bassuk et al., 2014).

Homeless Veterans

In January 2017, 40,056 homeless veterans represented approximately 9% of all homeless adults (Henry et al., 2017). Men accounted for 90% of the homeless veteran population. Women who are veterans are almost three times more likely to become homeless than other women (VA National Center on Homelessness among Veterans, 2016). Veterans' risk factors for homelessness include mental illness, substance abuse, and low income levels (Tsai & Rosenheck, 2015). Negative childhood experiences, social isolation, and a history of incarceration are other contributing factors that put veterans at risk of homelessness.

One partnership between HUD and the Department of Veterans Affairs is a very significant effort to reduce veteran homelessness. The Housing and Urban Development and Veterans Affairs Supportive Housing (HUD-VASH) program has had substantial success in housing outcomes but less success with mental health and substance abuse problems, and some research has found veterans served by the program continue to abuse substances (Tsai & Rosenheck, 2015). The Veterans Administration, HUD, and the U.S. Interagency Council on Homelessness all support utilizing the HF model with veterans, as discussed later in the section titled Housing Options.

Older Adult Homelessness

Homeless older adults have higher rates of health problems, including chronic illnesses such as arthritis and high blood pressure (Brown, Thomas, Cutler, & Hinderlee, 2013). Medical conditions associated with aging in the general population are experienced at younger ages by the homeless. Some older adults have experienced mental illness, substance abuse, and incarceration that put them at risk of homelessness. Other homeless older adults without problems earlier in life endure some kind of crisis in their later years, such as loss of their home, loss of a partner, or serious health challenges (Brown et al., 2013). Lack of family members, such as not having children, can also increase the risk of homelessness.

Adults older than 50 years are distinguished from the younger homeless population because they are less likely to engage in manual labor and less likely to have current technological skills (Watson, 2010). As just indicated, older homeless are more likely to have health problems. For older homeless persons, like younger homeless individuals, mental health problems can be either a cause or a consequence of their homelessness (Watson, 2010).

In a study of those who provide services to older homeless adults, the most pressing concerns were mental health, physical health, and housing (Watson, 2010). Subsidized housing is more likely to be available for older adults than it is for younger adults, but yet it is not likely to meet the current need (Aubry et al., 2016). NAMI advocates for providing the least restrictive housing alternatives and support services for older adults. It also advocates for the development of research on aging and mental illness and calls for the expansion of health provider education and training on the special needs of this population (NAMI, 2016).

Permanent supportive housing can help resolve homelessness for older adults (Brown et al., 2013). See Case Example 9.2 for a description of a successful supportive housing program for adults aged 50 or older in Boston, Massachusetts.

CASE EXAMPLE 9.2

HEARTH, INC.: A PERMANENT SUPPORTIVE HOUSING MODEL

Hearth, Inc., originally known as the Committee to End Elder Homelessness when founded in 1991, is a nonprofit organization whose mission is to reduce elder homelessness in Boston. Hearth serves clients aged 50 and older and currently has 188 housing units in seven buildings in Boston. The organization's goals include increasing the number of housing units available to older adults and preventing elder homelessness. Hearth also calls attention to older adult homelessness at the local, state, and national levels to support the development of special policies aimed toward helping this population (Hearth, 2018).

Hearth offers subsidized rental units and a multidisciplinary services team to help meet the physical and mental health needs of elderly homeless individuals. It works closely with staff from homeless shelters, who make referrals. Services include assessment, treatment planning, crisis intervention, and medication management. Services to address and support activities of daily living include meal assistance, personal care assistance, and homemaking services. Group activities prevent or reduce social isolation for older adults (Brown et al., 2013).

SOURCES: Brown, R. T., Thomas, M. L., Cutler, D. F., & Hinderlie, M. (2013). Meeting the housing and care needs of older homeless adults: A permanent supportive housing program targeting homeless elders. *Seniors Housing Care Journal, 21*(1), 126–135; Hearth. (2018). *Ending elder homelessness*. Retrieved from http://www.hearth-home.org/hearth-housing

Homeless Courts

Homeless courts are designed to facilitate a positive intervention for the homeless who have been accused of low-level crimes. The first homeless court was established in 1989 in San Diego, California (Coalition for the Homeless, 2016). In Houston, Texas, local social service agencies and homeless shelters refer clients to the Coalition for the Homeless of Houston/Harris County within the Houston Municipal Courts for assistance.

Another example is the homeless court in Orange County, California, where individuals who have misdemeanor charges and fines they cannot pay can receive help. Clients perform community service and collaborate with a case manager and lawyer to establish a plan to overcome homelessness, gain access to local social services, and locate affordable housing (Orange County Public Defender, 2018). Successful completion of the court program results in legal charges and fines being dropped.

▨ HOMELESS SHELTERS, TRANSITIONAL HOUSING, AND MOVING TOWARD PERMANENCY

Shelters for the homeless are designed to respond to their immediate needs. However, to ensure a successful outcome. the homeless must be motivated to seek shelter and be ready to make changes (Thompson et al., 2004). Depending on the requirements of specific programs, shelters may keep individuals and families for weeks or require that they stay just one night and return the next day to see if a bed will be available for them. Transitional housing can last up to 2 years to stabilize individuals and to plan for permanent housing (SAMHSA, 2017). Recently the trend has moved away from shelters and short-term or transitional housing, and toward long-term housing for the homeless. This trend has been documented in the United States, Canada, Australia, and Europe (O'Campo ct al., 2016).

In a 2-year follow-up study of single homeless people in a homeless shelter in Ottawa, Canada, there were several important findings (Aubry et al., 2016). The authors identified three resources that help individuals end homelessness and achieve a stable home. One resource was related to the characteristics of the homeless individual, such as higher level of education, skill level, and a feeling of empowerment. A second resource was having a sizable and supportive social network available to the individual. A third resource was the availability of economic supports, such as regular income and subsidized housing (Aubry et al., 2016). After 2 years, those persons with better mental health functioning did not have substance abuse problems, felt they had quality housing, and felt empowered in their lives. Those with substance abuse problems had a lower level of mental health functioning and were less likely to have achieved permanent housing.

Interestingly, Aubry et al. (2016) found that housing *stability* did not necessarily mean better mental health after 2 years. One explanation is that this may not have been a long enough period of time to see an improvement in mental health. Another explanation is that the experience of homelessness is traumatic, and the effects of trauma add to mental health problems. Also, those with mental health and substance use disorders likely had those problems prior to homelessness. The *quality* of housing was related to improved mental health status. Thus, when individuals felt they had nicer and more comfortable housing, their mental health was better.

Research confirms the importance of having a network of family and friends to provide support to the homeless (Johnstone, Parsell, Jetten, Dingle, & Walter, 2016). Hawkins and Abrams (2007) described several reasons that formerly homeless individuals with both mental illness and substance use disorder can have limited social connections to support their recovery. One reason is that family and friends may die at an early age. Another reason is individuals can choose to withdraw from family and friends and instead cultivate relationships with others who have similar problems. A third reason is that family and friends may have many problems of their own, such as poverty, and cannot provide assistance to homeless individuals. Family and friends can reject the homeless individual when their own basic needs are not being met.

A study of the formerly homeless in stable housing found that connections with family, friends, and social service professionals were very helpful in exiting homelessness (Thompson et al., 2004). For example, one respondent stated about family and friends: "They kept me going when I was stuck or confused. It's a person I go and talk to when I'm not sure about everything in life in general. … They'll at least listen" (Thompson et al., 2004, p. 426). Eighty percent of respondents indicated that service providers were helpful to them in ending homelessness. For example, one respondent stated, "I think she [social worker] helped me out with more responsibility, and when I was living alone she kept me going in the right direction and go off the bad stuff. A lot of nice people around here that help with finding employment" (p. 427).

In interviews with the formerly homeless, Thompson et al. (2004) found that mental illness was not often mentioned by study respondents. This could suggest that professionals attach a greater significance to the role of mental illness in homelessness than do the homeless themselves. The homeless may utilize mental health services because they were referred and expected to seek such help by those assisting them with housing. This could also mean that the homeless do not see that mental health services are necessary to access housing (Thompson et al., 2004).

Housing Options

Community resources are the most important factors in reducing homelessness (Aubry et al., 2016). They include access to subsidized housing, the ability to participate in job training, obtaining and maintaining a job, and adequate finances. Lack of affordable subsidized housing contributes heavily to the problem of homelessness (Aubry et al., 2016).

There are a number of different approaches to helping the homeless, making it difficult to evaluate and compare theoretical and practical approaches to housing this population. Today the best-known approach is Housing First (HF), which is both a philosophical orientation and a working model for providing assistance to the homeless, with the underlying premise that everyone deserves a home (Waegemakers Schiff & Schiff, 2014). The HF model provides immediate access to a home, typically a subsidized apartment, with supports to address mental health and other problems (O'Campo et al., 2016). HF can improve the quality of life by providing a stable place to live with such service supports as counseling and vocational training.

HF has garnered much attention due to its emphasis on immediate housing for the homeless before considering other problems such as mental illness and substance abuse. In HF programs, the homeless typically get immediate access to a permanent subsidized apartment with very few restrictions (Bassuk et al., 2014; Clifasefi, Malone, & Collins, 2013). Typically, there is no requirement for abstinence from drugs or alcohol. However, there are a wide range of needs in homeless families, with some requiring more social supports than others (Bassuk et al., 2014).

In contrast to HF, the Treatment First (TF) approach places priority on treating the symptoms of mental illness as well as other problems experienced by the homeless (Henwood, Derejko, Couture, & Padgett, 2015). TF offers a more traditional approach. In a comparison of HF and TF, one qualitative study of 63 clients found that 49% of TF clients did not complete the program as compared with 13% of HF clients who did not complete the program (Henwood et al., 2015). The ability to maintain clients over longer periods of time in housing is an important measure of success in any kind of supportive housing program. In another study comparing HF and TF programs, the HF program resulted in increased quality of life and fewer arrests. However, no differences were found in substance use and healthcare utilization (O'Campo et al., 2016).

One study of HF interviewed formerly homeless residents with a diagnosis of serious mental illness every 6 months over a 2-year period (Tsemberis, Gulcur, & Nakae, 2004). The respondents had an 80% success rate of remaining housed. The presence of a mental disorder did not have any impact on the ability to maintain housing. Tsemberis et al. (2004) concluded that there should not be a requirement that tenants participate in mental health or substance abuse treatment.

HF programs may not prohibit alcohol and legal substance use, which can create a very real challenge for those with substance use disorders. Homeless individuals with alcohol and drug problems are more likely to benefit from treatment before entering stable housing (Polcin, 2016). This means a TF approach may be preferable for those homeless persons with substance use disorders, who would benefit from a period of abstinence and treatment support before living on their own.

Overall, HF has received much attention and support in the literature (Henwood et al., 2015). However, HF models have had more political support than actual research evidence in their favor (Waegemakers Schiff & Schiff, 2014). Research that compares different kinds of permanent housing for the homeless is required to determine the most successful supportive housing approaches for all homeless individuals, but especially for those with mental illness and substance use disorders. Tips for the Field 9.1 summarizes NAMI's policy platform regarding housing.

TIPS FOR THE FIELD 9.1

DIGGING DEEPER INTO POLICY: NATIONAL ALLIANCE ON MENTAL ILLNESS'S POLICY PLATFORM REGARDING HOUSING

The National Alliance on Mental Illness (NAMI) advocates for community housing for the homeless mentally ill. Following are some of the main points of the NAMI policy platform regarding housing for the homeless mentally ill:

1. The homeless mentally ill need immediate access to affordable housing as part of their recovery. Options should include providing services to meet client needs, with priority given to independent living, if possible. Clients must be able to make their own choices regarding their housing preferences.

2. Housing choices should include rentals, ownership in independent living, supportive housing, and group homes. Housing options should help residents connect to transportation, as well as employment and educational opportunities. Funding from federal, state, and private housing alternatives should be better coordinated to establish linkages between housing and support services.

3. NAMI is opposed to restrictions in housing that discriminate on the basis of mental illness or co-occurring disorders. No individuals with mental illness should be placed

in a nursing home without evidence of a medical need that requires nursing home placement.

4. Individuals with mental illness should not lose their living situations due to a crisis, hospitalization, or inpatient treatment.

SOURCE: National Alliance on Mental Illness. (2016, December). *Public policy platform of the National Alliance on Mental Illness revised* (12th ed.). Arlington, VA: Author. Retrieved from https://www.nami.org/getattachment/Learn-More/Mental-Health-Public-Policy/Public-Policy-Platform-December-2016-%281%29.pdf

▨ SOCIAL WORK, MENTAL ILLNESS, AND THE HOMELESS

Social work has long had concern for the provision of adequate housing for all in American society. This includes arranging for foster homes for abused and/or neglected children, assisting refugees to relocate to a new country, arranging for group homes for the developmentally disabled and the mentally ill, finding housing for those released from substance abuse treatment programs, and working directly with homeless populations (Social Work Policy Institute, 2006).

It has long been acknowledged that from a clinical perspective, work with the homeless is complex, and the added issue of lack of community resources makes this an especially difficult area of social work practice (Mowbray, Thrasher, Cohen, & Bybee, 1996). This area of social work requires strong skills to develop close working relationships with clients and to advocate for the development of housing and other services needed by the homeless.

While the field of social work gives priority to the most vulnerable, marginalized, and oppressed within society, it has also been criticized for not giving sufficient attention to laws and policies that criminalize some behaviors of the homeless (Aykanian & Lee, 2016). Clearly, social work can achieve more in the development and implementation of policies to protect the homeless and lead them toward services that will provide permanent housing. Social workers must protect the human rights of the homeless, especially those with mental illness. They must protect the homeless from discrimination on the streets and in community services. An essential skill of social workers is to engage in collaborative processes with other professionals and organizations and encourage advocacy to resolve the problem of homelessness.

Social workers can screen and assess the homeless for a variety of problems, including mental illness, and then establish a therapeutic relationship that addresses the issues that underlie their homelessness

(Lorenzo, 2018). In addition to finding housing, social workers help clients adjust to new housing, provide ongoing support, and help them cultivate feelings of empowerment and self-sufficiency. Therefore, social work with the homeless incorporates both micro approaches in working with clients and macro approaches that seek adequate quality homes for those in need (Social Work Policy Institute, 2006). Overall, social workers should lend their voices to developing a comprehensive approach to combatting homelessness (Aykanian & Lee, 2016).

The National Center for Excellence in Homeless Services (2016, 2018) was founded in 2013. It is an excellent example of a social work collaboration through a network of schools of social work, homeless providers, policy makers, and others to develop a comprehensive approach to ending homelessness. The National Center seeks to develop leaders in eradicating homelessness, educate policy makers, and advocate for evidence-based practices. It also calls for increased attention to homelessness in undergraduate and graduate social work curricula, as well as the expansion of social work field placements within organizations that serve the homeless. The National Center provides leadership for the National Homelessness Social Work Initiative, which received funding from the New York Community Trust in January 2015. The initiative partnered with the Council on Social Work Education (CSWE) to develop and expand networks of social work schools. In addition, it seeks to give homelessness priority within the social work profession and expand community–university partnerships to prevent and end homelessness (National Homelessness Social Work Initiative, 2018). Finally, the initiative seeks to promote social work leadership in practice, policy, and research. The National Center for Excellence in Homeless Services' (2018) Regional Hub Social Work School Leaders is composed of the University of Texas at Austin, the University of Maryland, the University of Southern California, and California State University at Long Beach.

POLITICS, POLICY, AND RESPONSES TO HOMELESSNESS

Ending homelessness in the United States is a major undertaking that has failed to capture the political will of American policy makers. Both the increase in poverty in recent years in the United States and a lack of affordable housing and healthcare have been drivers of homelessness (Martin, 2015). The Patient Protection and Affordable Care Act of 2010 does not include policies to address mental health and homelessness or public health services for the homeless (Martin, 2015). Without major changes in state and national policies and politics, the lack of attention to the poor and homeless will only persist. According to Martin (2015, p. 74),

in the end, poverty, hunger, and homelessness persist because the conservative agenda of three administrations during the past twenty-five years granted capital the unrestricted right to accumulate wealth regardless of the social cost and the systematic discrediting and dismantling of the welfare state. At no time since the early twentieth century has the state's role in providing some sort of safety net for the least advantaged in society been so undermined.

It is very hard to imagine that the Trump administration will show concern for the homeless and seek to develop and expand homelessness services. See Tips for the Field 9.2 for the major recommendations of the National Alliance to End Homelessness.

TIPS FOR THE FIELD 9.2

THE 10 ESSENTIALS OF THE NATIONAL ALLIANCE TO END HOMELESSNESS

These 10 recommendations for communities to implement to prevent and bring about an end to homelessness are all of equal value.

1. *Plan.* Each community must develop strategies to end homelessness with the input of politicians, community service agencies, and organizations that serve the homeless. The participants in the planning must be able to obtain the necessary funding. For the homeless mentally ill, this likely means expanding the availability of social workers and other mental health professionals.

2. *Data.* Each community must develop information systems that can ascertain the number of homeless, the reasons they become homeless, the services they access, as well as the services they need. This information will help to determine the types of care needed by the mentally ill homeless.

3. *Emergency prevention.* Each community must have in place an emergency program to respond to financial need, such as emergency funds for rent, utilities, and other financial strategies to prevent eviction. This can reduce crises for the homeless, especially the more vulnerable with mental illness.

4. *Systems prevention.* Each community must ensure there is stable housing for those being released from public institutions, such as shelter, psychiatric hospitals, and substance abuse treatment programs. Community service providers such as child protective services and mental health agencies must assess the housing needs of their clients on a consistent basis.

5. *Outreach.* Each community must offer advocacy and outreach services to the homeless and link them with needed community services. Those experiencing episodes of severe mental illness may have difficulty connecting with services on their own and can benefit from outreach services.

6. *Shorten homelessness.* Each community must offer shelter and transitional housing to reduce the time that individuals and families spend in homelessness. Shorter periods in shelters can help to stabilize clients with mental illness.

7. *Rapid rehousing.* Each community must offer housing placement services that focus on quickly locating appropriate housing for those in need. An up-to-date list of housing vacancies in a community can help to streamline this process.

8. *Services.* When individuals and families are rehoused, they must have immediate access to services provided by community programs. For the mentally ill, this is especially important to avoid disruption in mental healthcare, including access to medications.

9. *Permanent housing.* Each community must develop a plan to ensure that there is an adequate supply of permanent supportive housing. This is no small undertaking and is likely to require considerable community effort.

10. *Income.* Each community must ensure that the homeless are receiving the federal and state financial benefits to which they are entitled. Some are likely to require assistance with employment and educational opportunities to help them afford new homes.

SOURCE: National Alliance to End Homelessness. (2003, August). *The ten essentials: What your community needs to do to end homelessness.* Washington, DC: Author. Retrieved from http://www.hmissummit.net/coc/10%20Year%20Plans/tenessentials.pdf

Better quality and quantity of mental health services can provide greater opportunities for those with mental disorders and can reduce homelessness (Martin, 2015; National Coalition for the Homeless, 2009). Innovations in serving the mentally ill are urgently needed. For example, the San Francisco Public Library employs a full-time psychiatric social worker to assist the homeless in obtaining mental health resources and permanent homes (Harrison, 2015).

As previously stated, it is imperative that the field of social work be more involved in policy, practice, and research to help prevent, reduce, and ultimately end homelessness. These are not merely political debates: Many lives are negatively impacted each day. Research tends to examine the problems of the homeless in isolation while failing to carefully examine the system that provides homeless services (Watson, 2010). Research is needed on the relationship between specific mental disorders and homelessness (Martens, 2001–2002). To develop specialized programs for children, women, and older homeless, more research must be completed (Martens, 2001–2002). Lack of research on homeless sexual and gender minorities is also a problem (Flentje, Leon, Carrico, Zheng, & Dilley, 2016). Overall, the quality of research regarding the homeless must improve to determine which approaches are best to meet their needs (Polcin, 2016).

▨ SUMMARY AND CONCLUSION

Despite many reform efforts throughout the years, homelessness continues to be a major social problem in the United States. The relationships among homelessness, mental illness, and substance abuse are among the most challenging to understand and address. Homeless families, veterans, women, children, and youth with mental illness have an especially difficult time. Homeless individuals and families must be screened for mental health, substance abuse, and medical issues to better understand their specific needs and to ultimately be matched with appropriate services. Shelters and transitional housing offer short-term solutions, while supportive housing offers the best opportunity for the formerly homeless to succeed. HF and TF are two different strategies to address homelessness, with HF programs tending to report better results. Supportive family and friends can provide crucial social supports to the homeless. Further research must be designed to better understand the role of mental illness in homelessness and to devise quality interventions.

Social workers play a critical role in efforts to prevent and reduce homelessness. In addition to providing clinical assessment and treatment services, social workers must engage in more research and policy development as noted in Tips for the Field 9.2.

▨ DISCUSSION QUESTIONS/TOPICS

1. Discuss the risk factors for homelessness in the United States.
2. Describe the relationship between homelessness and mental illness.
3. In what ways does having a co-occurring disorder such as mental illness and addiction complicate responses to the homeless?
4. Why has homelessness grown significantly in the United States since the 1980s?
5. What are short- and long-term effects of homelessness on the mental health of children and youth?
6. How effective do you think homeless shelters are in reducing homelessness?
7. Describe the challenges of veterans coping with homelessness.
8. Discuss the importance of family and friends for homeless individuals.
9. Describe the Hearth program as an example of serving elderly homeless individuals.
10. In what ways can the 10 essentials of the National Alliance to End Homeless be utilized to make the biggest impact?

▪ REFERENCES

American College of Obstetricians and Gynecologists. (2010, reaffirmed 2018). *Health care for homeless women: Committee opinion*. Retrieved from https://www.acog.org/Clinical-Guidance-and-Publications/Committee-Opinions/Committee-on-Health-Care-for-Underserved-Women/Health-Care-for-Homeless-Women?IsMobileSet=false

Amerson, R. (2008). Mental illness in homeless families. *Journal for Nurse Practitioners, 4*(2), 109–113. doi:10.1016/j.nurpra.2008.01.001

Aubry, T., Duhoux, A., Klokawsky, F., Ecker, J., & Hay, E. (2016). A longitudinal study of predictors of housing stability, housing quality, and mental health functioning among single homeless individuals staying in emergency shelters. *American Journal of Community Psychology, 58*(1–2), 123–135. doi:10.1002/ajcp.12067

Aykanian, A., & Lee, W. (2016). Social work's role in ending the criminalization of homelessness: Opportunities for action. *Social Work, 61*(2), 183–185. doi:10.1093/sw/sww011

Bassuk, E. L., & Beardslee, W. (2014). Depression in homeless mothers: Addressing an unrecognized public health issue. *American Journal of Orthopsychiatry, 84*(1), 73–81. doi:10.1037/h0098949

Bassuk, E. L., DeCandia, C. J., Beach, C. A., & Berman, F. (2014). *American's youngest outcasts: A report card on child homelessness*. Waltham, MA: National Center on Family Homelessness.

Brown, R. T., Thomas, M. L., Cutler, D. F., & Hinderlie, M. (2013). Meeting the housing and care needs of older homeless adults: A permanent supportive housing program targeting homeless elders. *Seniors Housing Care Journal, 21*(1), 126–135.

Burt, M. R. (1992). *Over the edge: The growth of homelessness in the 1980s*. New York, NY: Russell Sage Foundation.

Chamberlain, C., & Johnson, G. (2011). Pathways into adult homelessness. *Journal of Sociology, 49*(1), 60–77. doi:10.1177/1440783311422458

Clifasefi, S. L., Malone, D. K., & Collins, S. E. (2013). Exposure to project-based Housing First is associated with reduced jail time and bookings. *International Journal of Drug Policy, 24*(4), 291–296. doi:10.1016/j.drugpo.2012.10.002

Coalition for the Homeless. (2016). *Homeless court*. Houston, TX. Retrieved from http://www.homelesshouston.org/homeless-court

Flentje, A., Leon, A., Carrico, A., Zheng, D., & Dilley, J. (2016). Mental and physical health among homeless sexual and gender minorities in a major urban US city. *Journal of Urban Health, 93*(6), 997–1009. doi:10.1007/s11524-016-0084-3

Forge, N., & Ream, G. L. (2014). Homeless lesbian, gay, bisexual and transgender (LGBT) youth in New York City: Insights from the field. *Child Welfare, 93*(2), 7–22.

Gittelman, M. (2005). The neglected disaster: Homelessness and mental illness. *International Journal of Mental Health, 34*(2), 9–21. doi:10.1080/00207411.2005.11043402

Harrison, E. (2015, February 5). Mental illness and homelessness: 3 ways communities can help. *Bitfocus*. Retrieved from https:bitfocus.com/human-services-topics/mental-illness-homelessness-help

Hawkins, R. L., & Abrams, C. (2007). Disappearing acts: The social networks of formerly homeless individuals with co-occurring disorders. *Social Science & Medicine, 65,* 2031–2042. doi:10.1016/j.socscimed.2007.06.019

Henry, M., Watt, R., Rosenthal, L., & Shivji, A. (2017, December). *The 2017 annual homeless assessment report (AHAR) to Congress. Part 1.* U.S. Department of Housing and Urban Development, Office of Community Planning and Development. Retrieved from https://www.novoco.com/sites/default/files/atoms/files/hud_2017_ahar_p1_120617.pdf

Henwood, B. F., Derejko, K.-S., Couture, J., & Padgett, D. K. (2015). Maslow and mental health recovery: A comparative study of homeless programs for adult with serious mental illness. *Administrative Policy in Mental Health and Mental Health Research, 42*(2), 220–228. doi:10.1007/s10488-014-0542-8

Jackson, K. (2013). Reducing homelessness in veterans with mental illness. *Social Work Today, 13*(3), 8.

Jasinski, J. L., Wesely, J. K., Mustaine, E., & Wright, J. D. (2005). *The experience of violence in the lives of homeless women: A research report.* National Institute of Justice. Retrieved from https://www.ncjrs.gov/pdffiles1/nij/grants/211976.pdf

Johnson, G., & Chamberlain, C. (2008). Homelessness and substance abuse: Which comes first? *Australian Social Work, 61*(4), 342–356. doi:10.1080/03124070802428191

Johnstone, M., Parsell, C., Jetten, J., Dingle, G., & Walter, Z. (2016). Breaking the cycle of homelessness: Housing stability and social support as predictors of long-term well-being. *Housing Studies, 31*(4), 410–426. doi:10.1080/0267 3037.2015.1092504

Lam, C. N., Arora, S., & Menchine, M. (2016). Increased 30-day emergency department revisits among homeless patients with mental health conditions. *West Journal of Emergency Medicine, 17*(5), 607–612. doi:10.5811/westjem.2016.6.30690

Lorenzo, J. (2018). *Clinical social work with homeless people.* New York, NY: National Association of Social Workers. Retrieved from https://www.naswnyc.org/page/173

Martens, W. H. J. (2001–2002). Homelessness and mental disorders: A comparative review of populations in various countries. *International Journal of Mental Health, 30*(4), 79–96.

Martin, E. J. (2015). Affordable housing, homelessness, and mental health: What health care policy needs to address. *Journal of Health and Human Services Administration, 38*(1), 67–89.

McKenzie-Mohr, S., Coates, J., & McLeod, H. (2012). Responding to the needs of youth who are homeless: Calling for politicized trauma-informed intervention. *Children and Youth Services Review, 34*(1), 136–143. doi:10.1016/j.childyouth.2011.09.008

McNaughton, C. C. (2008). Transitions through homelessness, substance use, and the effect of material marginalization and psychological trauma. *Drugs: Education, Prevention and Policy, 15*(2), 177–188. doi:10.1080/09687630701377587

Morton, M. H., Dworsky, A. M., Matjasko, J. L., Curry, S. R., Schlueter, D., Chavez, R., & Farrell, A. F. (2018). Prevalence and correlates of youth homelessness in the United States. *Journal of Adolescent Health, 62*(1), 14–21. doi:10.1016/j.jadohealth.2017.10.006

Mowbray, C. Y., Thrasher, S. P., Cohen, E., & Bybee, D. (1996). Improving social work practice with persons who are homeless and mentally ill. *Journal of Sociology & Social Welfare, 23*(4), 3–24.

National Alliance on Mental Illness. (2016, December). *Public policy platform of the National Alliance on Mental Illness revised* (12th ed.). Arlington, VA: Author. Retrieved from https://www.nami.org/getattachment/ Learn-More/Mental-Health-Public-Policy/Public-Policy-Platform-December-2016-%281%29.pdf

National Center for Excellence in Homeless Services. (2016). *Category: National Homelessness Social Work Initiative.* Retrieved from https:// nationalcenterforexcellenceinhomelessservices.wordpress.com/category/ national-homelessness-social-work-initiative/page/2

National Center for Excellence in Homeless Services. (2018). *About us.* Retrieved from https://nationalcenterforexcellenceinhomelessservices .wordpress.com

National Coalition for the Homeless. (2009, July). *Mental illness and homelessness.* Retrieved from https://www.nationalhomeless.org/factsheets/ Mental_Illness.html

National Homelessness Social Work Initiative. (2018). The National Homelessness Social Work Initiative (2019). Retrieved from https:// socialwork.utexas.edu/projects/the-national-homelessness-social-work -initiative

Nonprofit Vote. (2018). *Voting and homelessness.* Retrieved from https://www .nonprofitvote.org/voting-in-your-state/special-circumstances/voting-and -homelessness

O'Campo, P., Stergiopoulos, V., Nir, P., Levy, M., Misir, V., Chum, A., … Hwang, S. W. (2016). How did a Housing First intervention improve health and social outcomes among homeless adults with mental illness in Toronto? Two-year outcomes from a randomized trial. *BMJ Open, 6*, 1–12. doi:10.1136/bmjopen-2015-010581

Orange County Public Defender. (2018). *Homeless outreach court.* Retrieved from http://www.pubdef.ocgov.com/programs/homeless_outreach_court .htm

Padgett, D. K., Hawkins, R. L., Abrams, C., & Davis, A. (2010). In their own words: Trauma and substance abuse in the lives of formerly homeless women with serious mental illness. *American Journal of Orthopsychiatry, 76*(4), 461–467. doi:10.1037/1040-3590.76.4.461

Padgett, D. K., Smith, B. T., Henwood, B. F., & Tiderington, E. (2012). Life course adversity in formerly homeless persons with serious mental illness: Context and meaning. *American Journal of Orthopsychiatry, 82*(3), 421–430. doi:10.1111/j.1939-0025.2012.01159.x

Perlman, S., Willard, J., Herbers, J. E., Cutuli, J. J., & Garg, K. M. E. (2014). Youth homelessness: Prevalence and mental health correlates. *Journal of the Society for Social Work & Research, 5*(1), 361–377.

Polcin, D. L. (2016). Co-occurring substance abuse and mental health problems among homeless persons: Suggestions for research and practice. *Journal of Social Distress and the Homeless, 25*(1), 1–10. doi:10.1179/157365 8X15Y.0000000004

Rog, D. J., Marshall, T., Dougherty, R. H., George, P., Daniels, A. S., Ghose, S. S., & Delphin-Rittmon, M. E. (2014). Permanent supportive housing:

Assessing the evidence. *Psychiatric Services, 65,* 287–294. doi:10.1176/appi
.ps.201300261

Smith, C. (2010, October 24). Homelessness can cause mental problems in
kids. *InvestigateWest.* Retrieved from https://www.seattlepi.com/local/
article/Homelessness-can-casue-mental-problems-in-kids-879396.php

Social Work Policy Institute. (2006, August 10). *Housing.* Retrieved from
http://www.socialworkpolicy.org/research/housing.html

Substance Abuse and Mental Health Services Administration. (2017,
April 19). *Housing and shelter.* Retrieved from https://www.samhsa.gov/
homelessness-programs-resources/hpr-resources/housing-shelter

Sun, A.-P. (2012). Helping homeless individuals with co-occurring disorders:
The four components. *Social Work, 57*(1), 23–37.

Thompson, S. J., Pollio, D. E., Eyrich, K., Bradbury, E., & North, C. S. (2004).
Successfully exiting homelessness: Experiences of formerly homeless
mentally ill individuals. *Evaluation and Program Planning, 27,* 423–431.
doi:10.1016/j.evalprogplan.2004.07.005

Treatment Advocacy Center. (2016, September). *Serious mental illness and
homelessness.* Office of Research and Public Affairs. Retrieved from http://
www.treatmentadvocacycenter.org/storage/documents/backgrounders/smi-
and-homelessness.pdf

Tsai, J., & Rosenheck, R. A. (2015). Risk factors for homelessness among US
veterans. *Epidemiologic Reviews, 37,* 177–195. doi:10.1093/epirev/mxu004

Tsemberis, S., Gulcur, L., & Nakae, M. (2004). Housing First, consumer
choice, and harm reduction for homeless individuals with a dual
diagnosis. *American Journal of Public Health, 94*(4), 651–656. doi:10.2105/
AJPH.94.4.651

VA National Center on Homelessness Among Veterans. (2016, July). *Women
veterans and homelessness: Homeless evidence & research roundtable series.*
Philadelphia, PA: Author.

Vostanis, P., Grattan, E., & Cumella, S. (1998). Mental health problems of
homeless children and families: Longitudinal study. *BMJ Clinical Research,
316*(7135), 899–902. doi:10.1136/bmj.316.7135.899

Waegemakers Schiff, J., & Schiff, R. A. (2014). Housing First: Paradigm or
program? *Journal of Social Distress and the Homeless, 23*(2), 80–104. doi:10.
1179/1573658X14Y.0000000007

Watson, D. P. (2010). The mental health of the older homeless population:
Provider-perceived issues related to service provision. *Journal of Applied
Social Science, 4*(1), 27–43. doi:10.1177/1936724410000400104

CHAPTER 10

VIEWS FROM THE FIELD: CHALLENGES IN MENTAL HEALTH SOCIAL WORK

LEARNING OUTCOMES

- Describe some of the most stressful situations for mental health social workers.

- Define social work confidentiality and its importance within the context of working with the mentally ill.

- Demonstrate an understanding of the challenges associated with determining whether an individual is a danger to himself or others and needs involuntary psychiatric hospitalization.

- Discuss the importance of the Tarasoff decisions in the duty to warn and duty to protect potential crime victims.

- Identify the symptoms of stress and burnout in social workers and ways to combat them.

▦ INTRODUCTION

Social work is a demanding and very stressful profession, but relatively little research attention has been given to coping with and managing stress in the mental health professions (Bennett, Evans, & Tattersall, 1993; Morse, Salyers, Rollins, Monroe-DeVita, & Pfahler, 2012). Clients have complex problems, and the settings in which social work services are provided can also present challenges. Generally, social workers can experience higher levels of stress than professionals in other fields (Coyle, Edwards, Hannigan, Fothergill, & Burnard, 2005). Sources of stress emanate from client issues as well as from the environments in which social workers work. Social workers must make critical decisions, sometimes in crisis situations (DeNard, Garcia, & Circo, 2017).

Mental health social work is particularly stressful when decisions must be made regarding treatment for individuals in emergency situations. Sources of stress also include a lack of support from the organizations in which they work, a lack of clinical supervision, and a lack of agency and community resources.

This chapter addresses some of the most demanding and stressful aspects of mental health social work. Some especially stressful responsibilities of social workers include the commitment of patients to psychiatric hospitals without their consent, child abuse and neglect reporting, and the duty to warn and protect when clients make threats to the safety of others. It examines the frustrations of dealing with health insurance companies for mental health social workers in private practice. The chapter also offers recommendations to prevent and reduce stress and burnout through enhancements of staff supports and organizational changes.

Social work with clients who have severe and persistent mental illness such as schizophrenia can present special challenges for social workers. Examples of the challenging behaviors of these clients can include not taking medication as prescribed and bizarre or manipulative behaviors (Eack & Newhill, 2008). Negative attitudes of mental health providers can lead to poorer clinical outcomes for clients. As discussed in Chapter 1, Social Work and the Mental Health System, social workers are not immune to negative attitudes and stigma, although often they have less stigmatizing attitudes than psychiatrists. In a survey of 2,000 MSW social workers who were members of the National Association of Social Workers (NASW), Eack and Newhill (2008) found attitudes toward working with individuals with serious and persistent mental illness were more influenced by frustrations with their clients, rather than frustrations with the mental health system.

The Mental Health Provider Stigma Inventory (MHPSI) is an effective tool for assessing stigma among social workers and other mental health providers (Kennedy, Abell, & Mennicke, 2017). The use of the MHPSI can raise the prospects of negative views from other colleagues if results are shared, but it is possible for workers to utilize the tool independently without reporting results to supervisors or others. The MHPSI is not intended to label mental health providers, but rather to provide feedback on attitudes as well as opportunities for self-reflection, including the influence of organizational structures in which social workers work. An important use of the MHPSI can be to provide feedback on the types of agency educational and training programs needed by staff (Kennedy et al., 2017). As discussed later in this chapter in the section on Stress and Burnout, stigma-related attitudes can also be related to stress and burnout (Ahmedani, 2011; Kennedy et al., 2017).

▥ SOCIAL WORK CONFIDENTIALITY

Confidentiality is a huge issue in the field of social work, and all schools of social work emphasize the importance of privacy and confidentiality in the therapeutic relationship. Adherence to ethical standards of confidentiality and state and federal laws is critical to professional social work practice. The NASW's *Code of Ethics* addresses confidentiality in detail. Revised in January 2018, Standard 1.07 addresses issues of privacy and confidentiality. Confidentiality refers to the social worker not sharing information that the client has divulged in a therapy session (Krase, 2013). This ensures that potentially embarrassing information stays with the social worker and helps foster a trusting relationship.

There are many responsibilities of social workers and other mental health professionals to protect the confidentiality of their clients, and these must be balanced with concerns for individual and public safety. Social workers have primary responsibility to their clients; however, there can be exceptions. Social workers have a legal obligation to arrange for involuntary psychiatric hospitalization when the client is considered a danger to himself or herself or to others. Social workers and other professionals have a legal obligation to report child abuse and neglect to the local or state child protection agencies. In addition to social workers, other mandated reporters of child abuse and neglect include police officers, teachers, physicians, nurses, and teachers. Social workers also have a duty to warn potential victims when a client makes a threat of bodily injury or a death threat. Moreover, social workers are expected to notify the police department in the community in which the potential victim lives. These situations present some of the most challenging decisions that social workers face in their professional practice.

▥ INVOLUNTARY PSYCHIATRIC HOSPITALIZATION

There are many difficulties in making the determination whether individuals, such as patients in hospital emergency rooms, require psychiatric hospitalization. There are concerns for the safety and health of the patient, for family and others around the patient, and for the effects of stigma. There are important legal considerations as well (Good, Walsh, Alexander, & Moore, 2014). It is important to obtain a social history for a patient in crisis, including contacts with family members and other clinicians involved in the individual's care, if possible. That is, informed consent from the patient must be granted to contact other mental health professionals who have treated the client. Social workers understand and appreciate that important clinical decisions cannot be made in a vacuum, and their extensive training in how to obtain a psychosocial history serves them well. This includes assessing a client for a history of violent behaviors, suicide attempts, the level of threat that the patient poses to himself or herself or to others, the family support system, and mental health service availability in the community (White, 2013). Simply put, "social workers are charged with the lofty task of weighing innumerable risk and protective factors while maintaining objectivity in the face of extreme emotions" (White, 2013, p. 26). This statement is a succinct summation of the tremendous responsibilities of social workers.

Today there are screening and assessment tools to help determine whether inpatient psychiatric care is warranted. For example, the Columbia—Suicide Severity Rating Scale (C-SSRS) developed in 2007 can be used to evaluate if a patient needs psychiatric hospitalization. While it has been endorsed by the Food and Drug Administration, it has also been the subject of controversy for not being comprehensive and for not adequately covering the full range of suicidal behaviors (Giddens, Sheehan, & Sheehan, 2014). The Prodromal Questionnaire—Brief Version (PQ-B) is an effective psychosis screening tool that can be used with adolescents and young adults (Loewy, Pearson, Vinogradov, Bearden, & Cannon, 2011). While screening and assessment tools for suicide risk and psychotic disorders can be useful, they are not a substitute for clinical expertise. Ideally, screening and assessment tools should be used in conjunction with a clinical interview and evaluation. Yet, determinations of the need for involuntary hospitalization can sometimes seem to be more art than science.

Hospital emergency rooms should rely on mental health social workers, psychiatrists, and psychologists to determine the need for psychiatric hospitalization. Emergency room physicians do not have the expertise to make these decisions and should contact mental health professionals to provide mental health evaluations (Good et al., 2014). Ideally, social workers will consult with others such as psychiatrists and psychologists in a team effort to determine whether the best care plan requires involuntary hospitalization. The Council on Social Work Education (CSWE, 2014) supports a team-based approach to mental health evaluation and treatment.

Inpatient psychiatric facilities present many opportunities for stressful situations. Patients may have severe behavioral problems when admitted and may need to be on locked wards for their safety as well as the safety of other patients and staff. It is well known that psychiatric facilities are among the most stressful institutions in which a person can work (prisons are another example). Not surprisingly, threats and risks of violence are higher in psychiatric facilities than in other healthcare facilities, with nurses most at risk of victimization (Johansson, Skarsater, & Danielson, 2013).

Violence is a concern for psychiatric inpatient units across the globe (d'Ettorre & Pellicani, 2017). In a review of studies on violence in psychiatric units, d'Ettorre and Pellicani (2017) found that between 24% and 80% of workers in acute psychiatric units have been verbally assaulted, threatened, or sexually harassed by a patient at some point in their careers. A risk assessment for violence within a psychiatric facility is important to help ensure the safety of other patients and staff (d'Ettorre & Pellicani, 2017).

Research on the staff of inpatient locked psychiatric facilities and their motivation to work in such challenging environments has been inadequate (Johansson et al., 2013). In a qualitative study of nurses, a psychiatrist, and other staff in a Swedish locked unit, respondents described the importance of being sensitive to the needs of patients, feeling a sense of responsibility, and the importance of delivering quality care to patients. They described mutual support among the staff as essential to delivering quality care (Johansson et al., 2013). The work also resulted in personal reflections such as "You gain insight into yourself, and sometimes you have some prejudices too that you get straightened out" (p. 10).

Social workers in inpatient facilities rely on their education and training, as well as their practical experience (Hyde, 2017). With a good understanding of the obstacles and vulnerabilities of a psychiatric inpatient, social workers can help promote a collaborative approach to treatment that emphasizes empathic listening and support to encourage optimism for the future (Hyde, 2017).

Social workers appreciate approval from their colleagues, patients, and their families as well. They welcome contact from psychiatric patients they have worked with, especially when things are going well for them. One social worker on an inpatient unit stated, "I've got a collection of letters that clients have actually given me thanking me ... and that's just so empowering" (Hyde, 2017, p. 128).

CHILD ABUSE AND NEGLECT MANDATED REPORTING

As previously noted, social workers are required to make critical decisions in crisis situations (DeNard et al., 2017). This can be the case especially when it comes to reporting suspected cases of child abuse and neglect, an important source of professional stress (McFadden, Mallette, & Leiter, 2017; McTavish et al., 2017). When social workers must make reports to child protection agencies, this reporting must be done in a way that is very respectful of the client (Krase, 2013). Here is where the sharp clinical skills of a social worker can ease this process. Social workers can engage with their clients in ways that will allow for interventions from child protection, while helping the client to see this intervention as useful to the family. Social workers can emphasize the types of services that can be accessed by child protection agencies, including the opportunity for family members to receive mental healthcare.

In a study of 258 mental health professionals in New York, social workers with MSW degrees filed almost half (49.4%) of the child abuse and neglect reports (Weinstein, Levine, Kogan, Harkavy-Friedman, & Miller, 2000). In more than half of these reported cases, the client was the suspected perpetrator. The filing of a report of suspected abuse did not necessarily result in termination or disruption of the therapeutic relationship. Other research has shown that reports of abuse and neglect can interfere with the therapeutic relationship (McTavish et al., 2017). Weinstein et al. (2000) found that in their sample of highly experienced social workers, 92% of those making reports acknowledged having consulted with at least one other professional about the report, such as a colleague, supervisor, or child protection hotline. It is important to consult with trusted colleagues or others when making these difficult determinations. Weinstein et al. (2000) acknowledged that "making a report about a client does not become routine with time" (p. 1326). This is an acknowledgment of the difficulties and stress involved in making child abuse and neglect reports, where each case is unique.

It is important to note that in their roles as mandated reporters, social workers do not have to prove abuse or neglect. They are only obligated by law to report cases where there is *suspicion* of abuse (Mignon, 2017). It is the responsibility of the child protection agency to investigate and make a formal determination of abuse and/or neglect. Sometimes cases of abuse and neglect can go awry with horrific consequences. See Case Example 10.1 for a case in which social workers were accused of failing to protect a child, resulting in death.

CASE EXAMPLE 10.1

SOCIAL WORKERS FACE TRIAL IN DEATH OF GABRIEL FERNANDEZ IN PALMDALE, CALIFORNIA

A judge in Los Angeles County, California, has allowed four social workers to be charged in court with criminal negligence in failing to protect Gabriel Fernandez, an 8-year-old boy. In 2013, paramedics were called to the child's home and found him unresponsive. Gabriel was murdered by his mother and her boyfriend. His body had bruises and burns, three of his ribs were broken, and he had BB pellets lodged in his lung and groin areas. The mother pleaded guilty and received a sentence of life in prison without parole. The mother's boyfriend received a death sentence.

In 2018, the Los Angeles County District Attorney filed charges against four social workers, including social work supervisors. The social workers were accused of failing to file timely reports on the boy's care and mishandling the evidence regarding abuse in the home. Prosecutors allege the social workers denied and ignored the severity of the maltreatment the child suffered. A schoolteacher stated reports were made to the child protection agency regarding the child's injuries, including bruises, a split lip, and swollen eyes. The boy acknowledged to the teacher that his mother had shot him with a BB gun.

The lawsuit alleges that the social workers failed to document the indicators of physical abuse and did not document the mother's consistent refusal to seek counseling. Further, a system used to score the level of risk to the child was not properly utilized, and therefore the risk was underestimated.

A motion to dismiss the case against the social workers was denied in September 2018. The judge stated the child's death was "foreseeable." If convicted, the social workers could get prison sentences of up to 10 years.

This tragic case reflects the failure of a bureaucratic organization designed to protect children but has promoted reforms within the L.A. County child protection agency. Were the social workers and their supervisors to blame for the child's death? In what ways should they be held accountable?

SOURCES: Etehad, M., & Winton, R. (2017, March 20). 4 LA County social workers to face trial in death of 8-year-old boy. *The Los Angeles Times*. Retrieved from https://www.latimes.com/local/lanow/la-me-ln-social-worker-charges-20170320-story.html; Winton, R., & Knoll, C. (2018, September 13). Charges upheld against social workers in death of 8-year-old Gabriel Fernandez. *The Los Angeles Times*. Retrieved from https://www.latimes.com/local/lanow/la-me-ln-gabriel-fernandez-social-workers-abuse-20180913-story.html

■ DUTY TO WARN AND PROTECT

The 1970s brought increased attention to the possible obligation of social workers and other mental health professionals to warn potential victims when threats of bodily harm had been made against them by clients. The 1969 murder of Tatiana Tarasoff, which resulted in the legal case of *Tarasoff v. Regents* in California, is considered the turning point regarding a duty to warn. See Case Example 10.2 for the case of *Tarasoff v. Regents of the University of California*.

CASE EXAMPLE 10.2

TARASOFF V. REGENTS OF THE UNIVERSITY OF CALIFORNIA: TATIANA TARASOFF AND THE "DUTY TO WARN"

Tatiana Tarasoff was an undergraduate student at the University of California, Berkeley (UC Berkeley) in 1969. Her life was tragically cut short that October when she was murdered by another student. Tarasoff apparently rejected advances from Prosenjit Poddar, including a marriage proposal, and he grew upset, angry, and depressed. He sought counseling from the Cowell Memorial Hospital at UC Berkeley and during his seventh counseling session told his therapist he planned to kill Tarasoff. The psychologist sent a letter to the UC Berkeley police chief regarding the threat, stating that Poddar had significant mental health issues and did pose a danger. University police talked with Poddar and released him after he promised to stay away from Tarasoff. Poddar himself is reported to have called the police and informed them that he killed Tatiana Tarasoff.

The Tarasoff family sued the police and staff of the University hospital due to failure to confine Poddar and because Tarasoff and her parents were not warned of Poddar's intent to kill her. The lawsuit was unsuccessful in both the Superior Court of Alameda County and the California Court of Appeal, which ruled that no "duty of care" or obligation to inform was present in this situation. The Tarasoffs appealed the case to the California Supreme Court, and in 1974 they were successful when the Court ruled that there was a "duty to warn" potential victims. In 1976, the California Supreme Court extended the Tarasoff ruling, known as Tarasoff II, to include the "duty to protect" a potential victim from foreseeable danger.

SOURCES: Casebriefs. *Tarasoff v. Regents of University of California*. Retrieved from https://www.casebriefs.com/blog/law/torts/torts-keyed-to-dobbs/the-duty-to -protect-from-third-persons/tarasoff-v-regents-of-university-of-california; Granich, S. (2012, Winter). Duty to warn, duty to protect. *The New Social Worker*. Retrieved from https://www.socialworker.com/feature-articles/ethics-articles/ Duty_to_Warn%2C_Duty_to_Protect/; Tapp, K., & Payne, D. (2011). Guidelines for practitioners: A social work perspective on discharging the duty to protect. *Journal of Social Work Values and Ethics, 8*(2) 2–13.

In 1974, the *Tarasoff* decision mandated warning the potential victim, but a 1976 expanded decision by the California Supreme Court also called for a duty to protect. Today, duty to warn and protect are among the few exceptions to a client's right to confidentiality and the social worker's (or other therapist's) ethical obligation to maintain confidential information related in the context of the therapeutic relationship. The professional may discharge this duty in one of several ways, including notifying the police, directly warning the intended victim, and taking reasonable steps to protect the threatened individual. The 1976 decision triggered passage of duty to warn laws for social workers and other mental health professionals in almost every state.

Some states have codified duties to warn, though the laws vary from state to state (National Conference of State Legislatures, 2018). The majority of states have duty to warn laws that are mandatory, including California, Massachusetts, and Wisconsin. Fewer states have laws that permit warning potential victims of crime, including Texas, Florida, and Alaska. Four states have no duty to warn laws: Maine, Nevada, North Dakota, and North Carolina (National Conference of State Legislatures, 2018).

In mental healthcare, the duty to warn typically arises in a clinic, a hospital, or a clinician's office (Tapp & Payne, 2011). For example, a client may confide in a therapist a desire to inflict harm or murder another person. In such situations, social workers and other mental health professionals must be ready to take "reasonable precautions" to warn potential victims (Yelen, 2018). Social workers must notify the local police department where the potential victim resides. The social worker should try to arrange for a voluntary psychiatric hospitalization for a client. If needed, the social worker should initiate the process for psychiatric evaluation and involuntary psychiatric hospitalization.

STRESS AND BURNOUT

For social workers, stress can be related to the disconnect between idealism and the actual duties of social workers (Lloyd, King, & Chenoweth, 2002). A study comparing mental health social workers, psychiatrists, and psychologists in health maintenance organizations found social workers experienced greater stress than these other professionals (Snibbe, Radcliffe, Weisberger, & Kelly, 1989).

One study of social workers working in a variety of settings and with a variety of populations, including mental health, child care, the disabled, and older adults, found high levels of stress, anxiety, and depression associated with their work (Bennett et al., 1993). In mental health settings where psychiatrists and psychologists are likely to have higher status than social workers, low autonomy and unclear job roles can be important contributors to stress (Lloyd et al., 2002). Social workers are exposed to *secondary or vicarious trauma* when clients relate their traumatic life events, which can contribute to stress (Wagaman, Geiger, Shockley, & Segal, 2015). In addition, the routine demands of helping clients, plus a lower level of professional esteem, contribute to stress and burnout for social workers (Lloyd et al., 2002).

Like all employees, social workers have personal feelings regarding their work, their employers, and their clients. It is not surprising that often concerns of social workers focus on *boundary* issues. In social work, ethical issues and establishing appropriate boundaries can be challenging (Reamer, 2003). Social workers must avoid conflicting roles such as serving first as a therapist and then socializing with therapy clients. These issues can extend to feelings of personal responsibility for clients (Mobray, Thrasher, Cohen, & Bybee, 1996). Reamer (2003) cites the example of a social worker in a private psychiatric facility who was the therapist for a patient diagnosed with paranoid schizophrenia. The deeply religious social worker would read the Bible to the patient during therapy sessions. This caused the patient to file a complaint against the therapist. As the foremost voice in social work ethics, Frederic Reamer (2003) reminds us that there is an "impressive range of boundary issues in the profession" (p. 123).

Social workers must avoid expecting their own emotional needs to be met by their clients and their work situations (Reamer, 2003). Another concern for social workers is their own competence to handle client problems. This includes concerns for their own personal safety and a lack of emotional support from the social worker's own network. One mental health social worker stated, "I feel like I'm out there alone" (Mobray et al., 1996, p. 14). Social workers and other mental health professionals working in prison mental health settings with clients who have committed murder can initially feel unprepared for the intensity of this work and also feel a lack of support from administrators (Harris, Happell, & Manias, 2015). This is a reminder of the value of strong clinical supervision, group supervision activities, and ongoing educational and training programs that can help to establish a strong sense of competence in social workers.

Mental health social workers can feel a lack of appreciation within society and also from their specific employers (Huxley et al., 2005). In a study of mental health social workers in the United Kingdom, respondents indicated that they highly valued their work and relationships with their clients and that these were the primary reasons social workers remained in their jobs (Huxley et al., 2005).

Burnout is the culmination of stress and leads social workers to change jobs or even leave the field altogether. Burnout is a combination of several factors: (a) *emotional exhaustion*, where workers feel overwhelmed and depleted in trying to accomplish their work; (b) *depersonalization* or cynicism, where workers feel negatively toward their work overall and which can include negative attitudes toward clients; and (c) *lack of a sense of personal accomplishment* in carrying out the responsibilities, including negative views of the effectiveness of one's own work (Morse et al., 2012).

In a review of studies of mental health workers, Morse et al. (2012) found that 21% to 67% experienced a very high rate of burnout. There may be higher levels of burnout in community social workers, although most studies fail to compare burnout rates across professions such as social work, nursing, and psychiatry. Research studies that compare professions can facilitate efforts to develop strategies for reducing stress and burnout (Morse et al., 2012). Stress and burnout may also be difficult to quantify, adding to the research challenges. Tools such as the Maslach Burnout Inventory developed in 1996 may be helpful in distinguishing between low, average, and high levels of burnout (Maslach, Jackson, Leiter, Schaufeli, & Schwab, 2018).

Social workers can pay a heavy price for stress and burnout. Social workers are at higher risk of substance abuse, mental health, and physical problems (Morse et al., 2012). A study of 182 mental health clinicians found that 52% were working more than their regular work hours, exceeding the time by an average of 5 hours per week (Luther et al., 2017). Those working additional hours were more likely to experience stress and burnout and were worried that they provided a lower level of care for clients.

Organizational challenges that result in stress and burnout for social workers include ambiguous roles in an organization, role conflicts with other types of professionals, and lack of autonomy (Lloyd et al., 2002). Environmental contributors to stress and burnout include an excessive workload, working under strict time pressures, lack of resources, lack of supervision, lack of involvement in policy making for the organization, inequitable pay, and limited recognition in the workplace for good job performance (Morse et al., 2012).

Role ambiguity has been and likely will continue to be a concern for social workers in mental healthcare. Forces within agencies and in the political arena as well as changes in healthcare and insurance organizations impact the delivery of social work services (Fraher, Richman, de Saxe Zerden, & Lombardi, 2018). In addition, there have been changes in attitudes toward specific types of services, such as the use of psychiatric hospitalization; recent developments in neuromodulation techniques; and changes in the licensure requirements of social workers and other mental health providers.

Organizational structures such as those that provide quality clinical supervision can reduce stress and increase overall job satisfaction for social workers (Antonopoulu, Killian, & Forrester, 2017; Lamb & Weinberger, 2017). Strong leadership and close collaboration and decision-making with a team of mental health professionals can improve job satisfaction of clinicians (Fleury, Grenier, & Bamvita, 2017). Since staff stress and burnout are associated with lower levels of client satisfaction, reducing and preventing worker stress and burnout will have benefits for clients as well (Salyers et al., 2017).

Social Work Students

Social work students themselves endure stress in earning a BSW or MSW degree (Reardon, 2012). Stress can impact the mental health of social work students, aggravating previously existing mental health issues or fostering the development of new issues. The field of social work is inclusive, and individuals with their own mental health issues can still become effective advocates and mental health clinicians (Reardon, 2012). Academic social work programs also want to ensure that they graduate social workers who can provide high-quality services. They strive to offer programs that give students a realistic perspective on mental health social work (Acker, 2010). In recent years more attention has been paid to developing academic policies to provide social work students with the help they need. This can take the form of reducing the academic workload from full time to part time and offering the option of postponing the fieldwork requirement (Reardon, 2012).

In a study of students in a social work program in Florida, about 34% said they experienced symptoms of depression (Horton, Diaz, & Green, 2009). Approximately 12% had previous thoughts of suicide, and 4% had recent thoughts of suicide. In another study of social work students, 50% had positive scores on a depression scale (Ting, 2011). Interviews with respondents revealed concern for seeking assistance due to stigma, fear, distrust, and worries about confidentiality.

Little research has been done on entering the field of social work with mental health issues and how over time this may affect the professional development of social workers (Goldberg, Hadas-Lidor, & Karnieli-Miller, 2014). Certainly, social workers and other therapists with mental health issues can be successful in the field. Social workers can use personal experiences in ways that benefit their therapy clients (Goldberg et al., 2014).

■ ECONOMICS OF MENTAL HEALTHCARE: MEDICAID AND PRIVATE INSURANCE

The ongoing lack of attention by federal and state governments to mental healthcare will ensure that it remains a low priority and will continue the systemic pattern of providing inadequate services (Ahmedani, 2011). This can clearly be seen in challenges in accessing outpatient mental healthcare. While agency organizational improvements may be made to improve quality of care and reduce stress and burnout in social workers, in reality, agencies have very little, if any, impact on improving the culture of health insurance companies and state and federal insurance programs such as Medicaid (Morse et al., 2012). Costs associated with inpatient and outpatient psychiatric care are very high, and lack of clarity in billing and insurance coverage can make it difficult to figure out the actual costs (Stensland, Watson, & Grazier, 2012).

The amount of paperwork associated with providing mental health-care on an outpatient basis is shocking. The authorizations required by health insurance companies, the amount of time necessary to complete the process, and the low compensation have all led many mental health practitioners to refuse to do business with insurance companies. Thus, clients are expected to pay on their own and hope their health insurance company will reimburse them. Actually, expecting mental health clients to handle their own paperwork with insurance companies can be an additional source of stress for them.

Outpatient mental healthcare can be extremely difficult to obtain. According to data from the University of Southern California Schaeffer Center, Massachusetts has the highest number of mental health providers of all states. It is second to Washington, D.C., in the number of psychiatrists, and third behind Rhode Island (Kowalczyk, 2018). Alabama has the lowest number of mental health providers. In Massachusetts, only approximately half of all licensed psychiatrists, psychologists, social workers, marriage and family therapists, and mental health counselors have contracts to accept payment from Medicaid, the state-funded health insurance program for low-income individuals (Kowalczyk, 2018).

With this trend of providers not accepting certain types of insurance, clients and families are left to their own devices in seeking mental healthcare. Accordingly, those with financial resources can get the care they want and need, and those without resources are stuck on long waiting lists. Private psychiatric care in Massachusetts can cost about $175 for a 20- to 30-minute session. However, Medicaid in Massachusetts pays about $92 for psychiatrists and the same amount for a 45-minute session with a psychologist. Thus, owing to the lower reimbursement, time spent appealing insurance denials, and time on other uncompensated paperwork, this type of practice is far less appealing for therapists. One man in Massachusetts spent 6 months trying to locate a therapist for a family member. He stated, "There's a lot of red tape and [therapists] don't want to bother anymore. The good therapists say, 'It's not worth it. We don't need this. We can charge whatever we want.' And they do" (Kowalczyk, 2018, p. A13).

The Blue Cross Blue Shield Foundation in Massachusetts, in holding focus groups with potential mental health clients, found that adults with private insurance waited 2 weeks to 3 months for an appointment with a mental health provider (Kowalczyk, 2018). Adults with Medicaid coverage waited 2 to 6 months for an appointment with a mental health provider. For children in Massachusetts, those with private insurance waited 4 to 9 months, and those with Medicaid waited 2 to 6 months.

Individual client experiences in seeking outpatient mental health-care contrasts with responses from mental health providers who felt they were overall doing a good job of responding to client need for appointments. One survey of mental health providers found that 81% see mental health patients within 2 weeks of an appointment request. Community mental health centers that are the most likely to serve clients with Medicaid coverage responded that 59% are offered appointments within 2 weeks (Kowalczyk, 2018). Imagine what it must be like to have to wait months for mental health treatment: Symptoms are likely to grow worse, and there is the message to the individuals that they are not important enough to deserve prompt mental healthcare. Swift access to appropriate mental healthcare is essential to meeting the needs of individuals and their families (Lester, Tritter, & Sorohan, 2005).

Payment systems for mental healthcare, especially for state-funded and federally funded care under the Medicaid program, can be abused, including improper billing and inappropriate care provided by unqualified staff. See Case Example 10.3 for the case of Medicaid fraud by a mental health agency.

CASE EXAMPLE 10.3

MEDICAID FRAUD BY A MENTAL HEALTH AGENCY

The attorney general of Massachusetts successfully sued South Bay Community Services, a mental health agency, in federal court for fraudulent billing. The company has 17 clinics in Massachusetts and provided mental health and substance abuse services to approximately 30,000 children and adults since 2009. The agency billed Medicaid, known in Massachusetts as MassHealth, for more than $123 million since that time. The suit alleged that clinicians were not properly trained and did not have the appropriate social work degrees, licenses, and supervision to provide mental healthcare. The attorney general's written statement included this comment: "This company provided substandard care to many vulnerable patients and fraudulently billed the state for its inadequate services" (McCluskey, 2018, p. B10). While initially disputing the allegations, South Bay Community Services agreed to pay $4 million to settle the lawsuit. A spokesperson for South Bay Community Services released the following statement: "We are pleased this matter has been resolved and look forward to continuing to provide quality services to those in need" (Micucci, 2018).

SOURCES: McCluskey, P. D. (2018, January 10). State alleges fraud in billings: AG sues provider of mental health care. *The Boston Globe*, B10, B12; Micucci, E. (2018, February 14). Mental health provider settles Medicaid fraud charges. *Worcester Business Journal*. Retrieved from http://www.wbjournal.com/article/20180214/ HEALTH/180219979/mental-health-provider-settles-medicaid-fraud-charges

This text has described the profit motive of pharmaceutical companies, and these same motives exist among healthcare organizations and health insurance companies. Case Example 10.4 explores the motivations to provide mental health services within the largest retail chain in the world.

CASE EXAMPLE 10.4

WALMART AND MENTAL HEALTHCARE: IS THIS A PLACE FOR SOCIAL WORKERS?

Headquartered in Boston, Beacon Health Options provides mental health and substance abuse treatment services throughout the United States and was founded in 1983. According to its website, Beacon Health Options has 4,500 employees and serves more than 40 million people in the United States. The company opened a mental health clinic in a Walmart store in Carrollton, Texas, in November 2018, with plans to open other clinics in Walmarts around the country. One social worker employed by Beacon Health Options provides services at the new mental health clinic.

Beacon staff members say they are trying to bring mental health services to geographic areas that do not have adequate services. The CEO indicated that this is also an effort to "mainstream behavioral health services" (Freyer, 2018, p. D1). The mental health services are aimed toward individuals with stress, anxiety, and depression. Clients may request an appointment by telephoning, walking in to the Walmart, or making an online request. Those with more serious mental illness will be referred to clinicians within the Beacon Health Options system. The clinic is seeking approval for Medicaid coverage. Alternatively, clients can pay on their own: $140 for an assessment and $110 for ongoing therapy.

The president of the Massachusetts Psychiatric Society said Beacon "would have to change a lot more about their business model for it to be successful" (Freyer, 2018, p. D2). Beacon is reputed to require a number of medical authorizations and is known for "putting up barriers to care" (p. D2). The president of the Association for Behavioral Healthcare in Massachusetts, a group of providers of mental health and substance abuse treatment, expressed concern about the low pay of the therapists. The organization president stated, "If Beacon were serious about expanding access to mental health services, it would focus on doing a better job.... What Beacon is really good at is limiting access to treatment" (Freyer, 2018, p. D2).

What is the motivation of Walmart and Beacon Health Options to provide mental health services within a retail store? Is it to meet the needs of those with mental disorders? Is it to find a new venue where a profit can be made? Is this an appropriate environment for social workers to provide mental health services?

SOURCES: Beacon Health Options. (2018). *Beacon Health Options.* Retrieved from https://www.beaconhealthoptions.com/beacons-mental-health-services; Freyer, F. J. (2018, November 26). A retail approach to mental health: Boston firms opens clinic at a Walmart. *The Boston Sunday Globe*, D1, D2.

FUTURE ISSUES IN SOCIAL WORK

In the development of healthcare policy, "social work has largely been absent from the planning table" (Fraher, Richman, de Saxe Zerden, & Lombardi, 2018, p. S282). Healthcare researchers have failed to include social work as a health profession, thereby ensuring inadequate attention to determining the numbers of social workers employed in healthcare and their specific roles in healthcare organizations. The Health Resources and Services Administration (HRSA), a federal agency under the Department of Health and Human Services, has worked to fill this gap. HRSA (2018), which was created in 1982, has primary federal responsibility for improving healthcare access for vulnerable members of society and those living in geographic isolation. It is also charged with strengthening the healthcare workforce. In 2014, 62 MSW programs received a total of $26 million through behavioral health workforce expansion training grants to better prepare social work students to work in mental health and primary care settings (Fraher et al., 2018).

Stress and the potential for burnout are concerns throughout the careers of social workers. The limited existing literature on stress and burnout reflects the need for developing more strategies and interventions and using more controlled research to evaluate these programs for staff (Morse et al., 2012). Interestingly, Europe, moving ahead of the United States on this front, has taken the lead on antistress and antiburnout research and the development of reduction and prevention efforts (Morse et al., 2012). Research on staff stress and burnout needs to examine the effects on clients and the effects on the institutions in which services are provided. These efforts, along with evaluating policies and practices, will improve outcomes for people with mental health disorders (Morse et al., 2012). See Tips for the Field 10.1 for strategies to reduce and prevent stress and burnout in mental health social workers and other providers.

TIPS FOR THE FIELD 10.1

DIGGING DEEPER: REDUCING AND PREVENTING STRESS AND BURNOUT IN SOCIAL WORKERS AND OTHER MENTAL HEALTH PROFESSIONALS

These recommendations are gleaned from various studies on how to reduce stress and burnout for social workers and other mental health professionals, as well as for direct care staff in psychiatric hospitals. The recommendations focus on both the needs of individuals who work in mental health organizations and those organizational changes that can help to prevent and reduce stress and burnout.

1. Create a program development committee to assess staff training needs. Programs on a variety of topics can be offered as one-time workshops as well as in sessions that can span several weeks and months. Importantly, training and educational programs can be shared across mental health disciplines. For example, topics can include interventions with clients with severe mental disorders, and training for administrators, supervisors, and staff in communication and social skills.

2. Promote greater feelings of equity across disciplines in an effort to acknowledge and appreciate the contributions of all mental health disciplines. Of course, this should include the direct care staff who supervise the patients in psychiatric hospitals and spend more time with the patients than do the clinical staff. Direct care staff can benefit from assertiveness training in their work with patients and the professional staff. Booster sessions for programs that target individuals should be offered to reduce the chances that staff will return to previous habits.

3. Provide opportunities for self-care for all levels of staff, such as developing ways to increase the sense of meaning and worth in helping those with mental illness. This can include yoga and meditation classes, and teaching cognitive behavioral coping skills.

4. Train and encourage administrators, managers, and supervisors to express gratitude to clinical and direct care staff alike.

5. Strategies aimed at reducing stress and burnout among mental health workers are not sufficient and must include efforts to improve the organizational environment. Agency administrators must ensure that social workers have a manageable workload, adequate resources to do their jobs, strong clinical supervision, opportunities for professional development, adequate and equitable compensation, and opportunities to participate in establishing agency policies and practices.

6. Explore the use of models for improving the organizational environment that have shown effectiveness in reducing stress and burnout. These can include the Availability, Responsiveness, and Continuity (ARC) organizational model and the Civil, Respect, and Engagement at Work (CREW) social relationship intervention model. These models are discussed in Chapter 11, Innovations in Mental Healthcare, as important innovations in improving mental healthcare for clients and reducing stress for those who provide mental health services.

7. Provide for continual assessment and revision of agency policies and practices that promote caring for all staff and the professional development of staff at all levels.

SOURCE: Adapted from Morse, G., Salyers, M. P., Rollins, A. L., Monroe-DeVita, M., & Pfahler, C. (2012). Burnout in mental health services: A review of the problem and its remediation. *Administration and Policy in Mental Health and Mental Health Services Research, 39*(5), 341–352. doi:10.1007/s10488-011-0352-1

Research on social work in mental healthcare must advance beyond descriptions of social work duties and responsibilities and focus on the unique contributions made to mental healthcare, including the positive effects on clients (Fraher et al., 2018). This is an important pathway to determining how best to enhance and reinforce the important roles of social workers in mental healthcare.

SUMMARY AND CONCLUSION

Social workers are at high risk of job-related stress and burnout. Mental health social work with individuals with severe and persistent mental illness can be especially challenging. Stressful situations for mental health social workers include decisions regarding the need for psychiatric hospitalization, making child abuse and neglect reports to child protection agencies, and duty to warn and duty to protect situations. Social workers may not get the quality clinical supervision they need or adequate organizational support. All mental health professionals need to address their own stigmatizing attitudes toward the mentally ill, especially clients with major mental disorders, who may be perceived as noncompliant with treatment.

The economics of mental healthcare can be problematic for social workers. Requirements of Medicaid, private insurance, and healthcare organizations make it difficult for social workers to receive appropriate compensation and to establish themselves in private practice. The trend toward expecting clients to pay out of pocket and then try to obtain reimbursement on their own is concerning.

Stress and burnout can be reduced in a variety of ways that focus on the individual needs of social workers as well as the organizational context in which they work. Improved clinical supervision and collaboration with other mental health professionals can help to reduce stress. More research is required to determine strategies for reducing stress among mental health social workers. Few antistress and antiburnout programs exist, and more and better-designed research is needed to evaluate their effectiveness.

▨ DISCUSSION QUESTIONS/TOPICS

1. Discuss the reasons that social work is a high-stress profession.

2. Why is a psychiatric team approach to care associated with higher job satisfaction?

3. Why is it important for all social workers to know the confidentiality laws in their own states?

4. What are the problems associated with determining whether an individual is a danger to himself or herself or to others and needs involuntary hospitalization?

5. What lessons should the field of social work take from the *Tarasoff v. Regents of the University of California* court case?

6. Why do mental health social workers and other professionals in private practice prefer to be paid directly by the client rather than by the client's insurance company?

7. What kinds of services do you think should be made available to social work students if they are experiencing mental health problems?

8. How can social workers and other mental health professionals address their own stigmatizing attitudes toward mental illness?

9. Discuss your own ideas for ensuring that all individuals with mental health problems can obtain prompt access to the care they need.

10. What are your suggestions for reducing stress and burnout in mental health social workers?

▨ REFERENCES

Acker, G. (2010). The challenges in providing services to clients with mental illness: Managed care, burnout and somatic symptoms among social workers. *Community Mental Health Journal, 46*(6), 591–600. doi:10.1007/s10597-009-9269-5

Ahmedani, B. K. (2011). Mental health stigma: Society, individuals, and the profession. *Journal of Social Work Values and Ethics, 8*(2), 4–16.

Antonopoulu, P., Killian, M., & Forrester, D. (2017). Levels of stress and anxiety in child and family social work: Workers' perceptions of organizational structure and support and workplace opportunities in Children's Services in the UK. *Children and Youth Services Review, 76*, 42–50. doi:10.1016/j.childyouth.2017.02.028

Bennett, P., Evans, R., & Tattersall, A. (1993). Stress and coping in social workers. *British Journal of Social Work, 23*, 31–44

Council on Social Work Education. (2014, October). The role of social work in mental and behavioral health care: Principles for public policy. Retrieved from https://www.cswe.org/getattachment/Advocacy-Policy/RoleofSWinMentalandBehavorialHealthCare-January2015-FINAL.pdf.aspx

Coyle, D., Edwards, D. M, Hannigan, B., Fothergill, A., & Burnard, P. (2005). A systematic review of stress among mental health social workers. *International Social Work, 48*(2), 201–211. doi:10.1177/0020872805050492

DeNard, C., Garcia, A., & Circo, E. (2017). Caseworker perspectives on mental health disparities among racial/ethnic minority youth in child welfare. *Journal of Social Service Research, 43*(4), 1–17. doi:10.1080/0148837 6.2017.1299827

d'Ettorre, G., & Pellicani, V. (2017). Workplace violence toward mental healthcare workers employed in psychiatric wards. *Safety and Health at Work, 8*(4), 337–342. doi:10.1016/j.shaw.2017.01.004

Eack, S. M., & Newhill, C. E. (2008). What influences social workers' attitudes toward working with clients with severe mental illness. *Family Sociology, 89*(3). doi:10.1606/1044-3894.3767

Fleury, M.-J., Grenier, G., & Bamvita, J.-M. (2017). Job satisfaction among mental healthcare professionals: The respective contributions of professional characteristics, team attributes, team processes, and team emergent states. *Sage Open Medicine, 5*, 1–12. doi:10.1177/2050312117745222

Fraher, E. P., Richman, E. L., de Saxe Zerden, L., & Lombardi, B. (2018). Social work student and practitioner roles in integrated care settings. *American Journal of Preventive Medicine, 54*(653), S281–S289.

Giddens, J. M., Sheehan, K. H., & Sheehan, D. V. (2014). The Columbia—Suicide Severity Rating Scale (C-SSRS): Has the "gold standard" become a liability? *Innovations in Clinical Neuroscience, 11*(9–10), 66–80. Retrieved from https://www.ncbi.nlm.nih.gov/pmc/articles/PMC4267801

Goldberg, M., Hadas-Lido, N., & Karnieli-Miller, O. (2014). From patient to therapatient: Social work students coping with mental illness. *Qualitative Health Research, 25*(7), 1–12. doi:10.1177/104973231455399

Good, B., Walsh, R. M., Alexander, G., & Moore, G. (2014). The acute psychiatric patient in the emergency room: Legal cases and caveats. *Western Journal of Emergency Medicine, 15*(3), 312–317. doi:10.5811/westjem.2013.8.18378

Harris, D. M., Happell, B., & Manias, E. (2015). Working with people who have killed: The experience and attitudes of forensic mental health clinicians working with forensic patients. *International Journal of Mental Health Nursing, 24*, 130–138. doi:10.1111/inm.12113

Health Resources and Services Administration. (2018). *About HRSA.* Retrieved from https://www.hrsa.gov/about/index.html

Horton, E. G., Diaz, N., & Green, D. (2009). Mental health characteristics of social work students: Implications for social work education. *Social Work in Mental Health, 7*(5), 458–475. doi:10.1080/15332980802467696

Huxley, P., Evans, S., Gately, C., Webber, M., Mears, A., Pajak, S., … Katona, C. (2005). Stress and pressures in mental health social work: The worker speaks. *British Journal of Social Work, 35*(7), 1063–1079. doi:10.1093/bjsw/bch218

Hyde, B. (2017, July). *The lived experience of acute mental health inpatient care: What's recovery got to do with it?* Doctoral dissertation submitted to Charles Sturt University, Australia.

Johansson, I. M., Skarsater, I., & Danielson, E. (2013). The experience of working on a locked acute psychiatric ward. *Journal of Psychiatric and Mental Health Nursing, 20*(4), 321–329. doi:10.1111/j.1365-2850.2012.01919.x

Kennedy, S. C., Abell, N., & Mennicke, A. (2017). Initial validation of the Mental Health Provider Stigma Inventory. *Research on Social Work Practice, 27*(3), 335–347. doi:10.1177/1049731514563577

Kowalczyk, L. (2018). Finding no help on mental issues. *The Boston Sunday Globe*, A1, A13.

Krase, K. (2013). Social workers as mandated reporters: Conflicted over confidentiality? Part IV. *The New Social Worker*. Retrieved from http://www.socialworker.com/feature-articles/practice/social-workers-as-mandated-reporters%3A

Lamb, H. R., & Weinberger, L. E. (2017). Understanding and treating offenders with serious mental illness in public sector mental health. *Behavioral Sciences and the Law, 35*, 303–318. doi:10.1002/bsl.2292

Lester, H. E., Tritter, J. Q., & Sorohan, H. (2005). Patients' and health professionals' views on primary care for people with serious mental illness: Focus group study. *BMJ, 330*(7500), 1122. doi:10.1136/bmj.38440.418426.8F

Lloyd, C., King, R., & Chenoweth, L. (2002). Social work, stress and burnout: A review. *Journal of Mental Health, 11*(3), 255–265. doi:10.1080/09638230020023642

Loewy, R. L., Pearson, R., Vinogradov, S., Beardon, C. E., & Cannon, T. D. (2011). Psychosis risk screening with the Prodromal Questionnaire—Brief version (PQ-B). *Schizophrenia Research, 129*(1), 42–46. doi:10.1016/j.schres.2011.03.029

Luther, L., Gearhart, T., Fukui, S., Morse, G., Rollins, A. L., & Salyers, M. P. (2017). Working overtime in community mental health: Associations with clinician burnout and perceived quality of care. *Psychiatric Rehabilitation Journal, 40*(2), 252–259. doi:10.1037/prj0000234

Maslach, C., Jackson, S. E., Leiter, M. P., Schaufeli, W. B., & Schwab, R. L. (2018). *Maslach Burnout Inventory*. Retrieved from https://www.mindgarden.com/117-maslach-burnout-inventory

McFadden, P., Mallette, J., & Leiter, M. (2017, May 23). Extending the two-process model of burn-out in child protection workers: The role of resilience in mediating burnout via organizational factors of control, values, fairness, reward, workload, and community relationships. *Stress and Health, 34*(6), 72–83. doi:10.1002/smi.2763

McTavish, J. R., Kimber, M., Devries, K., Colombini, M., MacGregor, J. C. D., Wathen, C. D., … MacMillan, H. L. (2017). Mandatory reporters' experiences with reporting child maltreatment: A meta-synthesis of qualitative studies. *BMJ Open, 7*(10), e013942. doi:10.1136/bmjopen-2016-013942

Mignon, S. I. (2017). *Child welfare in the United States: Challenges, policy, and practice*. New York, NY: Springer Publishing Company.

Mobray, C. T., Thrasher, S. P., Cohen, E., & Bybee, D. (1996). Improving social work practice with persons who are homeless and mentally ill. *Journal of Sociology & Social Welfare, 23*(4), 3–24.

Morse, G., Salyers, M. P., Rollins, A. L., Monroe-DeVita, M., & Pfahler, C. (2012). Burnout in mental health services: A review of the problem and its remediation. *Administration and Policy in Mental Health and Mental Health Services Research, 39*(5), 341–352. doi:10.1007/s10488-011-0352-1

National Conference of State Legislatures. (2018, October 12). *Mental health professionals' duty to warn.* Retrieved from http://www.ncsl.org/research/health/mental-health-professionals-duty-to-warn.aspx

Reamer, F. G. (2003). Boundary issues in social work: Managing dual relationships. *Social Work, 48*(1), 121–133. doi:10.1093/sw/48.1.121

Reardon, C. (2012). Supporting social work students with mental health challenges. *Social Work Today, 12*(5), 10.

Salyers, M. P., Bonfils, K. A., Luther, L., Firmin, R. L., White, D. A., Adams, E. L., & Rollins, A. L. (2017). The relationship between professional burnout and quality and safety in healthcare: A meta-analysis. *Journal of General Internal Medicine, 32*(4), 475–482. doi:10.1007/s11606-016-3886-9

Snibbe, J. R., Radcliffe, C., Weisberger, M., & Kelly, J. (1989). Burnout among primary care physicians and mental health professionals in a managed health care setting. *Psychological Reports, 65,* 775–780. doi:10.2466/pr0.1989.65.3.775

Stensland, M., Watson, P. R., & Grazier, K. L. (2012). An examination of costs, charges, and payments for inpatient psychiatric treatment in community hospitals. *Psychiatric Services, 63*(7), 666–671. doi:10.1176/appi.ps.201100402

Tapp, K., & Payne, D. (2011). Guidelines for practitioners: A social work perspective on discharging the duty to protect. *Journal of Social Work Values and Ethics, 8*(2), 2–13.

Ting, L. (2011). Depressive symptoms in a sample of social work students and reasons preventing students from using mental health services: An exploratory study. *Journal of Social Work Education, 47*(2), 253–268.

Wagaman, M. A., Geiger, J. M., Shockley, C., & Segal, E. A. (2015). The role of empathy in burnout, compassion satisfaction, and secondary traumatic stress among social workers. *Social Work, 60*(3), 201–209. doi:10.1093/sw/swv014

Weinstein, B., Levine, M., Kogan, N., Harkavy-Friedman, J., & Miller, J. M. (2000). Mental health professionals' experiences reporting suspected child abuse and maltreatment. *Child Abuse & Neglect, 24*(10), 1317–1328. doi:10.1016/S0145-2134(00)00191-5

White, R. (2013). The ethics of involuntary hospitalization. *Journal of Social Work Values and Ethics, 12*(2), 25–35.

Yelen, J. A. (2018, March/April). Ask our attorney armed and dangerous: Duty to warn. *Social Work* Voice, 8.

CHAPTER 11

INNOVATIONS IN MENTAL HEALTHCARE

LEARNING OUTCOMES

- Examine the advantages of integrating substance abuse and mental healthcare into primary care physicians' offices.

- Identify innovations in treatments for depression, neuroimaging, and psychiatric hospitalization.

- Describe the San Antonio model for delivering mental health services and the reasons it has become a national model.

- Evaluate strategies for creating healthier and more innovative organizations that provide mental health services.

- Discuss the knowledge and skills social workers bring to the development of innovative practices in mental healthcare.

■ INTRODUCTION

Mental health issues and services have been relegated to the periphery of healthcare and have not received the clinical and research attention they deserve (Brooks, Pilgrim, & Rogers, 2011). Unfortunately, few efforts have been made to address the fragmentation within the current mental health system (Geller, 2015). Fragmentation results in overall poorer outcomes for individuals and higher financial costs (Laderman & Mate, 2014). Not surprisingly, the mental health field is sorely in need of innovative clinical and systematic practices and policies.

This chapter addresses the fragmentation of the mental health system and examines barriers to innovation and service integration. It offers recommendations that may streamline and improve the system. It examines models for innovations in mental health, with a special focus on the successful efforts in San Antonio, Texas, to craft a comprehensive service approach to treatment of the mentally ill. The chapter examines organizational changes that can support service innovations. In addition, this chapter includes suggestions for promoting social workers as important innovators in mental healthcare.

The former Agency for Healthcare Research and Quality's (AHRQ) Health Care Innovations Exchange (2016) defined healthcare *innovation* as the implementation of new or revised products, services, systems, policies, organizational structures, or models to improve quality and/or reduce healthcare disparities. This is distinguished from *policy innovation*, which offers a new approach in a specific organizational context that leads to improved quality or reduction of disparities in the behavior of individuals, groups, or organizational entities (AHRQ, 2016).

In addressing the needs of the seriously mentally ill, Geller (2015) reminds us that those with major mental disorders have many needs beyond psychiatric care that should be addressed by community resources. Poor communication contributes significantly to fragmentation in mental health. This includes poor communication of mental health providers with clients as well as poor communication among mental health and other medical and social service organizations. If we are to succeed in designing integrated systems, we must ensure that the basics are provided: We must inform clients how to access services and how to advocate for themselves, and ensure they understand the instructions for taking medications and managing their follow-up care (Geller, 2015).

As we describe in this text, individuals with major mental disorders are likely to be assessed and treated in a wide variety of settings, such as medical offices and hospitals, mental health organizations, and the criminal justice system. It has taken many years to understand the importance of establishing connections among these providers to deliver more collaborative and comprehensive services. At this time we are still far from fully integrating medical and psychiatric healthcare. Geller (2015) offers a sobering insight: "It's a preposterous assumption to believe that two fragmented systems of care and treatment can be brought together with an outcome being an integrated system" (p. 910). However, integration and innovation efforts must continue.

Simple solutions such as ensuring that patients have a week's supply of medications upon hospital discharge can ease their transition back into the community. Emergency department and/or hospital discharge instructions should be provided to the patient as well as to the services to which he or she was referred. Patients should receive a telephone or text reminder a day or so before outpatient appointments to increase the chances they will attend. A client's failure to show up for an appointment should lead the clinician to seek follow-up contact with the client (Geller, 2015).

▨ IMPROVED TREATMENTS FOR DEPRESSION

A new development in mental health is the effort to distinguish subtypes of depression that can be more easily and specifically targeted for treatment. The idea of *precision medicine* utilized in the treatment of cancers may be the future of treatment for depression as well (Thielking, 2018). Regarding the causes of depression, the director of the Stanley Center for Psychiatric Research at the Broad Institute of MIT and Harvard University stated, "It's some grab bag of these thousands of [genetic] variants, plus bad luck as the brain develops, plus lived environments" (Thielking, 2018, p. B14). Currently, patients may have to try several different antidepressants to determine which will work best for them, a trial-and-error process that can last for months. Stanford University has recently established the Center for Precision Mental Health and Wellness to tackle this problem (Thielking, 2018). The effort to determine subtypes of depression relies on developing research that examines blood test results, MRI scans, and DNA testing. This is very challenging because symptoms can vary widely in patients with depression. The Stanford team involves a wide variety of professions—research scientists, geneticists, psychiatrists, and engineers. Once subtypes of depression can be identified, the next—and even more difficult—task requires determining how research results will guide treatment for individual patients. While seemingly daunting work, innovations in depression treatment are very much needed.

▨ PSYCHIATRIC HOSPITAL INNOVATION

History has taught us that public psychiatric hospitals are not likely to be sources of innovation, but this does not have to be the case. In recent years patients have been viewed as part of the treatment team, rather than being told to follow the instructions of the "professionals." An important new strategy is inviting recovered mental health patients into psychiatric hospitals to work with patients and staff. For example, New Jersey developed the *Recovery Network Project* to bring former state psychiatric patients back into hospitals to serve as consultants, where they teach wellness and recovery strategies to current patients and staff (Swarbrick & Brice, 2006). Former patients conduct weekly meetings to demonstrate that recovery is possible. Resources are offered to patients when they are ready to be discharged, so as to ease the transition back into the community through connections to self-help networks. Staff trainings include reminders that recovery is possible and that there is hope for the future. The development of this collaborative approach between the hospital staff and peer educators has been expanded into day psychiatric programs. The Recovery Network Project also fosters feelings of empowerment among former patients and provides them with the opportunity to serve as role models (Swarbrick & Brice, 2006).

In 2017, Nevada launched its own Recovery Network Project, funded by the Substance Abuse and Mental Health Services Administration (SAMHSA), to support connections of the recovery community and integrate peer supports into healthcare and mental health systems (Eagan, 2017). These recovery supports cannot replace professional mental health treatment, but rather serve as an important adjunct to mental healthcare.

INNOVATIONS IN NEUROIMAGING

Brain disease models of mental illness are dominant in Western psychiatry today (Borgelt, Buchman, & Illes, 2012). The appeal of the brain image approach is that it purports to provide objective information. Neuroimaging of a brain problem gives authority and validation to having a biologically based disorder, which can help reduce stigma in mental illness. However, the social context in which these tools are used must be considered. Major concerns are the current lack of knowledge and understanding regarding causes of brain disease. The overlap of symptoms in various brain disorders makes it very difficult to distinguish between psychiatric disorders (Arentshorst, de Cock Buning, & Broerse, 2016). Of course, innovations in neuroimaging must be provided within an ethical context (Borgelt et al., 2012). See Case Example 11.1 for the controversial brain imaging work of Dr. Daniel Amen.

CASE EXAMPLE 11.1

DR. DANIEL AMEN AND AMEN CLINICS: CONTROVERSIAL BRAIN SCAN-BASED TREATMENTS

Dr. Daniel Amen is a celebrity psychiatrist and the director of Amen Clinics, established in 1989, which provide brain scans, treatment plans, and therapies. Dr. Amen is also a best-selling author of numerous books on improving brain functioning. He appears on the Public Broadcasting Service (PBS) system and sells nutritional supplements to support brain function. His website boasts that he is the most popular psychiatrist in the United States. On his website, he makes this bold statement: "You are not stuck with the brain you have. You can make it better and I can prove it."

Amen Clinics offer SPECT (single photon emission computed tomography) brain imaging. SPECT imaging measures the flow of blood in the brain and the patterns of brain activity. According to Dr. Amen, SPECT imaging shows the parts of the brain that work well, that work too hard, and that do not work well. The Amen Clinics website (2018) states personnel at these clinics have done more than 140,000 scans on individuals ages 9 months up to 105 years and have worked with individuals from 111 countries. At this writing, the cost of an initial consultation is $400, according to the Amen Clinics website. In 2016, an evaluation consisting of two SPECT brain images, one while concentrating and one while at rest, cost $3,950 (Berstein, 2016). Typically, health insurance does not pay for these services, but payment plans are available.

Amen Clinics treat anxiety, depression, bipolar disorder, posttraumatic stress disorder (PTSD), addictions, concussion, and a variety of other disorders. Currently, Amen Clinics are located in New York City; Atlanta, Georgia; Bellevue, Washington; Reston, Virginia; Bannockburn, Illinois; and three California sites—Encino, Costa Mesa, and Walnut Creek.

While Amen Clinics are popular among the public and have made Dr. Amen very wealthy, a number of prominent psychiatrists and neurologists have taken issue with the claims about SPECT and its ability to diagnose and establish treatments for mental disorders. One criticism is that Dr. Amen's PBS shows are aired without a trace of the controversy that surrounds his work within the medical community (Bernstein, 2016). In 2012, the director for the Center for Neuroscience & Society at the University of Pennsylvania referred to one of Dr. Amen's research articles as "a sham" (Tucker, 2012). A professor of psychiatry, neurology, and radiology at Emory School of Medicine stated, "He's making claims that are outrageous and not supported by any research" (Tucker, 2012). Jeffrey Lieberman, chairman of the Department of Psychiatry at Columbia College of Physicians and Surgeons, and former president of the American Psychiatric Association, stated the following: "Basically, he's conning people" (Bernstein, 2016). Perhaps what Dr. Amen is best at is selling hope for recovery and a better future.

SOURCES: Amen D. (2018). Retrieved from http://danielamenmd.com; Amen Clinics. (2018). Retrieved from https://www.amenclinics.com/faq; Amen, D. G. (1998, revised 2015). *Change your brain, change your life*. New York, NY: Harmony Books; Bernstein, R. (2016, August 3). Head case: Why has PBS promoted controversial shrink Dr. Daniel Amen? *Observer*. Retrieved from https://observer.com/2016/08/head-case-why-has-pbs-promoted-controversial-shrink-dr-daniel-amen; Tucker, N. (2012, August 9). Daniel Amen is the most popular psychiatrist in America: To most researchers and scientists, that's a bad thing. *The Washington Post Magazine*. Retrieved from https://www.washingtonpost.com/lifestyle/magazine/daniel-amen-is-the-most-popular-psychiatrist-in-america-to-most-researchers-and-scientists-thats-a-very-bad-thing/2012/08/07/467ed52c-c540-11e1-8c16-5080b717c13e_story.html?noredirect=on&utm_term=.6c179e9644ce

One newer area of brain research focuses on individuals who have had repetitive brain trauma, such as the multiple concussions that can be experienced by professional football players. For example, researchers at Boston University Medical Center examined the brains of deceased professional football players and found that a significant number had chronic traumatic encephalopathy (CTE). CTE is characterized by difficulties with memory, depression, personality changes, and aggressive behavior. In a study of 111 brains of former National Football League players examined at Boston University, 110 brains showed evidence of CTE (Ward, Williams, & Manchester, 2017). Perhaps the best-known case is that of Aaron Hernandez, who was a tight end for the New England Patriots for three seasons. Hernandez received a life sentence for killing a friend and was acquitted of two other murders. In hindsight, he displayed classic symptoms of CTE. Hernandez hanged himself in a Massachusetts prison in April 2017 at the age of 27. The autopsy of his brain at Boston University Medical Center confirmed that his brain was "ravaged" by CTE (Pfeiffer, Healy, Hohler, Ryan, & Wen, 2018, A7).

The future is likely to bring about significant contributions from neuroimaging to the diagnosis and treatment of mental disorders. This will include increased efforts to distinguish mental illness from brain injury. Borgelt et al. (2012) conclude, "Neuroimaging is expected to have a profound, expansive impact on the conceptualization of mental illness and provision of mental healthcare. The magnitude and nature of the effects of neuroimaging on its end-users and social context must continue to be elucidated to inform policy and practice in the future."

MEDICAL INSURANCE CHALLENGES

As described in Chapter 10, Views From the Field: Challenges in Mental Health Social Work, insurance directives and funding regulations present obstacles to accessing mental healthcare. These challenges also extend to integration and innovation in the provision of mental health services. Federal funding for programs such as Supplemental Security Income (SSI) and Medicaid, which cover services for a wide variety of low-income and needy individuals, including those with disabilities, has only added to the lack of coordination between psychiatric hospitals and outpatient services. For example, federal and state regulations lead to patients being shunted from the hospital emergency department to a private psychiatric hospital for stabilization, then perhaps being moved to a state hospital or into a nursing home, or even remaining in the emergency department for weeks because beds are not available (Geller, 2015).

The Institution for Mental Disease (IMD) exclusion is a good example of the restrictive regulations governing mental healthcare; it has been in force since the development of Social Security and Medicaid in 1965

(Legal Action Center, n.d.). The intent of the IMD exclusion is to ensure that states, rather than the federal government, have primary responsibility for paying for psychiatric hospitalization. It prohibits Medicaid patients aged 18 to 64 from receiving mental health and substance abuse inpatient treatment in facilities that have more than 16 beds and, therefore, reduces care options (Legal Action Center, n.d.). With Medicaid recipients unable to access the care they need, the access disparities become more significant. In 2014 in the United States, Medicaid covered only 25% of inpatient mental health services and 21% of inpatient services for substance use disorders (Musumeci, 2018). Waivers to these requirements for those persons with mental health disorders are the most commonly sought, and the most commonly obtained waivers. (Just imagine the time and effort that could be redirected more fruitfully if waivers were not needed!) In 2017, the federal Centers for Medicare and Medicaid Services (CMS) prohibited Medicaid funding for managed healthcare organizations to cover members in IMDs for more than 15 days within each calendar month (Mercy Care Plan, 2017). Thus, payment requirements and restrictions can severely reduce the opportunities for patients to get the treatment they need. Since the IMD exclusion is part of the federal Medicaid statute, only an act of Congress can overturn it, something it has not been willing to do in all these years. It would be a huge step forward in the treatment of mental illness and substance abuse—an "innovation"—if Congress was willing to act to remove the IMD exclusion. This is an important national advocacy issue for the National Association of Social Workers (NASW), and an extension of its important work to improve access to mental healthcare.

Sometimes, it can be difficult to distinguish innovation from the repackaging of services with a much higher price tag (Kowalczyk, 2018). See Case Example 11.2 for a description of recent inpatient psychiatric care alternatives.

CASE EXAMPLE 11.2

PRIVATE-PAY PSYCHIATRIC INPATIENT CARE PROGRAMS AT MCLEAN HOSPITAL: INNOVATION OR PROFIT?

As discussed in Chapter 10, Views From the Field: Challenges in Mental Health Social Work, the trend toward not accepting health insurance for outpatient psychotherapy has been accompanied by a recent trend toward providing psychiatric inpatient care on a private-pay basis only. McLean Hospital in Belmont, Massachusetts, widely considered the top psychiatric hospital in the country, has a number of private-pay-only programs. One specialty care program of McLean, the Pavilion in Belmont, Massachusetts, costs $55,300 for a 2-week stay.

Another specialized care unit is Borden Cottage in Camden, Maine, which provides care in luxurious surroundings. There, the minimum stay of 1 month costs $2,150 per day. The wealthy can afford this—but others must remortgage their homes, use their credit cards, or use retirement savings to pay for such care.

On average, in McLean Hospital, insurance typically covers only 3 to 7 days of psychiatric care to stabilize patients. In 2018, only about 17% of McLean Hospital patients were paid for by Medicaid. The hospital now has 40% of its psychiatric beds and outpatient programs available exclusively for those who can pay privately.

McLean Hospital administrators justify the very high costs charged by the hospital by asserting that private-pay patients subsidize the costs of treatment for those on Medicaid or other private insurance plans that do not cover the complete costs of care. An attorney with Mental Health Legal Advisors in Boston is supportive of this approach: "Patients are treated as guests and clients. This is less stigmatizing to patients, and that could improve outcomes" (Kowalczyk, 2018, A10). The executive director of the advocacy group Massachusetts Chapter of the National Alliance on Mental Illness said that this level of care should be available to all individuals with a psychiatric need, not just those with private funds. A vice president of the nonprofit advocacy group Mental Health America commented, "Only in America do we have insurance [that] doesn't cover what we need and then we pay extra" (p. A10).

SOURCE: Kowalczyk, L. (2018, October 1). Exclusive psychiatric care, for a price. *The Boston Globe*. A1, A10.

INTEGRATION OF MENTAL HEALTH, SUBSTANCE ABUSE, AND PRIMARY CARE

The move toward integration of primary care and mental health has received more clinical and research attention in recent years. Integrated care focuses on trying to meet various patient healthcare needs in one location. The Affordable Care Act has helped move the U.S. healthcare system toward this integration (Horevitz & Manoleas, 2013). One model includes placing social workers and other mental health professionals within primary care physicians' offices. Another model is for primary care physicians to provide medical care within mental health settings (Gerrity, 2014).

Several important arguments support the need for the integration of services. One argument is that primary care physicians already see a large number of patients with mental illness and provide a significant proportion of medications for depression treatment, as previously discussed. Also, those individuals with mental health and/or substance use disorders have higher rates of chronic health problems and, therefore, require increased medical attention (National Institute of Mental Health, 2017). Another argument is that many individuals do not know how to access mental health services and may feel more comfortable seeking assistance from their primary care physician (National Institute of Mental Health, 2017). Other reasons to support integrated care are that it is typically closer to home and offers greater continuity of care because individuals tend to stay with primary care doctors over long periods of time.

One integrated model is known as the patient-centered medical home (PCMH) model of care. It provides a variety of services in one-stop shopping, with mental health services as a critical component (Mann et al., 2016). The Affordable Care Act of 2010 provided Medicaid coverage for PCMHs for individuals with chronic health problems (National Institute of Mental Health, 2017).

A far less common model is integrating the services of primary care physicians into mental health settings such as psychiatric day treatment programs and group homes. The Milbank Memorial Fund examined 12 examples of this model over a 10-year period, starting in 2004 (Gerrity, 2014). Millbank concluded that utilizing this model of integration improves client mental health outcomes, especially for those persons with serious mental disorders.

It can be complicated to integrate medical and mental health services (Mann et al., 2016). Not surprisingly, there are financial barriers to implementation, such as obtaining insurance coverage for added services (Butler et al., 2008). Staff needs and appropriate training must be taken into account—for example, determining when it is appropriate for a physician to request social work services. The integration of medical records is also a challenging but important move toward integration of services (Geller, 2015). See Tips for the Field 11.1 for a description of collaborative care components, a model that has shown effectiveness in treating anxiety and depression.

TIPS FOR THE FIELD 11.1

COLLABORATIVE CARE COMPONENTS FOR INTEGRATED CARE

In a review of 79 randomized controlled studies, this collaborative model showed significant improvement for the short-, medium-, and long-term treatment of anxiety and depression (Archer et al., 2012). The model focuses on the following components:

1. Support patient self-care.

2. Ensure responsibility for care management lies with the care team.

3. Provide for outcomes measurement, including systematic tracking of the severity of the illness.

4. Utilize a stepped care model: Utilize the least restrictive and least expensive treatments first, and then increase the intensity of treatment, if needed.

5. Develop a system of caseload, consultation, and referral reviews.

6. Develop patient tracking and registry mechanisms.

7. Utilize evidence-based guidelines and interventions.

8. Collaborate with social service agencies to address patient needs.

SOURCES: Archer, J., Bower, P., Gilbody, S., Lovell, K., Richards, D., Gask, L., ... Coventry, P. (2012, October). Collaborative care for depression and anxiety problems. *Cochrane Database Systemic Review, 10*, CD006525. doi:10.1002/14651858.CD006525.pub2; Laderman, M., & Mate, K. (2014, March/April). Integrating behavioral health into primary care. Reprinted from Healthcare Executive. *Institute for Healthcare Improvement.* Retrieved from http://www.ihi.org/resources/Pages/Publications/IntegratingBehavioralHealthPrimaryCare.aspx

Social Work and Integrated Care

Social workers are key to the successful integration of physical health and mental health services. Social workers are skilled at screening and assessing for a variety of problems and have a far greater awareness of community resources than any other group of mental health professionals. Most often social work services within primary care focus on short-term interventions, using a team approach focused on patient outcomes (Horevitz & Manoleas, 2013; Mann et al., 2016). For example, this strategy can include social workers taking on the role of helping patients complete Medicaid applications. Patients who have had social work services in the past may expect longer-term assistance from a social worker, and patients should be informed of the brief nature of these interventions.

With social work offices within medical practices, physicians can introduce social workers to patients at the time of the medical appointment to facilitate social work assistance. Social workers help physicians with time management by relieving them of patient discussions on selected topics such as alcohol and drug use, smoking cessation, stress management, and the importance of exercise (Mann et al., 2016). Also, social workers can arrange appointments for patients within a variety of community resources. Of course, psychiatric emergencies can challenge the most well-integrated office, and these integrated approaches are more suitable for those with mild-to-moderate mental health disorders (Horevitz & Manoleas, 2013).

The integration of mental health and substance abuse screening, assessment, and treatment into primary care physician offices is showing positive outcomes (Butler et al., 2008). This is especially the case for the treatment of depression, as patients are more likely to be treated in this setting for depression than in a psychiatrist's office (Butler et al., 2008). A recent study compared satisfaction with specialized mental healthcare with care in primary settings and found equally strong satisfaction with both models (Fortin, Zhirong, & Fleury, 2018). Having a case manager and fostering continuity of care were important to both models. Healthcare insurers and policy makers will benefit from education regarding the important roles of social workers within the integrated model (Mann et al., 2016).

It can be hard for research to establish differences between increased professional attention to mental health disorders and the effect of different specific integration strategies (Butler et al., 2008). This points to the importance of devising research studies that can measure the effects of different models and strategies of integrated health and mental healthcare.

Future integration is likely to include an expansion into high-risk specialty clinics, such as cardiology clinics, where a wide variety of needs are usually present (Laderman & Mate, 2014). Integration is also likely to expand beyond specific organizations to include larger regions and states. Colorado, for example, developed the State Health Care Innovation Plan to integrate physical health and mental healthcare, and it is expected to be available to most residents by 2019. Integration also requires rethinking funding and payment mechanisms and offering more opportunities for innovation in healthcare financing (Laderman & Mate, 2014).

COLLABORATION ACROSS THE MENTAL HEALTH SERVICE SYSTEM: THE CASE OF SAN ANTONIO, TEXAS

A novel coalition to develop a comprehensive "soup-to-nuts" approach to mental healthcare is taking place in San Antonio, Texas. This wide-ranging effort has been under way for the past 16 years, and it is receiving much attention as a national model. The first line of mental health intervention is often with the police department, though individuals can seek these services on their own. San Antonio officers have participated in crisis intervention team (CIT) training, and it is now a requirement for new police recruits. A seven-person unit has considerable mental health training, such that one to two specially trained officers respond to crisis calls, including potential suicides and completed suicides. These officers must deal with the most dreadful circumstances, such as two officers who had the horrific experience of helping a mother cut down her son who hanged himself in a closet (Helman, Cramer, Russell, Rezendes, & Wallack, 2016).

The San Antonio coalition developed a crisis center for psychiatric and substance abuse emergencies. This means that patients can avoid hospital emergency departments and be taken directly to a mental health facility, known as the Restoration Center, designed to treat their specific problems. The facility is open 24 hours a day, 7 days a week, and a client deemed potentially suicidal or homicidal can receive an evaluation within 15 minutes of arrival (Helman et al., 2016). Clients receive stabilization services and then can move on to the Haven for Hope program, located literally across the street. Haven for Hope provides a wider range of mental health services and helps residents arrange for permanent housing.

Judges in San Antonio have instituted involuntary outpatient commitments for clients who are treatment resistant. Operating for 10 years, this specialized court serves those persons with severe mental illness and a history of psychiatric hospitalization. There are gender-specific courts for youth with mental health problems. A reentry center for inmates was opened in 2016 to smooth the transition back to the community, with special attention being paid to the needs of mentally ill inmates.

Over the past 8 years, more than 10,000 individuals have avoided trips to the hospital emergency department and have been diverted from jail at an estimated savings of $100 million (Helman et al., 2016). While the San Antonio experience has taken many years to develop, it is an excellent example of what can happen when the police, courts, correctional facilities, and mental health professionals choose collaboration and integration over fragmentation.

INNOVATIONS IN MENTAL HEALTH SERVICES FOR CHILDREN

A number of innovations have been developed to support mental health services for children. In keeping with the integration of these services into primary care in general, efforts are under way to improve access to mental health services specifically for children. In the greater Boston area, a $10 million grant from the private Richard and Susan Smith Family Foundation is focused on three mental health centers to create a model to integrate mental health services for children into primary care (Quintana, 2016). This includes mental health screening, expansion of the number of mental health providers, and a stringent evaluation plan to determine the effectiveness of the programs. The chief medical officer at one of the community health centers stated, "It is so comforting to see a patient and just walk out of my office and ask someone to come into the room and talk with the family" (Quintana, 2016, p. B5).

The Methuen Public School District in Massachusetts has developed a comprehensive innovative program for students with mental health problems. In partnership with the University of Maryland Center for School Mental Health, and as part of the Massachusetts School Mental Health Consortium (MASMHC), the program aims for early intervention to ensure that students and families receive the mental health support services they need (Lefferts, 2018). Beginning in the third grade, all students are evaluated for depression and anxiety and, if needed, receive referrals for services. A school guidance counselor said, "Not every student needs therapy, but every student needs to learn the skills that will insulate them from stress" (Lefferts, 2018, p. H1). The MASMHC (2018) raises awareness of mental health problems among students, focuses on prevention by fostering mental well-being through social and emotional learning (SEL) instruction, and increases access to community mental health services.

Another recent innovation is providing assistance to children and youth returning to school after a psychiatric hospitalization. This is a challenging time for the child, the family, and school personnel. The child must reintegrate into family life and deal with the academics that were interrupted during hospitalization, as well as cope with the responses and attitudes of his or her peers (Savina, Simon, & Lester, 2014). It is recommended that one professional organize the child's care and coordinate services among the family, hospital, and outpatient mental health services. Social workers are ideally suited to serve in this role and to develop a *school reintegration plan* (Savina et al., 2014, p. 736). Savina et al. (2014) recommend that each state develop a standardized protocol for the reintegration of children and youth into school—again, social workers have the knowledge and experience to lead the development of such a protocol.

Increasingly, clinical and research attention is focused on the responses of children to disasters, both natural and human made. Some examples of disasters are mass shootings, war experiences, hurricanes, volcanic eruptions, explosions, and family violence (Grolnick et al., 2018). Children, as well as adults, need a fast response, known as "psychological first aid," immediately after a disaster, even if they are unlikely to seek assistance on their own. For some children, a disaster experience can intensify symptoms of mental illness; for other children, new mental disorders will be diagnosed. After the initial crisis, helpful interventions include trauma-focused cognitive behavioral therapy (Grolnick et al., 2018). The development of partnerships among organizations can be very helpful to a coordinated response strategy. For example, in New York City in the aftermath of the September 11, 2001 terrorist attacks, social service agencies that already had existing relationships with schools were able to respond far more quickly to the needs of students than agencies that lacked such connections (Grolnick et al., 2018).

Evidence-based practices have yet to be fully integrated into mental healthcare for children and youth. A recent national study of mental health providers found that evidenced-based treatment practices were more likely to be used by providers who had recently obtained a college degree, had more positive attitudes toward innovation, and utilized standardized assessment tools (Wood, Taylor, Hausman, Andrews, & Hawley, 2019).

ROLE OF TECHNOLOGY IN MENTAL HEALTHCARE

Much recent attention has been given to the role of technology in improving the delivery of mental health services. Telepsychiatry or telemental health is an important form of telemedicine, through which screening and assessments for the need for mental healthcare can be done online. It includes forms of videoconferencing where both individual and group psychotherapy can be provided. Given that people with stigmatizing conditions are more likely to seek information using technology, it is reasonable to look to technological innovations as methods of treatment delivery (Grolnick et al., 2018). Technology can be very helpful in eliminating the barriers to care, as those concerned about stigma do not have go to a mental health clinic (Luo, 2017).

Telepsychiatry can also be very useful when transportation is not readily available in geographically isolated regions. Online psychotherapy can significantly reduce patients' symptoms (Omrani, Alavi, Rivera, & Khalid-Khan, 2017). Further, it can reduce waiting time for services as well as increase treatment compliance in patients (Omrani et al., 2017).

In responding to disasters, technology-based interventions can be especially important because they are able to reach a large population very quickly. Although many affected individuals may not have immediate Internet access post disaster, when needs for food and shelter take a higher priority, Internet access can be helpful in the subsequent days and weeks (Grolnick et al., 2018).

In Chapter 4, Mental Illness Across the Life Cycle: Children, Adolescents, Adults, and Older Adults, we discussed the important role of college counseling centers and the increasing number of mental health service requests on campuses. However, long waiting lists for services for students remain a national problem. A very recent technological innovation offers colleges the opportunity to better assist students with mental health needs. Technology firms can offer online mental health screenings, links to campus resources, and suggestions for reducing stress (Fernandes, 2018). Some firms offer online short-term counseling as well as referral to community therapists for long-term counseling. A firm called YOU at College (2018) describes its approach as providing a "well-being portal" that includes assessments and resources geared to the individual needs of colleges and their students. YOU at College is currently working with more than 20 college campuses in the United States (Fernandes, 2018). In response to long waiting lists and out-of-date referral information, Zencare (2018) was established 3 years ago to provide a faster and more accurate effort to connect students and others with community therapists through an online search process. Those using Zencare can search for therapists based on insurance coverage, as well as based on therapy approach and preferred therapist characteristics. Individuals using Zencare are not charged for the services, but therapists must pay to be listed in the registry (Fernandes, 2018).

The need for providers to have access to patients' medical records has existed for many years, but it has been a struggle to make this happen. Health information technology has received much attention in recent years in the effort to improve integration of care. Systems that work well allow different providers, across different healthcare systems, to access medical records to ensure continuity of care. New York developed one such system, in which patients can give informed consent in one process rather than have to provide consent to each specific healthcare provider (Gerrity, 2014).

LIFESTYLE AND MENTAL HEALTH

To be effective, treatment for mental health problems must coexist with a healthy lifestyle. This holistic approach to mental healthcare includes eating nutritious meals on a daily basis, getting adequate sleep, and having opportunities for relaxation and exercise. Medication alone cannot address mental health recovery, and healthy living and working environments are also essential for recovery (Slade, 2009). Alternative and complementary medicine can be of value to some individuals with mental illness. They do not have to choose between Western medicine and alternative medicine, but rather are free to incorporate elements of both into their recovery plans.

Many forms of exercise can be part of a healthy living regimen, including tai chi, weight training, jogging, and yoga. In recent years, more research attention has been paid to the role of yoga in improving a range of health problems (Bridges & Sharma, 2017). In a review of 24 studies of women with breast cancer, Cramer et al. (2017) found there is support of yoga for improving quality of life and reducing fatigue and sleep problems when compared with no therapy. Another study of yoga that reviewed 23 research studies found that yoga practice was effective in depression reduction (Bridges & Sharma, 2017). Additional research is needed to determine if specific forms of exercise and meditation are more helpful than others.

A variety of self-help and peer support programs can help with recovery from mental disorders (Copeland, 2002; Loumpa, 2012; Marshall,

Oades, & Crowe, 2009; Meehan, King, Beavis, & Robinson, 2008). The Wellness Recovery Action Plan (WRAP) program was developed in the United States in 1997 (Hyde, 2017). WRAP (2018) is a self-designed wellness plan used for mental health and physical health promotion. It includes an individualized self-monitoring tool to help people relieve their symptoms. WRAP focuses on hope, personal responsibility for recovery, education regarding an individual's disorder, self-advocacy, and cultivating a support network. It helps individuals to understand early warning symptoms and develop action and crisis plans (WRAP, 2018). Similar programs include the Expert Patient Program, the Manic Depression Fellowship Course, and the Rethink Self-Management Course (Hyde, 2017). See Tips for the Field 11.2 for advocacy recommendations and supports for individuals to ensure they are receiving the most up-to-date care.

TIPS FOR THE FIELD 11.2

NEUROLOGY NOW ADVOCACY RECOMMENDATIONS FOR RECEIVING THE MOST UP-TO-DATE CARE

The neurology magazine *Neurology Now* has suggested ways that patients, families, and advocates can access the most up-to-date care for a variety of medical problems, including mental health disorders.

1. Invest in research. Use the website EurekAlert.com to obtain information on new research studies. Ask mental health professionals to provide published research on the specific mental health problem.

2. Sign up for clinical trials. A service of the National Institutes of Health, ClinicalTrials .gov provides information on clinical trials that are funded by both the government and private organizations.

3. Weigh your options. Review potential trials with your physician and/or medical team to see if a trial may be helpful to you. It could grant early access to a new treatment.

4. Join a support group. Request information on support groups from the medical practice or social worker. If a social worker is not available, call the local hospital and seek this information from the social service or discharge planning department.

5. Consider a second opinion. This can be especially meaningful in the diagnosis and treatment of mental illness, as there can be differing views of the problems and alternative treatments such as different medications to choose from.

6. Engage with patient organizations. Become a member of national and local organizations that advocate on behalf of those with mental illness. These include the National Alliance on Mental Illness, Mental Health America, the National Mental Health Association, First Nations Behavioral Health Association, and the National Latino Behavioral Health Association.

7. Enlist family and friends. Allow others to seek information on your behalf, but avoid getting overwhelmed by data. A friend or family member may be able to set up a computer system to monitor for new information and clinical trials.

8. Manage expectations. Follow medication protocols and maintain regular follow-up appointments to maximize health.

SOURCE: Adapted from Kritz, F. (2017, February, March). Quick tips: 8 ways to access cutting-edge care. *Neurology Now*, 10–12.

CREATING HEALTHIER AND MORE INNOVATIVE ORGANIZATIONS

It is very difficult to locate evidence of successful strategies for changing the culture of an organization (Brooks et al., 2011). There are many barriers to organizational change, such as resistance from the corporate level and middle management, as well as from the finance and human resources departments. Other barriers are policies and practices in especially large organizations characterized by strong bureaucracy with adherence to the status quo, limited financial and other resources within organizations, and the complex nature of innovation (Brooks et al., 2011). On a larger scale, the policy context and organizational context must be understood to bring about change. At the clinical level, as described in Chapter 10, Views From the Field: Challenges in Mental Health Social Work, staff turnover, low wages, and low expectations by the staff regarding innovation can be barriers to change.

In a study of innovative mental health projects in the United Kingdom, Brooks et al. (2011) found that certain factors favored innovation, such as the knowledge, skills, and experience of a supportive team and strong leadership of the "project champion." Successful projects also were an integral part of the core mission, rather than ancillary to the organization. Regarding the processes and outcomes, the project champion had to be assertive in ensuring support from the funding source, support from the clients themselves, and positive contributions from the staff. Of course, cost-effectiveness is important as well (Brooks et al., 2011).

Examples of Organizational Innovations

A variety of innovations have been making headway in changing organizational cultures. It is a challenge to transfer innovations from one organization to another, as each organization has to find its own way (Brooks et al., 2011). The two models discussed in this section are important innovations in improving mental healthcare for clients and those who provide mental health services.

The Civil, Respect, and Engagement at Work (CREW) social relationship intervention model is an initiative introduced by the Veterans Administration (VA) in 2005. Its goal is to improve the organizational climate by promoting civil and respectful interactions among coworkers through a process of positive engagement (National Center for Organization Development, 2017). Facilitators meet regularly with staff groups to support positive working relationships and problem-solve. There is no specific manual on implementing CREW in an organization, so each agency can tailor the components to its own specific needs. A review of the CREW programs in 23 VA sites found significant improvements in both civility and the work environment (Osatuke, Moore, Ward, Dyrenforth, & Belton, 2009). Increases in civility in organizations are also associated with a reduction in staff burnout among healthcare providers (Maslach & Leiter, 2017).

The Availability, Responsiveness, and Continuity (ARC) organizational model is an effort to improve organizational culture within mental health and child welfare agencies (California Evidence-Based Clearinghouse for Child Welfare, 2017). It supports the adoption of evidence-based practices, seeks to reduce staff turnover, and improves outcomes for mental health clients. ARC adheres to five principles of effective organizations: Such organizations are "mission-driven, results-oriented, improvement-directed, relationship-centered, [and] participation-based" (Glisson, Williams, Hemmelgarn, Proctor, & Green, 2016, p. 713). ARC also promotes collaboration and alliances among community agencies. Thus, efforts are targeted at the individual level to develop relationships with community leaders, at the organizational level to deliver high-quality services to clients, and at the community level to cultivate an effective advocacy group (Glisson & Schoenwald, 2005). ARC creates a process for clinicians to build their commitment to improving services and supports them in addressing barriers in achieving high-quality services (Glisson, Hemmelgarn, Green, & Williams, 2013). A study of ARC in community mental health programs found that youth outcomes are improved by using this organizational model (Glisson et al., 2013). Youths who showed the most improvement were found in the most improved organizational social contexts. In subsequent research, youth outcomes were improved when the organizations adhered to the five key principles of ARC (Glisson et al., 2016).

Unfortunately, the concept of innovation is not frequently addressed in the mental health field (Brooks et al., 2011). As a result, there is insufficient research regarding the adoption and success of innovative practices. See Tips for the Field 11.3 for the critical components of innovative care in mental health.

TIPS FOR THE FIELD 11.3

DIGGING DEEPER INTO POLICY: CRITICAL COMPONENTS OF INNOVATIVE PRACTICES IN MENTAL HEALTHCARE

1. Organizations that study innovation against a backdrop of social context and outcome evaluation.

2. Support from management.

3. Leaders and managers who engage in a continuous process of learning and adaptation within mental health organizations.

4. Stability within the overall organization, including low staff turnover.

5. Clear lines of reporting within minimal role conflicts among multidisciplinary professionals.

6. Reasonable caseloads for clinicians.

7. Participation in research studies to determine the effectiveness of services.

8. Both short- and long-term views of the future of mental health services.

SOURCE: Adapted from Brooks, H., Pilgrim, D., & Rogers, A. (2011). Innovation in mental health services: What are the key components of success? *Implementation Science, 6*, 120. doi:10.1186/1748-5908-6-120

■ SUMMARY AND CONCLUSION

Innovation in mental healthcare has been lacking over the years. Innovation can be something as simple as ensuring that a client is provided with instructions and that other organizations know the client's treatment plan. Other innovations require a huge advocacy effort, such as making legislative changes to overturn the IMD exclusion, which limits Medicaid funding for inpatient psychiatric and substance abuse treatment. The integration of physical health and mental healthcare will continue to develop and expand. In addition, innovations in neuroimaging and technology will have strong impacts on the delivery of mental health services in the future.

Social workers have much knowledge and skill in developing and implementing innovations. Becauses they take "a person in the environment" and "whole person" approach, social workers are well qualified to work in primary medical offices as part of integrated care. Through NASW, social workers can challenge the IMD exclusion and expand opportunities for patients to benefit from psychiatric hospitalization. They can provide telemental health services to individuals and groups. They are well equipped to assist students in reintegrating into their schools after psychiatric hospitalization and to direct school reintegration plans. Social workers can help disaster victims with both short- and long-term recovery. They can help to create healthier mental health organizations. Overall, there are rich opportunities for social workers to advance innovations in mental healthcare.

DISCUSSION QUESTIONS/TOPICS

1. Discuss the importance of innovations in mental healthcare.
2. What are the advantages of integrating mental healthcare into primary care settings?
3. What are the challenges and barriers to integrating health and mental healthcare?
4. What makes the work of Dr. Daniel Amen controversial?
5. Why has the San Antonio model for delivering mental health services become a national model?
6. Discuss the role of complementary and alternative approaches in the treatment of mental health disorders.
7. Discuss the impacts of organizational change models such as CREW and ARC on the provision of mental health services.
8. What roles can social workers play in the integration of mental health and primary care services?
9. Discuss suggestions for mental health clients and their families to ensure they are receiving excellent mental healthcare.
10. What are your own ideas for changes that can be made in mental health organizations to improve the quality of care and the morale of the staff?

REFERENCES

Agency for Healthcare Research and Quality. (2016). *AHRQ healthcare innovations exchange.* Retrieved from https://innovations.ahrq.gov/faq

Arentshorst, M. E., de Cock Buning, T., & Broerse, J. E. W. (2016). Exploring responsible neuroimaging innovation: Visions from a societal actor perspective. *Bulletin of Science, Technology, & Society, 36*(4), 229–240. doi:10.1177/0270467617727457

Borgelt, E. L., Buchman, D. Z., & Illes, J. (2012). Neuroimaging in mental health care: Voices in translation. *Frontiers in Human Neuroscience, 6,* 293. doi:10.3389/fnhum.2012.00293

Bridges, L., & Sharma, M. (2017). The efficacy of yoga as a form of treatment for depression. *Journal of Evidence-Based Complementary & Alternative Medicine, 22*(4), 1017–1028. doi:10.1177/2156587217715927

Brooks, H., Pilgrim, D., & Rogers, A. (2011). Innovation in mental health services: What are the key components of success? *Implementation Science, 6,* 120. doi:10.1186/1748-5908-6-120

Butler, M., Kane, R. L., McAlpine, D., Kathol, R. G., Fu, S. S., Hagedorn, H., & Wilt, T. J. (2008, October). *Integration of mental health/substance abuse and primary care*. Evidence reports/technology assessment, No. 173. AHRQ Publication No. 09-E003. Rockville, MD: Agency for Healthcare Research and Quality.

California Evidence-Based Clearinghouse for Child Welfare. (2017). *Availability, Responsiveness, and Continuity* (ARC). Retrieved from http://www.cebc4cw.org/program/availability-responsiveness-and-continuity-arc

Copeland, M. E. (2002). Wellness recovery action plan: A system for monitoring, reducing and eliminating uncomfortable or dangerous physical symptoms and emotional feelings. *Occupational Therapy in Mental Health, 17*(3–2), 127–150.

Cramer, H., Lauche, R., Klose, P., Lange, S., Langhorst, J., & Dobos, D. J. (2017, January). Yoga for improving quality of life, mental health and cancer-related symptoms in women diagnosed with breast cancer. *Cochrane Database Systemic Review, 1*, CD010802. doi:10.1002/14651858.CD010802.pub2

Eagan, S. (2017, November 6). FFR launches statewide recovery network project, first of its kind in the state. Retrieved from https://forrecovery.org/immediate-release-new-statewide-recovery-network-project-launched-support-nevadas-recovery-community-first-kind-state

Fernandes, D. (2018, December 12). Tech firms eye campus mental health services. *The Boston Globe*, B6, B9.

Fortin, M., Zhirong, C., & Fleury M.-J. (2018). Satisfaction with primary and specialized mental health care among patients with mental disorders. *International Journal of Mental Health, 47*(2), 97–117. doi:10.1080/00207411.2018.1448661

Geller, J. L. (2015). The first step in health reform for those with serious mental illness: Integrating the dis-integrated mental health system. *Journal of Nervous and Mental Disease, 203*(12), 909–918. doi:10;1097/NMD.0000000000000396

Gerrity, M. (2014). *Integrating primary care into behavioral health settings: What works for individuals with serious mental illness: Executive summary*. New York: NY.Milbank Memorial Fund.

Glisson, C., Hemmelgarn, A., Green, P., & Williams, N. J. (2013). Randomized trial of the Availability, Responsiveness and Continuity (ARC) organizational intervention for improving youth outcomes in community mental health programs. *Journal of the American Academy of Child & Adolescent Psychiatry, 52*(5), 493–500. doi:10.1016/j.jaac.2013.02.005

Glisson, C., & Schoenwald, S. K. (2005). The ARC organizational and community intervention strategy for implementing evidence-based children's mental health treatments. *Mental Health Services Research, 7*(4), 243–259. doi:10.1007/s11020-005-7456-1

Glisson, C., Williams, N. J., Hemmelgarn, A., Proctor, E., & Green, P. (2016). Aligning organizational priorities with ARC to improve youth mental health service outcomes. *Journal of Consulting and Clinical Psychology, 84*(8), 713–725. doi:10.1037/ccp0000107

Grolnick, W. S., Schonfeld, D. J., Schreiber, M., Cohen, J., Cole, V., Jaycox, L., … Zatzick, D. (2018). Improving adjustment and resilience in children following a disaster: Addressing research challenges. *American Psychologist, 73*(3), 215–229. doi:10.1037/amp0000181

Helman, S., with Cramer, M., Russell, J., Rezendes, M., & Wallack, T. (2016, December 11). A better way. San Antonio has done in Texas what Massachusetts has not come close to: Making mental health care a community priority. *The Boston Sunday Globe,* A1, A12–A14.

Horevitz, E., & Manoleas, P. (2013). Professional competencies and training needs of professional social workers in integrated behavioral health in primary care. *Social Work in Health Care, 52*(8), 752–757. doi:10.1080/0098 1389.2013.791362

Hyde, B. (2017, July). *The lived experience of acute mental health inpatient care: What's recovery got to do with it?* Doctoral dissertation submitted to Charles Sturt University, Australia.

Kowalczyk, L. (2018, October 1). Exclusive psychiatric care, for a price. *The Boston Globe.* A1, A10.

Laderman, M., & Mate, K. (2014, March/April). *Integrating behavioral health into primary care.* Reprinted from *Healthcare Executive.* Institute for Healthcare Improvement. Retrieved from https://micmrc.org/system/files/ ihi_behavhealth90dayreport.pdf

Lefferts, J. F. (2018, September 30). School choice. *The Boston Sunday Globe,* H1.

Legal Action Center. (n.d.). *The Medicaid IMD exclusion: An overview and opportunities for reform.* Retrieved from https://lac.org/wp-content/ uploads/2014/07/IMD_exclusion_fact_sheet.pdf

Loumpa, V. (2012). Promoting recovery through peer support: Possibilities for social work practice. *Social Work in Health Care, 51*(1), 53–65. doi:10.1080/ 00981389.2011.622667

Luo, J. (2017, December 25). Introduction: Innovations to improve mental health outcomes. *Psychiatric Times, 34*(12). Retrieved from http://www .psychiatrictimes.com/special-reports/introduction-innovations-improve -mental-health-outcomes

Mann, C. C., Golden, J. H., Cronk, N. J., Gale, J. K., Hogan, T., & Washington, K. T. (2016). Social workers as behavioral health consultants in the primary care clinic. *Health Social Work, 41*(3), 196–2000. doi:10.1093/hsw/hlw027

Marshall, S., Oades, L., & Crowe, T. (2009). Mental health consumers' perceptions of receiving recovery-focused services. *Journal of Evaluation in Clinical Practice, 15,* 654–659. doi:10.1111/j.1365-2753.2008.01070.x

Maslach, C., & Leiter, M. P. (2017). New insights into burnout and health care: Strategies for improving civility and alleviating burnout. *Medical Teacher, 39*(2), 160–163. doi:10.1080/0142159X.2016.1248918

Massachusetts School Mental Health Consortium. (2018, March 6). *The Massachusetts School Mental Health Consortium.* Retrieved from http:// www.methuen.k12.ma.us/departments/special-education/guidance/ massachusetts-school-mental-health-consortium-masmhc

Meehan, T. M., King, R. J., Beavis, P. H., & Robinson, J. D. (2008). Recovery-based practice: Do we know what we mean or mean what we know? *Australian and New Zealand Journal of Psychiatry, 42,* 177–182. doi:10.1080/00048670701827234

Mercy Care Plan. (2017, September 5). *Provider communication: Implementing the new federal IMD regulation.* Retrieved from https://myemail. constantcontact.com/Implementing-the-new-federal-IMD-regulation. html?soid=1118183724642&aid=xgGtVynJ0Uo

Musumeci, M. B. (2018, June 18). Key questions about Medicaid payment for services in "institutions for mental disease." *Henry J. Kaiser Family Foundation.* Retrieved from https://www.kff.org/medicaid/issue-brief/

key-questions-about-medicaid-payment-for-services-in-institutions-for-mental-disease

National Center for Organization Development. (2017). Civility, Respect, and Engagement in the Workplace (CREW). Retrieved from https://www.va.gov/NCOD/CREW.asp

National Institute of Mental Health. (2017). *Substance use and mental health.* Retrieved from https://www.nimh.nih.gov/health/topics/substance-use-and-mental-health/index.shtml

Omrani, M., Alavi, N., Rivera, M., & Khalid-Khan, S. (2017). Online clinic, a new method of delivering psychotherapy. *European Psychiatry, 41*(suppl), S148. doi:10.1016/j.eurpsy.2017.01.1997

Osatuke, K., Moore, S. C., Ward, C., Dyrenforth, S. R., & Belton, L. (2009). Civility, Respect, Engagement in the Workforce (CREW): Nationwide organization development intervention at Veterans Health Administration. *Journal of Applied Behavioral Science, 45*, 384–410. doi:10.1177/0021886309335067

Pfeiffer, S., Healy, B., Hohler, B., Ryan, A., & Wen, P. (2018, October 19). Gladiator: Aaron Hernandez. A terrible thing to waste. *The Boston Globe,* A1, A6–A8.

Quintana, O. (2016, September 15). Grant funds program to boost children's mental health care. *The Boston Globe,* B5.

Savina, E., Simon, J., & Lester, M. (2014). School reintegration following psychiatric hospitalization: An ecological perspective. *Child and Youth Care Forum, 43*, 729–746. doi:10.1007/s10566-014-9263-0

Slade, M. (2009). The contribution of mental health services to recovery. *Journal of Mental Health, 18*(5), 367–371. doi:10.3109/09638230903191256

Swarbrick, M., & Brice, G. H. Jr. (2006). Sharing the message of hope, wellness, and recovery with consumers' psychiatric hospitals. *American Journal of Psychiatric Rehabilitation, 9*, 101–109. doi:10.1080/154877/60600876196

Thielking, M. (2018, May 10). Can precision medicine do for depression what it's done for cancer? It won't be easy. *The Boston Globe,* B11, B14.

Ward, J., Williams, J., & Manchester, S. (2017, July 25). 110 N.F.L. brains. *The New York Times.* Retrieved from https://www.nytimes.com/interactive/2017/07/25/sports/football/nfl-cte.html

Wellness Recovery Action Plan. (2018). *WRAP is...* Retrieved from http://mentalhealthrecovery.com/wrap-is

Wood, P. K., Taylor, E., Hausman, E., Andrews, J. H., & Hawley, K. M. (2019). Evidence-based treatment strategies in youth mental health services: Results from a national survey of providers. *Administration and Policy in Mental Health and Mental Health Services, 46*(1), 71–81. doi:10.1007/s10488-018-0896-4

YOU at College. (2018). YOU at College. Retrieved from https://youatcollege.com

Zencare. (2018). Zencare. Retrieved from https://www.zencare.co

CHAPTER 12

PREVENTION AND FUTURE ISSUES IN MENTAL HEALTH SOCIAL WORK

LEARNING OUTCOMES

- Define primary, secondary, and tertiary prevention in mental health and provide examples of each.

- Examine social determinants of mental health problems and explore ways to overcome them.

- Describe the relationship between mental health and climate change.

- Discuss the importance of community coalitions in preventing and reducing mental illness.

- Identify ways social workers can provide leadership in the field of mental health.

INTRODUCTION

Mental health is a vital part of an individual's overall health (Padhy, Sarkar, Panigrahi, & Paul, 2015). Yet mental illness receives considerably less clinical and research attention than other medical conditions. Additionally, historically the clinical and research focus has been heavily weighted toward mental illness rather than toward understanding and promoting mental health (Canadian Association of Social Workers, 2018). Much recent research focuses on brain dysfunction as it relates to mental disorders, with less attention paid to the societal factors that influence mental health and illness. However, to more fully understand the causes of mental illness, social work provides a broader understanding of the family, social, economic, and environmental influences on mental health. As discussed in this text, risk factors for mental disorders are strongly associated with social inequality, poverty, and discrimination (World Health Organization [WHO], 2014). Factors that constitute and promote mental health are feelings of well-being, living in harmony with oneself and others, mental flexibility, ability to adapt to one's environment, and opportunities for self-actualization and growth (Canadian Association of Social Workers, 2018).

This chapter addresses promotion of mental health and the prevention of mental disorders. Types and examples of mental health prevention are described. The chapter examines a recovery model that is based on the premise that individuals with mental health problems must take responsibility for their recovery while setting their own treatment goals. Social work leadership and social work research make valuable contributions to advances in treatment for those with mental illness. The chapter also discusses the need to promote mental health social work as a satisfying career to address the workforce shortage.

It is crucial to work to prevent mental disorders (Shekhar, Jane-LLopis, & Hosman, 2006). Mental illness prevention focuses on reducing risk factors and promoting protective factors. As discussed, risk factors include poverty, inadequate housing, poor nutrition, lack of access to education, lack of access to healthcare, and involvement in the criminal justice system (Shekhar et al., 2006). Unfortunately, it is not possible to prevent all mental health disorders. For example, schizophrenia and bipolar disorder are known to be biologically based major mental disorders. Nevertheless, while prevention may be a more difficult task, these disorders can be managed in ways that promote improved overall health.

There is an important distinction between mental health promotion and mental disorder prevention (Shekhar et al., 2006). Mental health promotion refers to activities that encourage individual and group well-being and support feelings of competence and resilience. Health promotion activities support maintaining good health and can lead to achieving better overall health (Min, Lee, & Lee, 2013). This includes various forms of exercise and emotional support from others in times of adversity. Conversely, the goal of mental disorder prevention is to reduce symptoms in an effort to prevent the onset of mental illness and/or to minimize the effects. It focuses on the causes of risk factors and seeks to avoid illness (Min et al., 2013). Rather than mental health promotion and mental disorder prevention representing opposite ends of a continuum, they actually overlap. Accordingly, often mental health promotion and mental illness prevention coexist within prevention strategies (Shekhar et al., 2006).

Research has found that while individuals with mental health problems may want to cultivate a healthy lifestyle, they sometimes feel that it is impossible (Verhaeghe, De Maeseneer, Maes, Van Heeringen, &

Annemans, 2011). Some important barriers to developing a healthy life-style can include lack of motivation, lack of energy, substance abuse, and side effects of medications (Verhaeghe et al., 2013).

Interventions for mental disorders are generally based on following the recommendations of professionals. As discussed, mental health services usually focus on symptoms while encouraging individuals with mental illness to remain engaged with treatment services, especially in cases where medication is recommended. Services also typically focus on trying to determine whether those persons with mental illness are a risk to themselves or others (Davidson, Brophy, & Campbell, 2016). The innovations discussed in Chapter 11, Innovations in Mental Healthcare, focus on including clients in decision-making and nurturing recovery-based approaches (Davidson et al., 2016). This encourages and supports more of a person-centered approach, tailoring services to the needs of individual clients, rather than simply providing clients with generic services. This process, known as "personalization," seeks to ensure that services meet the client's self-identified goals (Allen, Carr, Linde, & Sewell, 2016, p. 14).

A theme of this text is that many states and communities do not offer adequate services to meet the mental health needs of their residents. However, certain geographic locations with poor access to mental health services can respond in helpful ways during times of crisis. Nevada is an example of a state that provides inadequate services, yet was able to respond appropriately to a mass shooting in 2017. See Case Example 12.1 for a description of the Nevada response to the massacre in Las Vegas.

CASE EXAMPLE 12.1

2017 MASSACRE IN LAS VEGAS: AN UNDER-RESOURCED MENTAL HEALTH SYSTEM RESPONDS TO A CRISIS

The state of Nevada has the dubious distinction of having one of the worst mental health systems in the country. The national advocacy group Mental Health America ranked Nevada at the bottom of all 50 states for access to mental healthcare, with long waiting lists to access therapy—and this was before the massacre at a country music festival in Las Vegas on October 1, 2017. During that event, a lone gunman killed 58 people and injured more than 500 people in a mass shooting.

Within hours, volunteer mental health professionals, including social workers, responded to the call for help. Some were local clinicians; some came from great distances. One social worker traveled from Michigan to provide crisis counseling for survivors. He described the importance of helping survivors understand their reactions to the traumatic shootings and to identify coping mechanisms for short- and long-term adjustment.

The executive director of the Kenny Guinn Center for Policy Priorities in Nevada, who had just completed an analysis of the Nevada's mental health system, stated, "I think this crisis and now this surge in short-term demand for mental health services will place a lot of stress on the pretty thin, poorly resourced system that we have currently" (Robbins, 2017, p. 3). Despite its under-resourced mental health system, Nevada was able to mount a commendable crisis response in the immediate aftermath of the gunman's attack. This massacre serves as another wake-up call to cities about the importance of immediate mental health response plans. It also calls attention to the need to shore up mental health services to be better prepared.

SOURCE: Robbins, R. (2017, October 15). Nevada's mental health system was in dire straits. Then came Las Vegas. *SundaySTAT*. Retrieved from statnews.com

■ PREVENTION

In light of the emotional and financial costs of mental illness to individuals, families, communities, and society at large, prevention is key. Mental health prevention and promotion must be a part of a public policy approach that addresses the environment, housing, welfare supports, work, education, and criminal justice responses (Shekhar et al., 2006). Prevention partnerships among social service agencies are necessary to help meet the many needs of some mentally ill individuals (Allen et al., 2016).

The purpose of prevention is to reduce mental disorders in specific populations by decreasing stress in the environment and bolstering an individual's ability to cope (Canadian Association of Social Workers, 2018). This includes a wide variety of activities, such as education on the importance of self-care and the promotion of healthy relationships with others. The research evidence that supports mental illness prevention is stronger for the diagnosis of depression than for schizophrenia and bipolar disorders (Arehart-Treichel, 2013).

Most often, three forms of mental illness prevention activities are described, all of which fall solidly within the purview of social workers. This is in contrast to psychiatrists and psychologists, who do not typically acknowledge that they can play a role in mental illness prevention and mental health promotion (Min et al., 2013).

Primary Prevention

Primary prevention is concerned with preventing mental illness from occurring in the first place. It is focused on education aimed at the general population. *Universal prevention* is a type of primary prevention that is offered to everyone, not just to those who have risk factors for mental illness or substance abuse (Borsari, 2014; Mignon, 2015). Examples are mental health–related educational programs for students, including programs that focus on preventing students from using alcohol and/or drugs. *Selective prevention*, also a type of primary prevention, focuses on subgroups at increased risk, such as children and adolescents living in poverty. Laws that restrict access to alcohol and firearms that can be used in suicides are primary prevention practices (Petersen et al., 2016).

Secondary Prevention

Secondary prevention seeks early detection and intervention to reduce the number of cases of mental illness and to minimize the impact of mental disorders (Mignon, 2015; Min et al., 2013). *Indicated prevention*, a type of secondary prevention, focuses on activities for those persons with early or minimal symptoms that do not yet meet the criteria for a mental health disorder (Shekhar et al., 2006). In some cases, secondary prevention can have more significant impacts than primary prevention does. For example, secondary prevention can prevent future episodes of mania or depression in someone with an initial episode of bipolar disorder (Arehart-Treichel, 2013). This serves as a reminder of the importance of screening for mental health and substance abuse disorders in hospital emergency rooms, urgent care centers, and doctors' offices, and among court defendants. Examples of secondary prevention are school-based referrals for assistance for students showing early symptoms of depression. For individuals with heroin addiction, needle exchange programs are another example of secondary prevention that has reduced transmission of the AIDS virus (Mignon, 2015).

Tertiary Prevention

Tertiary prevention involves intervening in mental health problems so that they do not become worse. This type of prevention helps reduce the level of disability experienced by the individual and seeks to prevent relapses of mental illness (Min et al., 2013; Shekhar et al., 2006). Examples include both outpatient and inpatient mental health services. While most people do not consider treatment to be a form of prevention, treatment can reduce the severity of the effects of mental illness on the individual as well as the negative impacts on family members and the community (Mignon, 2015).

WHO has provided global leadership in the prevention of mental disorders. WHO (2014) recommends that all mental health policies and programs developed by each nation should focus on a life-span and intergenerational-family approach. See Tips for the Field 12.1 for a description of WHO recommendations for national and local prevention strategies.

TIPS FOR THE FIELD 12.1

WORLD HEALTH ORGANIZATION RECOMMENDATIONS FOR IMPROVEMENTS TO GLOBAL MENTAL HEALTH

The World Health Organization (WHO) has made it clear that mental health needs must be given greater priority across the globe. Policies to improve mental health must reflect a strong knowledge of the social and financial costs of mental disorders and must support the development of clinical and educational responses that will endure over the long term.

The following are some WHO recommendations for national strategies to promote mental health:

1. Reduce poverty.
2. Increase social protections for people throughout the life course.
3. Increase attention to preventing violence and wars.
4. Promote access to education, housing, jobs, and healthcare.
5. Support early childhood development programs.
6. Screen for and treat maternal depression.
7. Review alcohol policies, including access to alcohol.
8. Provide welfare benefits for the unemployed.
9. Develop special programs for families living in poverty that have members with mental illness.

Prevention strategies developed by each nation should provide the framework for reducing inequalities in power, money, and other resources. This framework can serve as the base from which local action can be taken. To develop localized strategies to improve mental health, knowledge and data must be collected in several domains:

1. The types and prevalence of mental disorders in a community.
2. The ease or difficulty in accessing mental healthcare and determining the amount of unmet need for care.
3. Knowledge of local social, economic, and environmental stressors that contribute to mental health problems.

4. Knowledge of local social, economic, and environmental factors that reduce stress.

5. An appraisal of local services and initiatives and their impacts on mental health.

This information can lead to the development of strategies for community action such as community coalitions, as described in this chapter.

SOURCE: Adapted from World Health Organization & Calouste Gulbenkian Foundation. (2014). *Social determinants of mental health.* Geneva, Switzerland: World Health Organization. Retrieved from http://apps.who.int/iris/bitstream/handle/10665/112828/9789241506809_eng.pdf?sequence=1

Regarding mental health promotion and prevention, social work has an important place in college and team sports. To this end, the University of Michigan School of Social Work established a graduate student organization, the Social Work & Sport Association (Laurio, 2018/2019b). Social workers can be helpful in reducing the stigma of mental illness among athletes and coaches, and social workers can train coaches to be aware of symptoms of mental illness and substance abuse. They can also offer stress reduction strategies to athletes.

Suicide Prevention

Suicide is associated with a number of problems, including depression, social isolation, and poor economic conditions. Among individuals with severe mental illness such as schizophrenia and bipolar disorder, suicide is a common cause of death (Bhatia et al., 2006; Latalova, Kamaradova, & Prasko, 2014).

Unfortunately, the suicide rate in the United States has been rising for years. According to the National Center for Health Statistics, male and female suicides increased 33% between 1999 and 2017 (Hedegaard, Curtin, & Warner, 2018). In 2016, suicide was the second leading cause of death in individuals ages 10 to 34 and the fourth leading cause of death in those ages 35 to 54 (Hedegaard et al., 2018).

Warning signs for suicide include changes in energy level, mood changes, and social isolation (Laurio, 2018/2019c). Safety planning is essential to prevent suicide. Those with suicidal ideation or previous suicide attempts need to think about their warning signs and ways to improve self-care. They need to identify other people to whom they can reach out, including emergency contacts such as a suicide hotline. Some find it helpful to make a list of reasons to stay alive. This plan should include removing firearms and poisonous household cleaning products from the home (Laurio, 2018/2019c). Social workers can play a crucial role in suicide prevention by working to expand mental healthcare, especially crisis responses (Scobie-Carroll, 2018).

The Veterans Administration (VA) was in the news in late 2018 for failure to utilize federal funds for suicide prevention for veterans. Certainly, this is unacceptable when approximately 20 veterans die by suicide each day (U.S. Government Accountability Office [U.S. GAO], 2018). The reduction in outreach and prevention activities in 2017 and 2018 was attributed to lack of leadership within the agency. The VA spent only $57,000 of the $6.2 million allocated for prevention purposes (Burke, 2018). The VA was also reproached for not having clear goals by which prevention activities could be evaluated (U.S. GAO, 2018).

The National Suicide Prevention Hotline has trained volunteers to take telephone calls on a 24/7 basis. The national hotline phone number is 1-800-273-8255. One of the oldest organizations working to prevent suicide is the Boston Samaritans (Samaritans Boston, 2018). In 2015, it established a program where individuals can text volunteers rather than having to make a telephone call. Initial responses have been very positive, as those texting average longer connections with the suicide prevention volunteer than those who call in. Further, those individuals texting tend to share more details about their problems (Russell, 2018).

The field of social work has not given much research attention to suicide and suicide prevention until recently (Joe & Niedermeier, 2006). In a review of social work research on suicide between 1980 and 2006, social workers contributed "limited evidence-based knowledge … on the treatment or prevention of suicide or suicide-related behaviours" (Joe & Niedermeier, 2006, p. 507). The lack of social work research on suicide can lead to social workers being unprepared to deal with suicidal clients. With insufficient knowledge of evidence-based practices for the treatment of suicidal clients, the field of social work needs to turn its attention to making clinical and research contributions in this area (Joe & Niedermeier, 2006). Tips for the Field 12.2 focuses on social work and suicide prevention.

TIPS FOR THE FIELD 12.2
SUICIDE PREVENTION AND SOCIAL WORK

Recommendations to help social workers engage in prevention and treatment of suicidal clients:

1. Understand the statistical patterns and trends regarding those individuals who take their own lives.

2. Give special attention to older male adolescents and young adults as well as older adult males, who are at high risk of suicide.

3. Understand the psychological, social, and cultural suicide risk factors that are global in nature.

4. Utilize suicide screening and risk assessments to focus on those persons facing extreme stress, such as long-term unemployment, divorce, or entry into a nursing home.

5. Seek to reduce access to firearms and poisonous products in the home.

SOURCE: Joe, S., & Niedermeier, D. (2006). Preventing suicide: The neglected social work research agenda. *British Journal of Social Work, 38*(3), 507–530. doi:10.1093/bjsw/bcl353

Overall, prevention efforts should be viewed as part of the continuum of care in addressing mental health issues. Mental health promotion strategies underlie the continuum of mental healthcare and support individuals in making healthy responses to life's challenges (SAMHSA, 2016). Prevention strategies focus on avoiding certain behaviors such as alcohol and substance abuse. Treatment programs offer a variety of strategies to help those diagnosed with a mental health or substance use disorder. And, as we have discussed, the recovery process fosters individuals who take responsibility for getting better (SAMHSA, 2016).

■ RECOVERY APPROACHES

Newer approaches to treating mental health disorders rely heavily on engaging with clients to determine their own goals and strategies for achieving them. As noted, "client self-determination" is a hallmark of social work. Recovery is most often defined by the clients themselves, and there is no one specific formula or framework to respond to the "lived experience" of those with mental illness (Meehan, King, Beavis, & Robinson, 2008). Social work is well equipped to take a leadership role in recovery-oriented programs (Hyde, Bowles, & Pawar, 2014).

With a definitive shift in practice, policy, and law, today there is more "supportive decision making" with clients (Campbell, Brophy, Davidson, & O'Brien, 2018, p. 139). Specifically, those who use mental health services are becoming better organized in the effort to get their needs met (Ramon, 2009). For example, the Collaborative Recovery Model used in Australia encourages the therapeutic relationship between social worker and client to be an "alliance" (Marshall, Oades, & Crowe, 2009, p. 654). As discussed, this gives greater responsibility for recovery to the client, and it can include homework exercises and other activities that clients find meaningful for their own recovery (Marshall et al., 2009). These collaborative approaches can be more comfortable for social workers, who are often adverse to coercive treatment measures (Davidson et al., 2016). Models that focus on client responsibility for recovery are exerting considerable influence within mental health services (Meehan et al., 2008).

Supports outside of clinical services can be instrumental to a client's recovery. For example, the Connecting People Intervention (CPI) was developed in 2012 in the United Kingdom. It assists clients who utilize social and/or health services to expand their social networks (CPI, 2012). This approach views clients as equal partners in developing new social opportunities for clients with mental illness and disabilities. The team-based approach more fully places social workers and other mental health professionals within the community to better establish partnerships between clients and workers (Webber et al., 2018). Clients and social workers together set goals for greater social involvement and a deeper and more expansive social network. For example, clients may start to participate in sports and/or to work out regularly at a gym. Clients can also expand their social networks by volunteering within community agencies such as homeless shelters and community food pantries.

A recent study found that participants in the CPI program experienced significant social improvements and had an overall improved sense of well-being (Webber et al., 2018). This adds to the evidence base indicating that for clients with mental health problems, assistance must extend far beyond medical treatment of mental illness. As the recovery approach garners additional clinical and research attention, more remains to be discovered about the philosophy that underlies recovery approaches and about the processes of recovery (Leamy, Bird, Le Boutillier, Williams, & Slade, 2011).

▉ THE CONTINUUM OF CARE: FEDERAL, STATE, AND LOCAL EFFORTS

As described in this text, prevention and treatment of mental health problems can come from a variety of sources, but most rely on federal, state, and local funding and resources.

Federal Efforts

On the federal level, the Substance Abuse and Mental Health Services Administration (SAMHSA) is responsible for formulating prevention and early intervention strategies to reduce mental disorders and substance use disorders. The *SAMHSA Strategic Prevention Framework* is a five-step public health approach to prevent mental illness and substance abuse. The framework can be utilized by states and communities to devise sustainable prevention activities: (a) assess prevention needs based on epidemiological data; (b) build prevention capacity; (c) develop a strategic plan; (d) implement effective community prevention programs, practices, and policies; and (e) evaluate prevention efforts for outcomes (SAMHSA, 2017). Current top priorities for SAMHSA are reducing prescription and illegal use of opioids among those ages 12 to 25, and reducing underage drinking among those ages 12 to 20. As indicated previously, SAMHSA's framework is designed to be utilized by states in carving out their own prevention strategies.

The advocacy organization Mental Health America (2018a) has issued *Position Statement 14* regarding the responsibilities of the federal government for providing mental health services. Tips for the Field 12.3 describes these responsibilities.

TIPS FOR THE FIELD 12.3

DIGGING DEEPER INTO POLICY: RESPONSIBILITIES OF THE FEDERAL GOVERNMENT IN PROVIDING AND IMPROVING MENTAL HEALTH SERVICES

1. Protect individual rights to avoid abuses of those with mental illness and substance use disorders.

2. Repair holes and deficiencies in the treatment safety net so that those with mental illness can access food, housing, employment, and healthcare.

3. Stop discrimination in social and economic life by enforcing antidiscrimination laws.

4. Ensure a fair distribution of resources by providing a foundation for the provision of health and mental health services.

5. Address public health crises with a coordinated national response.

6. Empower people with information so consumers can make informed choices about the services they receive.

7. Focus on prevention and early intervention in mental disorders.

8. Improve competition so that consumers get high-quality mental health services at the lowest cost.

9. Fund research on prevention and treatment of mental disorders.

10. Disseminate knowledge of successful innovative programs and support states in their implementation of proven policy and practice strategies.

SOURCE: Mental Health America. (2018). *Position Statement 14: The federal government's responsibilities for mental health services.* Retrieved from http://www.mentalhealthamerica.net/positions/federal-role

State Efforts

Mental Health America (2018b) also addresses the roles of states in providing mental health services. While states must adhere to federal standards in providing care, there is considerable latitude in the types of care and the amount of services they offer to those with mental illness. All states receive Medicaid funding, but they have considerable discretion in utilizing those funds. Ultimately, each state is responsible for designing and implementing its own system of care.

States vary in their requirements for duty to warn and duty to protect. They also vary in their requirements for involuntary psychiatric hospitalization.

Finally, states have an important role to play in mental health research and reporting outcomes. Successful models can then be adopted in other states (Mental Health America, 2018b).

Local Efforts: Community Coalitions

While local efforts to address mental disorders and prevention can vary widely, often they rely on state and/or federal funding for treatment programs. Neighborhood community mental health centers may also obtain funding for programs through private donations and foundations. Community coalitions have increased in recent years and can be at the core of local prevention and treatment efforts. These coalitions include health, social service, and educational organizations united in an effort to prevent and reduce mental disorders and substance abuse. Typically, coalitions include professionals and community residents, and together they offer activities that include prevention, education, community action, and empowerment to improve responses to mental health disorders (SAMHSA, 2016). Successful coalitions identify and develop new resources to ensure that the coalition continues over time. More research attention is needed to identify the factors that will allow community coalitions to be successful over time.

■ SOCIAL WORK LEADERSHIP

As Angelo McClain, CEO of the National Association of Social Workers (NASW), stated, "Social work and leadership; it's just a natural fit" (Laurio, 2018/2019a, p. 14). Many former and current U.S. leaders representing diverse professions have educational and career backgrounds in social work. For example, U.S. Senator Barbara Mikulski represented the state of Maryland from 1987 to 2017. Prior to that, she served in the House of Representatives from 1977 to 1987. She stands as the longest-serving woman in the legislature in the United States (United States Senate, 2018). Another example of a social worker in a leadership position is Suze Orman, a financial advisor who gained acclaim for her Public Broadcasting Service (PBS) finance specials. A final example is Wendy Sherman, who served as U.S. Undersecretary of State for political affairs from 2011 to 2015. Among her many accomplishments was negotiating a nuclear arms agreement with Iran (Laurio, 2018/2019a). With much less fanfare, many other social workers in leadership positions are helping to improve lives by ensuring clients receive high-quality care and by developing and expanding innovative, evidence-based programs.

Examples abound of leadership training and opportunities for social workers. The NASW's Supervisory Leaders in Aging (SLA) program began in 2015 with funding from the John A. Hartford Foundation (Laurio, 2018/2019a). The SLA program is designed to strengthen clinical supervision for social workers providing services for older adults (John A. Hartford Foundation, 2015). The program provides trainings and online continuing education offerings, including advanced training for social work supervisors (NASW, 2017).

The Council on Social Work Education (CSWE) Leadership Institute in Social Work Education (2018) offers three programs to promote social work leadership. First, the CSWE Program Director Academy is a certificate program for social workers in their positions for fewer than 3 years, with a focus on the development of leadership skills and management tools. Seond, the CSWE Leadership Scholars in Social Work Education Program provides mentoring and training for faculty positions, program directorship, and college deans. Third, the CSWE Networking Reception takes place at the annual CSWE program meeting to foster new leadership in the social work profession (CSWE, 2018).

The Social Work Healthcare Education and Leadership Scholars (HEALS) program is a partnership between the NASW Foundation and CSWE to provide leadership opportunities in social work education in healthcare. More than 160 scholarships have been awarded from the bachelor's level through postdoctoral studies in social work (Laurio, 2018/2019a). This project supports the principle that social workers at all levels of the profession must be involved in strengthening the delivery of healthcare services through the use of evidence-based practices, and by developing practice and policy innovations (NASW Foundation, 2018).

At the George Warren Brown School of Social Work at Washington University in St. Louis, Missouri, teaching leadership skills has become a high priority (Laurio, 2018/2019a). This reflects a move by the CSWE toward increasing macro education. The curriculum includes foci on defining and analyzing problems, analysis of power within an organization, leadership influences, and team and coalition building (Laurio, 2018/2019a). Management and leadership skills can be utilized in a wide range of settings, such nonprofits, for-profits, and government agencies, and to support social activism. Dr. Barry Rosenberg, chair of the MSW Management Specialization concentration at George Warren Brown School of Social Work, opines that social workers can be more effective in leadership roles compared to members of other professions for several reasons: (a) Social workers possess knowledge of the needs of clients and the resources that can and cannot meet those needs; (b) social workers have knowledge of the social and cultural contexts in which social work services operate, including legislative, regulatory, and organizational contexts; and (c) social workers have a very strong commitment to social justice and the provision of both equitable and ethical services (Laurio, 2018/2019a).

TRANSLATIONAL RESEARCH AND SCIENCE

There has been an increasing focus on the process of translating research into practice in all fields of health and social services. This focus has shed considerable light on the potential for social workers to play a pivotal role in conducting translational research. Social work needs to have a strong presence in translational science in mental healthcare. Translational science in this context refers to quickly enacting successful research findings into mental health settings and developing partnerships between researchers and clinicians that can overcome long delays in implementation. The initial focus must be on the success of clinical interventions, with these evidence-based practices then being incorporated into mental healthcare in the community (Brekke, Ell, & Palinkas, 2007). To accomplish this, four important actions are needed: (a) training in specialized areas of mental health research, including doctoral and postdoctoral training as well as research field placements for MSW students; (b) special funding mechanisms, including the expansion of funding from the National Institute of Mental Health and other sources, that can bolster interdisciplinary research efforts; (c) national activities such as national social work meetings that can help develop strategies to enhance the role of social work in translational research; and (d) consortium development, including expansion of community partnerships among social work researchers, clients, and clinicians (Brekke et al., 2007). Tips for the Field 12.4 describes the steps needed to improve intervention research, defined as a systematic study of strategies for change.

TIPS FOR THE FIELD 12.4

STEPS IN INTERVENTION RESEARCH: PRODUCING HIGH-QUALITY SOCIAL WORK RESEARCH AND IMPROVING OUTCOMES

Intervention research is an effort to produce high-quality social work research that leads to improved outcomes for clients, groups, organizations, and communities. The design and development of interventions is a critical component of evidence-based practices.

The steps developed by Fraser and Galinsky (2010) and DePanfilis and Herman (2015) have been adapted for mental health research as follows:

Step 1: *Define the problem and program theories.*
The nature and extent of the problem must be explored before interventions can be devised. Determining the factors associated with mental health problems will help facilitate development of theories about appropriate interventions.

Step 2: *Create and revise program materials.*
Components of programs must be defined, and specific interventions must be determined. This includes mental health treatment and intervention protocols, and possibly the development of a manual or toolkit that gives instructions for implementation. There must be evidence that an intervention follows the established protocol (a concept known as fidelity), and that it is properly designed to evaluate whether the intended outcomes are achieved.

Step 3: *Refine program components and perform efficacy testing.*
Social work program components such as assessment measures must be reviewed and refined on an ongoing basis. It must be determined whether the mental health intervention produces the intended outcomes for clients.

Step 4: *Test effectiveness in a variety of settings and circumstances.*
Interventions should be tested within a number of different studies to determine if they are effective. This will identify the conditions under which interventions are most useful and the clients for whom the interventions are most successful.

Step 5: *Disseminate program findings and materials.*
Social work interventions must increase knowledge and understanding of how successful interventions can be implemented to benefit the community. This includes the study of the implementation and dissemination processes within the wider community.

SOURCES: DePanfilis, D., & Herman, D. (2015). Heeding the call: Advances in social work intervention research. *Journal of the Society for Social Work and Research, 6*(4), 459–465. doi:10.1086./684140; Fraser, M. W., & Galinsky, M. J. (2010). Steps in intervention research: Designing and developing social programs. *Research on Social Work Practice, 20*(5), 459–466. doi:10.1177/1049731509358424

Research action is needed on local, national, and international levels and must address evaluation methods for various interventions. The translation of evidence into innovative policy and practice requires advocacy, mainstreaming mental health into public health, and expanding service networks (Shekhar et al., 2006).

WORKFORCE ISSUES

There are insufficient numbers of psychiatrists, psychologists, and social workers to meet the demand for mental health services both currently and in the future (Health Resources and Services Administration, 2018; Kepley & Streeter, 2018; U.S. Department of Health and Human Services, 2018). This is especially the case in areas with high poverty rates.

The Health Resources and Services Administration (HRSA, 2016) report on the supply of and demand for professionals working in mental health is eye opening. HRSA researchers reviewed six types of providers of mental health services: psychiatrists, psychologists, social workers, mental health counselors, substance abuse counselors, and school counselors. In 2013, approximately 110,880 social workers with a specialty in mental health and/or substance abuse were in the workforce. HRSA (2016) estimates that in 2025, approximately 31,990 social work full-time equivalents (FTEs) in mental health and substance abuse will enter the workforce, and 33,350 FTEs will leave the workforce. This will be a net reduction of 1,660 FTEs, accounting for a 1% decrease in social workers. However, the demand for social workers specializing in mental health and substance abuse is expected to increase by 14%, with aging and population growth accounting for most of the increased need. In light of this prediction, it is time to design and implement recruitment strategies for mental health and substance abuse social workers and to improve social work curricula attention to mental health.

CLIMATE CHANGE AND MENTAL HEALTH

Individuals may have different physical and emotional adaptations to exposure to climate change based on the geographic areas in which they live, their age, and their place in the life course. Social determinants of physical health and mental health such as socioeconomic factors are important factors that are related to climate change (Trombley, Chalupka, & Anderko, 2017). As discussed in Chapter 11, Innovations in Mental Healthcare, mental health service responses to those who experience disasters, whether natural or human made, are especially important. Posttraumatic stress disorder (PTSD) and depression are the most common mental health problems associated with climate change, including natural disasters such as floods, hurricanes, and wildfires (Padhy et al., 2015; Trombley et al., 2017). Climate change brings greater exposure to intense heat, drought, poor nutrition, and outdoor pollution. Increases in these conditions can be associated with increases in violence and crime (Trombley et al., 2017). Further, increased temperatures are associated with aggressive behaviors and suicides, and long-term drought is especially associated with suicides among farmers (Padhy et al., 2015). Individual, family, and community preparations can be helpful in reducing anxiety about natural disasters. Also, promoting positive mental health can help to safeguard against the psychological stress brought on by climate change (Padhy et al., 2015). Finally, social workers can choose to become advocates in national and global efforts to reduce human-related climate change.

■ FUTURE OF MENTAL HEALTHCARE

The future of mental healthcare is expected to bring even greater involvement from consumers of mental health services and increased focus on improving the environmental and social factors associated with mental illness. This will include more online mental health services, and likely greater bureaucratic and governmental efforts to control access to and costs of care (Giacco et al., 2017).

Globalization can bring advantages to mental healthcare. Globalization provides the opportunity to compare approaches to care, work collaboratively with other nations, and improve care in the United States (Ramon, 2009). The Social Progress Imperative was established in 2014 and is based in Washington, D.C. It publishes the Social Progress Index (2018), an innovative way to determine the success of individual nations: in this index, social progress is designed to be an addition to economic health with a focus on the quality of life. The Social Progress Imperative collects and shares data on environmental and social health and can help establish priorities in social progress. At this writing, the United States ranks 25th of all countries on social progress. While the United States spends the most on healthcare, it ranks only 62nd on maternal mortality, 40th on child morality, and 47th on premature deaths. In terms of violence and discrimination against minorities, the United States ranks 67th. In terms of equality of political influence among lower socio-economic groups, the United States ranks 65th. These figures should be of great concern for our citizens and policy makers. According to a professor at Harvard Business School: "The fracturing of our society is grounded not in the weaknesses of a particular leader but in the inability of our institutions to deliver meaningful social progress for the average citizen" (Porter, 2018, p. A10).

Historically, social workers have made enormous contributions to mental healthcare in the United States. It comes as no surprise, however, that far more remains to be done. As stated by Allen et al. (2016), "Social work is at the heart of social and community innovations in mental health" (p. 6). It is time to take action.

■ SUMMARY AND CONCLUSION

Given the continued emphasis on social and emotional determinants of health and mental health, social workers have a lot of work to do. Mental illness prevention and mental health promotion are critical in reducing mental disorders. Primary prevention is focused on educational activities to deter individuals from developing mental disorders. Secondary prevention refers to early intervention to reduce the number of cases of mental illness and to minimize the impact of mental disorders. Tertiary prevention seeks to reduce the level of disability experienced by those with mental illness and seeks to prevent relapse.

A focus on a client's strengths, rather than symptoms of illness, can help promote positive functioning and hope for the future. Innovative collaborations between social workers and clients are becoming more mainstream: Social workers have the clinical and leadership skills needed to forge strong partnerships with clients as well as strong partnerships with other mental health professionals and researchers. The continuum of care across federal, state, and local mental health efforts adds support to this important structure of service delivery.

No country is exempt from mental disorders, so a global perspective on mental health can be beneficial for all. Countries' sharing of research data on mental healthcare, such as responses to climate change, can lead to enhancements in their own systems.

It is time to recruit more mental health social workers to specialize in clinical practice and research to meet the needs of those with mental disorders. Social workers possess the interest, experience, advocacy skills, and leadership qualities to move the mental health field toward innovation and the provision of equitable and high-quality services.

DISCUSSION QUESTIONS/TOPICS

1. Discuss the importance of efforts to prevent the development of mental disorders in individuals.

2. Discuss the importance of clients with mental illness taking on greater responsibility for setting and achieving goals in their recovery process.

3. Compare and contrast mental illness prevention with mental health promotion.

4. In what ways is tertiary prevention a form of mental illness prevention?

5. Discuss the relationship between climate change and mental health.

6. Discuss the role of community coalitions to address mental disorders.

7. In what ways can social workers provide leadership within the field of mental health?

8. What are your own suggestions for increasing the number of social workers specializing in mental illness?

9. Discuss the social determinants of mental health and what can be done to improve them to prevent mental disorders.

10. Discuss the importance of social work research for the future of mental health treatment.

REFERENCES

Allen, R., Carr, S., Linde, K., & Sewell, H. (2016). *Social work for better mental health: A strategic statement.* Department of Health. Retrieved from https:// assets.publishing.service.gov.uk/government/uploads/system/uploads/ attachment_data/file/495500/Strategic_statement_-_social_work_adult _mental_health_A.pdf

Arehart-Treichel, J. (2013, January 18). Future looks promising for mental illness prevention. *Psychiatric News.* Retrieved from http://psychnews .psychiatryonline.org/doi/10.1176/appi.pn.2013.10b1

Bhatia, T., Thomas, P., Semwal, P., Thelma, B. K., Nimgaonkar, V. L., & Deshpande, S. N. (2006). Differing correlates for suicide attempts among patients with schizophrenia or schizoaffective disorder in India and USA. *Schizophrenia Research, 86*(1–3), 208–214. doi:10.1016/j.schres.2006.04.015

Borsari, B. (2014). Universal prevention for alcohol use disorders: 1940–2014. *Journal of Studies on Alcohol* Supplement, 75, Suppl 17, 89–97.

Brekke, J. A., Ell, K., & Palinkas, L. A. (2007). Translational science at the National Institute of Mental Health: Can social work take its rightful place? *Research on Social Work Practice, 17*(1), 123–133. doi:10.1177/1049731506293693

Burke, M. (2018, December 18). VA left millions unspent for veterans suicide prevention: GAO. *The Hill.* Retrieved from https://thehill.com/homenews/ administration/422000-va-left-millions-unspent-for-veterans-suicide -prevention-gao-report

Campbell, J., Brophy, L., Davidson, G., & O'Brien, A-M. (2018). Legal capacity and the mental health social worker role: An international comparison. *Journal of Social Work Practice, 32*(2), 139–152. doi:10.1080/02650533.2018 .1439458

Canadian Association of Social Workers. (2018). *The role of social work in mental health.* Retrieved from https://www.casw-acts.ca/en/role-social- work-mental-health

Connecting People Intervention. (2012, April 10). *Introducing the Connecting People Intervention.* Retrieved from https://connectingpeoplestudy. net/2012/04/10/introducing-the-connecting-people-intervention/

Council on Social Work Education. (2018). *Leadership Institute.* Retrieved from https://www.cswe.org/Centers-Initiatives/Centers/Leadership-Institute

Davidson, G., Brophy, L., & Campbell, J. (2016). Risk, recovery, and capacity: Competing or complementary approaches to mental health social work. *Australian Social Work, 69*(2), 158–168. doi:10.1080/03124 07X.2015.1126752

Giacco, D., Amering, M., Bird, V., Craig, T., Ducci, G., Gallinat, J., … Priebe, S. (2017). Scenarios for the future of mental health care: A social perspective. *Lancet Psychiatry, 4*(3), 257–260. doi:10.1016/S2215-0366(16)30219-X

Health Resources and Services Administration. (2016, November). *National projections of supply and demand for selected behavioral health practitioners: 2013–2025.* Rockville, MD: National Center for Health Workforce Analysis, Substance Abuse and Mental Health Services Administration/Office of Policy, Planning and Innovation. Retrieved from https://bhw.hrsa.gov/ sites/default/files/bhw/health-workforce-analysis/research/projections/ behavioral-health2013-2025.pdf

Health Resources and Services Administration. (2018). *Behavioral health workforce projections, 2016–2030: Psychiatrists (adult), child and adolescent psychiatrists*. Retrieved from https://bhw.hrsa.gov/sites/default/files/bhw/nchwa/projections/psychiatrists-2018.pdf

Hedegaard, H., Curtin, S. C., & Warner, M. (2018, November). *Suicide mortality in the United States, 1999–2017*. NCHS Data Brief, no 330. Hyattsville, MD: National Center for Health Statistics. 2018. Retrieved from https://www.cdc.gov/nchs/products/databriefs/db330.htm

Hyde, B., Bowles, W., & Pawar, M. (2014). Challenges of recovery-oriented practice in inpatient mental health settings: The potential for social work leadership. *Asia Pacific Journal of Social Work and Development, 24*(1–2), 5–16. doi:10.1080/02185385.2014.885205

Joe, S., & Niedermeier, D. (2006). Preventing suicide: The neglected social work research agenda. *British Journal of Social Work, 38*(3), 507–530. doi:10.1093/bjsw/bcl353

John A. Hartford Foundation. (2015, September 24). *NASW launches Supervisory Leaders in Aging program*. Retrieved from https://www.johnahartford.org/newsroom/view/nasw-launches-supervisory-leaders-in-aging-program

Kepley, H., & Streeter, R. A. (2018). Closing behavioral health workforce gaps: A HRSA program expanding direct mental health service access in underserved areas. *American Journal of Preventive Medicine, 54*(6S3), S190–S191. doi:10.1016/j.amepre.2018.03.006

Latalova, K., Kamaradova, D., & Prasko, J. (2014). Suicide in bipolar disorder: A review. *Psychiatria Danubina, 26*(2), 108–114.

Laurio, A. (2018/2019a, December–January). Stepping up: Profession trains social workers to become leaders. *Social Work Advocates,* 12–21.

Laurio, A. (2018/2019b, December–January). College athletes learn skills, find support. *Social Work Advocates,* 22–29.

Laurio, A. (2018/2019c, December–January). Suicide rates on the rise: Know the signs, as the right questions to help stem the tide. *Social Work Advocates,* 12–21.

Leamy, M., Bird, V., Le Boutillier, C., Williams, J., & Slade, M. (2011). Conceptual framework for personal recovery in mental health: Systematic review and narrative synthesis. *British Journal of Psychiatry, 199,* 445–452. doi:10.1192/bjp.bp.110.083733

Marshall, S. L., Oades, L. G., & Crowe, T. P. (2009). Mental health consumers' perceptions of receiving recovery-focused services. *Journal of Evaluation in Clinical Practice, 15,* 654–659. doi:10.1111/j.1365-2753.2008.01070.x

Meehan, T. J., King, R. J., Beavis, P. H., & Robinson, J. D. (2008). Recovery-based practice: Do we know what we mean or mean what we know? *Australian & New Zealand Journal of Psychiatry, 42*(3), 177–182. doi:10.1080/00048670701827234

Mental Health America. (2018a). *Position Statement 14: The federal government's responsibilities for mental health services*. Retrieved from http://www.mentalhealthamerica.net/positions/federal-role

Mental Health America. (2018b). *The federal and state role in mental health*. Retrieved from http://www.mentalhealthamerica.net/issues/federal-and-state-role-mental-health

Mignon, S. I. (2015). Substance abuse treatment: Options, challenges, and effectiveness. NY: Springer Publishing Company.

Min, J.-A., Lee, C.-U., & Lee, C. (2013). Mental health promotion and illness prevention: A challenge for psychiatrists. *Psychiatry Investigation, 10*(4), 307–316. doi:10.4306/pi.2013.10.4.307

National Association of Social Workers. (2017). *Supervisory Leaders in Aging 2017*. Retrieved from https://www.nasw-md.org/page/SLA

National Association of Social Workers Foundation. (2018). *Social work HEALS*. Retrieved from http://www.naswfoundation.org/Our-Work/Special-Projects/Social-Work-HEALS

Padhy, S. K., Sarkar, S., Panigrahi, M., & Paul, S. (2015). Mental health effects of climate change. *Indian Journal of Occupational and Environmental Medicine, 19*(1), 3–7. doi:10.4103/0019-5278.156997

Petersen, I., Evans-Lacko, S., Semrau, M., Barry, M. M., Chisholm, D., Gronholm, P., … Thornicroft, G. (2016). Promotion, prevention and protection: Interventions at the population- and community-levels for mental, neurological, and substance use disorders in low- and middle-income countries. *International Journal of Mental Health Systems, 10*(1), 30. doi:10.1186/s13033-016-0060-z

Porter, M. E. (2018, September 24). America has traded one recession for a far more serious one. *The Boston Globe*, A10.

Ramon, S. (2009). Adult mental health in a changing international context: The relevance to social work. *British Journal of Social Work, 39*(8), 1615–1622. doi:10.1093/bjsw/bcp066

Russell, J. (2018, January 28). Silent Samaritans. *The Boston Globe*. A1, A12.

Samaritans Boston. (2018). Samaritans. Retrieved from https://samaritanshope.org/

Scobie-Carroll, A. (2018, September/October). Hands and hearts extended for suicide prevention month. *Social Work Voice*, 3.

Shekhar, S., Jane-LLopis, E., & Hosman, C. (2006). Prevention of mental and behavioural disorders: Implications for policy and practice. *World Psychiatry, 5*(1), 5–14.

Social Progress Imperative. (2018). *Social progress index*. Retrieved from https://www.socialprogress.org/about-us

Substance Abuse and Mental Health Services Administration. (2016). *Prevention of substance abuse and mental illness*. Retrieved from https://www.samhsa.gov/find-help/prevention

Substance Abuse and Mental Health Services Administration. (2017). *SAMHSA's efforts related to prevention and early intervention*. Retrieved from https://www.samhsa.gov/prevention/samhsas-efforts

Trombley, J., Chalupka, S., & Anderko, L. (2017). Climate change and mental health: An evidence-based review of the emotional health risks associated with a changing climate. *American Journal of Nursing, 117*(4), 44–52. doi:10.1097/01.NAJ.0000515232.51795.fa

United States Senate. (2018). *Barbara Mikulski: A featured biography*. Retrieved from https://www.senate.gov/artandhistory/history/common/generic/Featured_Bio_Mikulski.htm

U.S. Department of Health and Human Services, Health Resources and Services Administration, National Center for Health Workforce Analysis. (2018). *State-level projections of supply and demand for behavioral health occupations: 2016–2030*, Rockville, MD: Author. Retrieved from https://bhw.hrsa.gov/sites/default/files/bhw/nchwa/projections/state-level-estimates-report-2018.pdf

U.S. Government Accountability Office. (2018, November 15). *VA health care: Improvements needed in suicide prevention media campaign outreach oversight and evaluation.* Retrieved from https://www.gao.gov/products/GAO-19-66

Verhaeghe, N., De Maeseneer, J., Maes, L., Van Heeringen, C., & Annemans, L. (2011). Perceptions of mental health nurses and patients about health promotion in mental health care: A literature review. *Journal of Psychiatry and Mental Health Nursing, 18*(6), 487–492. doi:10.1111/j.1365-2850.2011.01692.x

Verhaeghe, N., De Maeseneer, J., Maes, L., Van Heeringen, C., & Annemans, L. (2013). Health promotion in mental health care: Perceptions from patients and mental health nurses. *Journal of Clinical Nursing, 22*(11–12), 1569–1578. doi:10.1111/jocn.12076

Webber, M., Morris, D., Howarth, S., Fendt-Newling, M., Treacy, S., & McCrone, P. (2018). Effect of the Connecting People Intervention on social capital: A pilot. *Research on Social Work Practice.* Retrieved from http://clok.uclan.ac.uk/21520/1/21520%20RSWP%20CPI%20pilot%20findings%20paper%20MW%20et%20al.pdf

World Health Organization & Calouste Gulbenkian Foundation. (2014). *Social determinants of mental health.* Geneva, Switzerland: World Health Organization.

INDEX

Abilify. *See* aripiprazole (Abilify)
abuse
    child, 69–70, 215, 217–219
    of mentally ill, 24, 27, 35, 101
        Titicut Follies (1967), 36–37
    sexual, 106, 176
    substance. *See* substance abuse
access to care, 3, 7, 41, 166, 207
    for children/adolescents, 73
    disparities, 140, 143–144
    of foster care children, 121
    of immigrants, 156
    and insurance, 144
    of minorities, 143–144, 149
    psychiatrists, access to, 124
ACLU. *See* American Civil Liberties Union
ADD. *See* attention deficit disorder
Adderall. *See* methylphenidate (Ritalin/
    Adderall)
addiction. *See also* substance use disorder
    heroin, 263
    opioid, 105
    substance, 78, 104
ADHD. *See* attention deficit hyperactivity
    disorder
adolescents
    African American, 148
    and ARC organizational model, 252
    dialectical behavior therapy for, 102
    homeless, 197–198
    LGBT, 197
    mental health challenges, 68–74
    mental illness survey data for, 6–7
    Native American, 152, 153
    prescription of antipsychotics to,
        122–123, 128

    psychiatric hospitalization for, 72–74
    and race/ethnicity, 145–146
    reintegration into school after
        psychiatric hospitalization, 247
    sexual minority/gender nonconforming,
        154–155
    teenage pregnancy, 142
    trends in mental healthcare for, 70–72
adults
    emerging. *See* emerging adults
    mental health challenges, 79–80
    mental illness survey data for, 7
    older, 80–82
    with serious mental illness, 7
advocacy, 28, 39, 154, 181, 206, 250–251
Affordable Health Care Act (2010), 182,
    205, 242, 243
African Americans, 147–149
    college students, 75
    and labeling, 181
Agency for Healthcare Research and
    Quality (AHRQ), Health Care
    Innovations Exchange, 236
AHRQ. *See* Agency for Healthcare
    Research and Quality, Health Care
    Innovations Exchange
alcoholism, 34, 79, 103
All the Things We Never Knew (Hamilton),
    60
alternative and complementary medicine,
    249
Alzheimer's disease, 81
Amen, Daniel, 238–239
Amen Clinics, 238–239
American Association of Hospital Social
    Workers, 29